# Space Groups for Solid State Scientists

# Space Groups for Solid State Scientists

GERALD BURNS

*IBM Thomas J. Watson Research Center*
*Yorktown Heights, New York*

A. M. GLAZER

*Fellow of Jesus College, Oxford*
*and*
*Clarendon Laboratory, Oxford*

ACADEMIC PRESS New York San Francisco London 1978
*A Subsidiary of Harcourt Brace Jovanovich, Publishers*

ACADEMIC PRESS, INC.
111 Fifth Avenue, New York, New York 10003

*United Kingdom Edition published by*
ACADEMIC PRESS, INC. (LONDON) LTD.
24/28 Oval Road, London NW1 7DX

Burns, Gerald, Date
Space groups for solid state scientists.

Bibliography: p.
Includes index
1. Solid state physics. 2. Lattice theory.
3. Symmetry (Physics). I. Glazer, Anthony
Michael, joint author. II. Title.
QC176.B865 530.4'1 78-9773
ISBN 0-12-145760-5

PRINTED IN THE UNITED STATES OF AMERICA

81 82 9 8 7 6 5 4 3 2

# Contents

# Preface

For a number of years there has been a growing interest in a variety of solid state problems (electronic band theory, lattice dynamics, various types of spectroscopy) embracing crystals that have quite complicated structures. Because of this, solid state physicists, chemists, engineers, and others (for lack of a better term we call them solid state scientists) have become increasingly more interested in the symmetry properties of crystals. This interest ultimately leads to the microscopic symmetry of crystal structures, the proper description of which requires a knowledge of space groups. X-Ray crystallographers have been dealing with space groups since 1913 (almost 25 years after they were determined) and have developed a nomenclature and a way of dealing with them in a manner that has been accepted on an international basis by this group of scientists. For crystallographers there is already a very convenient compilation of the 230 space groups in "The International Tables for X-Ray Crystallography: Vol. I" published for the International Union of Crystallography, which, for the sake of brevity, we shall refer to simply as the **International Tables.** This was first published in 1952 and was derived from an earlier version published in 1935. The International Tables provide a wealth of information for each of the 230 space groups. However, most solid state scientists, even if they know of the existence of this volume, find it overwhelming. They also find that the information given there does not always appear at first sight to fit in with the solid state scientist's own view of space groups; for example, there appear to be many more symmetry elements than might be expected.

It is the intention of the present book to show the interested solid state scientist how to obtain all the symmetry and related information from this compilation of space groups as well as how to understand, generate, and use the symmetry operations of a crystal. Thus, given the space group symbol, and sometimes the atomic positions, the object is to know what this really means, what the implications are for the symmetry, what the point group of the space group is, what the possible site symmetries are, why some space groups have sites with symmetry the same as the point group symmetry while others do not, which character tables one uses for the space group symmetry operations, and many other topics. These are the kinds of questions we hope the reader will be able to answer after reading this book. As such, this book is not a standard crystallographer's approach, which, at any rate, is well documented in many other books.

We shall present the symmetry of space groups in the following order, with a chapter devoted to each main topic. These are

Chapter 1: symmetry operations
Chapter 2: 7 crystal systems
Chapter 3: 14 Bravais lattices
Chapter 4: 32 crystallographic point groups
Chapter 5: description of the 230 space groups.

Chapter 6 shows how one can use the International Tables to obtain all the symmetry information about space groups needed for most solid state crystal problems. Many solid state scientists may be able to obtain the information that they want merely by reading this chapter and consulting the index as required. Chapter 7 discusses, very briefly, several applications of space group symmetry. Finally there are several appendices that summarize the bulk of the symmetry information and should serve as a useful reference. The ideas we use throughout are very simple, relying in the main on matrix multiplication, and only requiring a slight knowledge of group theory. We have tried to adopt a tutorial approach throughout.

The proliferation of notation used for symmetry operations, point groups, space groups and irreducible representations has been so great that often communication between scientists in different fields is greatly hampered. Fortunately, the two most popular notations for symmetry operations are gaining wider recognition, whereas most of the other notations are hardly used at all in the literature. We shall use both the **International notation** (elsewhere sometimes called the **Hermann–Mauguin notation**) and the **Schoenflies notation** side by side throughout this book, with the latter usually written in brackets. Thus, a typical space group would be written as $P2_1/c(C_{2h}^5)$, a point group as $2/m(C_{2h})$, and a symmetry operation as $2(C_2)$. While this might be slightly cumbersome for the writer and the typesetter, it should be clear and helpful to the reader. The student will probably spend a little extra time at the beginning in learning two notations at the same time, but we hope that the dividend will be that more of the literature will be understood with ease. However, we should emphasize that elsewhere it is normal for only one notation to be used at any one time. For example, a point group would be written either as 2/m or $C_{2h}$, depending on the choice of the writer.

In the Schoenflies system there are many ways of denoting the direction about which a symmetry operator acts, whereas in the International system the directions are not explicitly represented, except in the sense that the positions of certain symbols in the space group symbol may reveal them. Faced with this profusion of different notations the solid state scientist is to be forgiven if he feels that the task of understanding space groups is daunting. It is for this reason that, whenever some ambiguity might arise, we have adopted the approach of always specifying the direction about which an operator acts by following the symmetry symbol by [u v w], where u, v, and w are the normal crystallographic indices for directions (this will be explained in Chapter 1). Planes of symmetry are described by the directions of their normals. We shall use this in both the International as well as in the Schoenflies symbols. While this is undoubtedly a more lengthy way of writing the symmetry symbols than is convenient, it does have the distinct advantage of being unambiguous.

We hope that this book will help in clearing up the confusion that many solid state scientists encounter when starting to study solid state symmetry. How many well-established scientists still believe that all cubic crystals must have axes of fourfold symmetry, for example? In a similar vein, how many of them would define a crystal system according to the lengths of the unit cell axes and their interaxial angles? How many know which character tables to use for a crystal that has a glide plane or screw axis? If we can clarify a few of these kinds of problems, and nothing else, we shall feel that writing this book will have been worthwhile.

# Acknowledgments

It is a pleasure to have this opportunity to thank the many people who helped to improve the presentation of this book. We would, in particular, like to thank C. J. Bradley, S. A. Mabud, H. D. Megaw, I. Wood, and R. Whatmore for useful comments. F. H. Dacol took care of the logistics of keeping the problems, captions, figures, and appendices together with the text, as well as sketching many of the figures. This took an enormous job off our shoulders and we are grateful to him. Various stages of the manuscript were typed by J. L. Butcher and C. Hughes, and it is a pleasure to acknowledge them. However, the final typing, which was really typesetting on an IBM experimental printer system, was done by L. J. Callahan and we are indeed grateful for her patience and herculean effort. The first draft of this book was written at the Cavendish Laboratory, Cambridge University. We would both like to acknowledge the stimulating atmosphere there and thank our many colleagues for helping us. We are also grateful for the help from the experimental-printing group, particularly A. C. Hohl who helped in so very many ways to make the computer do what we thought we were telling it to do. We would also like to acknowledge and thank the authors and publishers of the several books from which we have used figures and tables. They are

N. F. M. Henry and K. Lonsdale, Kynoch
O. V. Kovalev, Gordon and Breach
D. and C. McKie, Nelson and Sons
H. D. Megaw, Saunders Co.
G. Weinreich, Wiley

Chapter 1

# POINT SYMMETRY ELEMENTS

*And I made a rural pen,*
*And I stain'd the water clear,*
*And I wrote my happy songs,*
*Every child my joy to hear.*

*Blake, "Songs of Innocence"*

## 1-1 Introduction

The fact that certain objects possess various types of symmetry is a common form of expression. We might say a pencil "has symmetry" along its long axis or a human being "has symmetry through a bisecting plane." In this chapter we wish to make mathematically clear what we mean when we say an object possesses a certain symmetry, and furthermore, we should like to develop a notation for these symmetry operations.

In this book we shall be dealing in the main with symmetry in crystals, rather than in other every day objects. Thus, before we go on to deal with symmetry operations, we briefly explain what we mean when we use the word, **crystal**. On a macroscopic scale we may define a crystal as a solid of uniform chemical composition which is formed with plane faces each making precise angles with one another. This is not a very rigorous definition, and in fact, it can only be made so by considering the microscopic nature of crystals. The really important aspect that makes crystals different from all other objects is that they are solids which consist of atoms or groups of atoms repeated regularly in three dimensions. This regular repetition of groups of atoms is a form of symmetry known as **translational symmetry**, a subject to be dealt with at great length in the chapters that follow. For the moment however we shall just deal with the problem of point symmetry.

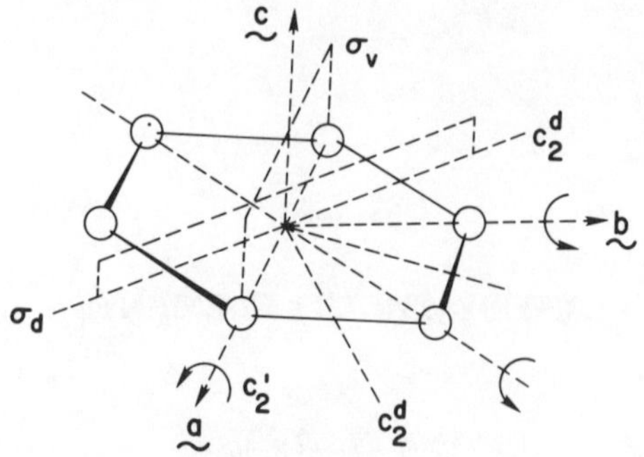


**Fig. 1-1** A benzene molecule with some of the symmetry operations indicated.

In order to understand what we mean by a symmetry operation, consider a molecule such as benzene ($C_6H_6$), as shown in Fig. 1-1. (As a **convention**, in all figures, a wavy underscore indicates a vector.) For simplicity, only the six carbon atoms are shown. If this molecule is rotated by 60° about the axis perpendicular to the molecular plane, then it will appear exactly the same as before the rotation. We would then say that a rotation by 60° is a symmetry operation of this molecule. Hence a **symmetry operation** for a molecule or crystal is defined as an operation which interchanges the positions of the various atoms and results in the molecule or crystal appearing exactly the same (being in a **symmetry-related position**) as before the operation. Furthermore, when the operation is carried out repeatedly the molecule or crystal must end up in some other symmetry-related position. It is worth noting that rotations by 120°, 180°, 240°, 300°, and 360° are also symmetry operations in this molecule. As we shall see there are many other symmetry operations in benzene. Some are rotations about other axes and some are symmetry operations other than rotations. The various types of point symmetry operations needed for crystals will now be discussed.

## 1-2 Point Symmetry Operations

A **point symmetry operation** is a symmetry operation specified with respect to a point in space which does not move during the operation. For example, the rotations discussed in the last section are point symmetry operations. In later chapters of this book, as we have already mentioned, symmetry operations that involve translations will also be considered. Translations, although they may be symmetry operations as defined in the

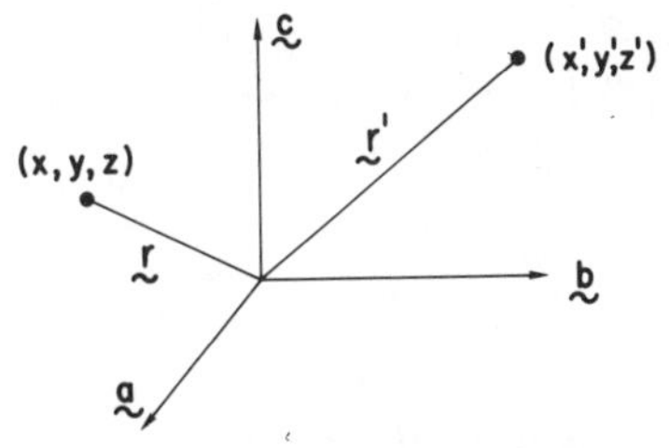


**Fig. 1-2** A point in space before and after a symmetry operation.

last section, cannot be considered to be taken with respect to any fixed point. When we talk about point groups (this term will be defined later) we shall consider a set of point symmetry operations all taken with respect to the same fixed point.

We should also like to describe the symmetry mathematically. In order to do this, we take three vectors, **a**, **b**, and **c**, measured from a common origin, in such a way that **a** and **b** are not collinear and **c** is not coplanar with the **ab**-plane. Note that these three vectors act as **axes of reference** and need not be orthogonal. There are basically two ways of describing the effect of symmetry operations. We can set up a symmetry operator which moves all points or position vectors of space with all vectors referred to a fixed set of axes. Alternatively, the symmetry operator can be made to move the axes of reference leaving all points in space, and hence position vectors, unmoved. The former type of operator is called an **active operator**, and the latter, which is its inverse, is called a **passive operator**. We shall use only active operators here. In order to illustrate what we mean, consider Fig. 1-2 where we show two points whose coordinates with respect to the axes of reference are (x,y,z) and (x′,y′,z′). Note that throughout this book, unless specifically indicated otherwise, we adopt a right-hand **convention** of axes with **a** down the page, **b** to the right, and **c** out of the page toward the reader. This is the same convention as used in the International Tables. In Fig. 1-2, the axes of reference are right-handed but are drawn so that **c** points up and **b** to the right. The point in space given by the primed coordinates is obtained after operating with a point operator R on the point given by the unprimed coordinates. In this book the operator R is a symmetry operator, although what we are saying here is generally applicable to all operators. Thus, we consider the axes **a**, **b**, and **c** fixed in space (but not necessarily orthogonal) and the point operators move the objects in various ways. Then, after carrying out the point symmetry operation, we can describe the new position in terms of the old position by a matrix transformation:

$$\begin{bmatrix} x' \\ y' \\ z' \end{bmatrix} = \begin{bmatrix} a_{11} & a_{12} & a_{13} \\ a_{21} & a_{22} & a_{23} \\ a_{31} & a_{32} & a_{33} \end{bmatrix} \begin{bmatrix} x \\ y \\ z \end{bmatrix} \tag{1-1a}$$

or

$$\mathbf{r}' = \mathbf{R}\,\mathbf{r} \tag{1-1b}$$

where Eq. (1-1b) is the short-hand matrix equation of Eq. (1-1a) in which R stands for the matrix of the point operation. This will become clearer when we write out some of the matrix operators. Let us now deal with the various point symmetry operations in turn.

**1-2a Identity** Although it may sound trivial, the most important symmetry operation is the operation that can describe all objects; that is, the operation of doing nothing to the object. This symmetry operation is given the symbol 1 in the International notation or E in the Schoenflies notation. The matrix, Eq. (1-1), which describes this operation contains 1's along the diagonal and 0's off the diagonal, the so-called unit or identity matrix. This matrix, along with matrices for all the other symmetry operations, is given in Appendix 1 (see under heading, Direction [000]).

**1-2b Rotations** If rotation about an axis by 180° ($2\pi/2$) is a symmetry operation for a particular object, then in the International (Schoenflies) notation we write it as $2(C_2)$. In general, if the symmetry operation is a rotation by an amount $2\pi/n$, where n is called the **order** of the rotation, the symbol is $n(C_n)$. This is sometimes called a **pure** or **proper rotation**. (We shall see later that an improper rotation is a rotation followed by either an inversion or a reflection.) In this book only n = 1, 2, 3, 4, 6 will be discussed since it turns out that for crystals these are the only allowed rotations. This point will be justified in the next chapter. Since rotations are taken about certain rotation axes in the crystal it is sometimes convenient to specify the orientation of a particular rotation axis. While there is no generally accepted way of doing this, in this book we shall, when we think necessary, specify the orientation directly after the symbol for the rotation operator. Since the rotation axis is a line with a specific direction, we can describe it with respect to the **a**-, **b**-, and **c**-axes by a vector

$$\mathbf{S} = u\mathbf{a} + v\mathbf{b} + w\mathbf{c} \tag{1-2}$$

where the length of the vector **S** is adjusted to make u, v and w integers. The crystallographic **convention** for denoting this vector is to write it as

[uvw]. (Note that in some books it is written as (uvw); we prefer to write it with brackets since to crystallographers parentheses signify planes rather than directions.) The rotation operation is then **conventionally** written as n[uvw] in the International notation or as $C_n$[uvw] in the Schoenflies notation.

Let us take an example of a rotation operation. In Fig. 1-3a we see a schematic diagram of two right hands with their palms up; these are related to each other by the symmetry operation 2($C_2$). (Of course in a crystal we do not really have "hands" but collections of atoms. The hands in our diagrams serve only to illustrate the effects of the various symmetry operations in a convenient way.) Thus, when this operation is applied about an axis perpendicular to the paper, which we may denote symbolically by 2[001] or $C_2$[001], the hand pointing to the top of the page will rotate into the position of the hand pointing to the bottom of the page and vice versa. Notice that the hands both have their palms up and that both are right hands. (One cannot be a left hand, unless both are left hands.) We could think of this operation in a slightly different manner. Just consider the hand that points to the top of the page and operate on it by a 2-fold or $C_2$ operation. Then, the hand that points to the bottom of the page is generated by this operation and the composite picture has the point symmetry 2($C_2$).

**Stereograms** are another way of representing these symmetry operations and these are discussed in Chapter 4 and Appendix 5. Here we discuss still another way of pictorially representing this symmetry operation. Beside the two hands two circles with a + sign next to them are drawn. The circles are a convenient way of representing any general object such as a hand or a collection of atoms. The system of circles is used because it is compact and is the adopted symbol in the International Tables. The + sign refers to the fact that each circle is above the plane of the paper. A – sign would mean that the circle in question were below the plane of the paper. Under a 2($C_2$) operation, it is clear that these two circles interchange and that both remain at the same height above the paper, so that the circles are in symmetry-related positions. The fact that only right hands are needed under this operation is denoted by the use of open circles. As will be discussed later, if we had started with a right hand, open circle, and then generated a left hand, we would have put a comma in the circle to indicate this change in handedness. Notice that the 2-fold operation acts about a particular axis, [001] in this example, and that this is indicated on the diagram by a symbol similar to the shape of an American football. We also show, in the figure, two circles related by a 2-fold axis but observed perpendicular to the axis of rotation, [010] in this

Point Symmetry Operations
International notation (Schoenflies notation)

Rotation Axes–Symbol
(also called pure or proper rotation)

2($C_2$)

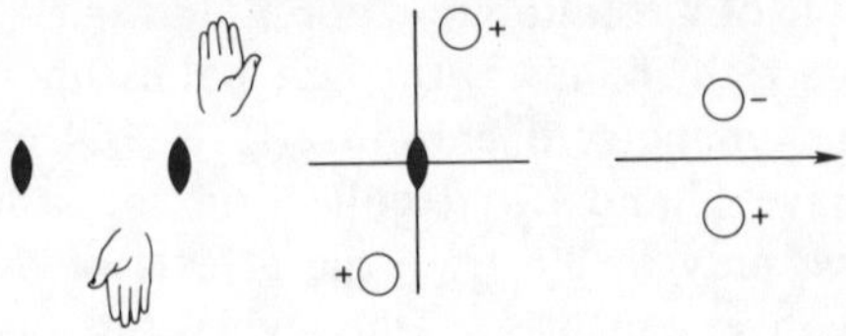

3($C_3$)

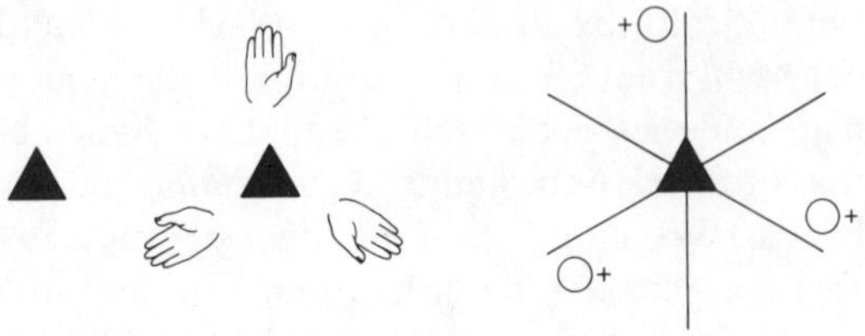

4($C_4$)

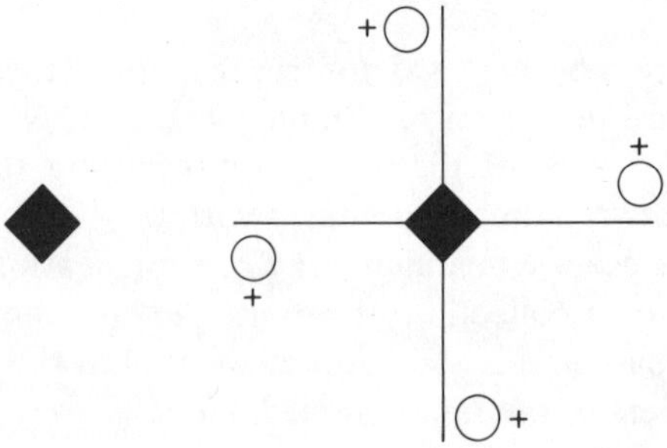

6($C_6$)

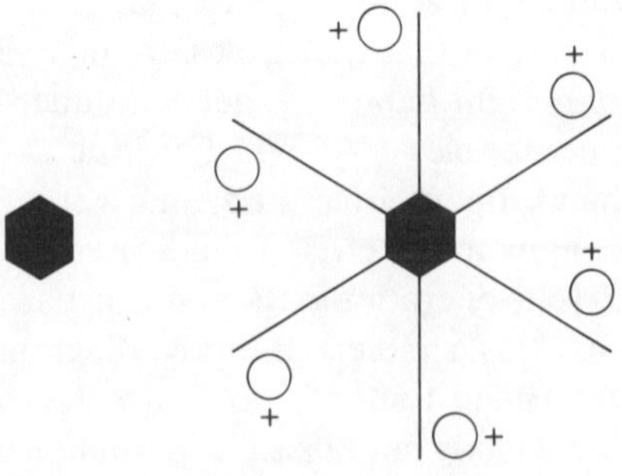

## Inversion through a center
## (also called inversion or center)

$\bar{1}$ (i)

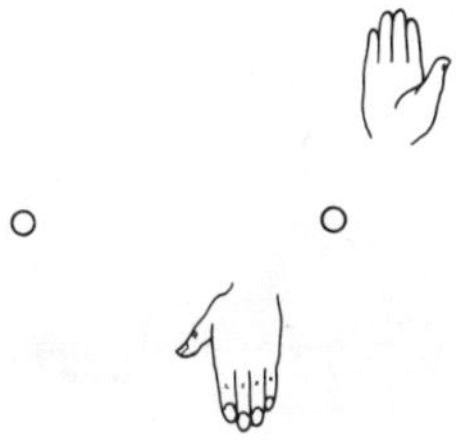

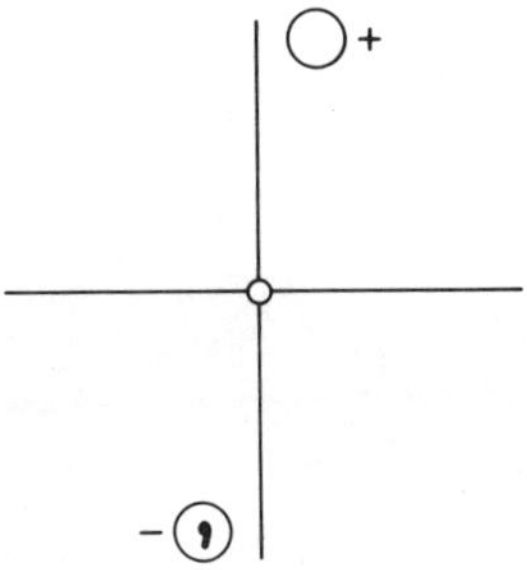


Rotatory inversion axes
(also called improper rotation)
$\bar{1}$ = inversion
$\bar{2}$ = mirror plane

$\bar{3}(S_6^5)$

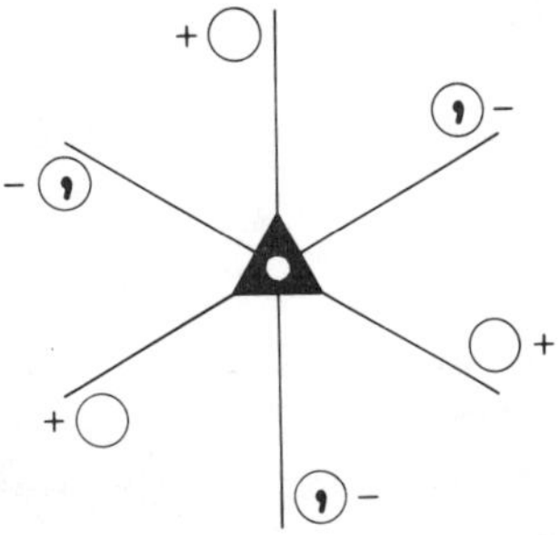


## Mirror plane
## (also called reflection across a plane)

Looking perpendicular to the plane

m($\sigma$)

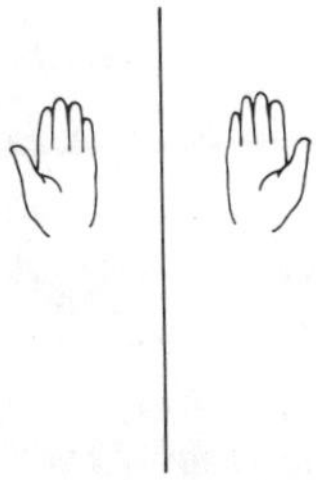

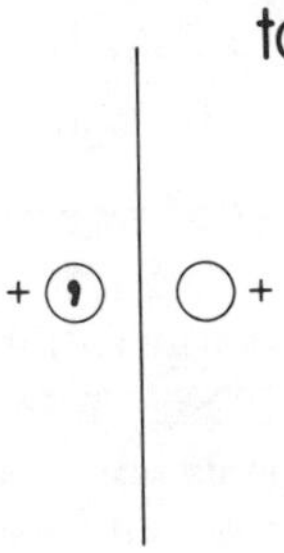


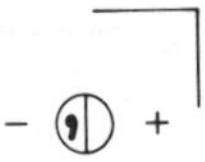

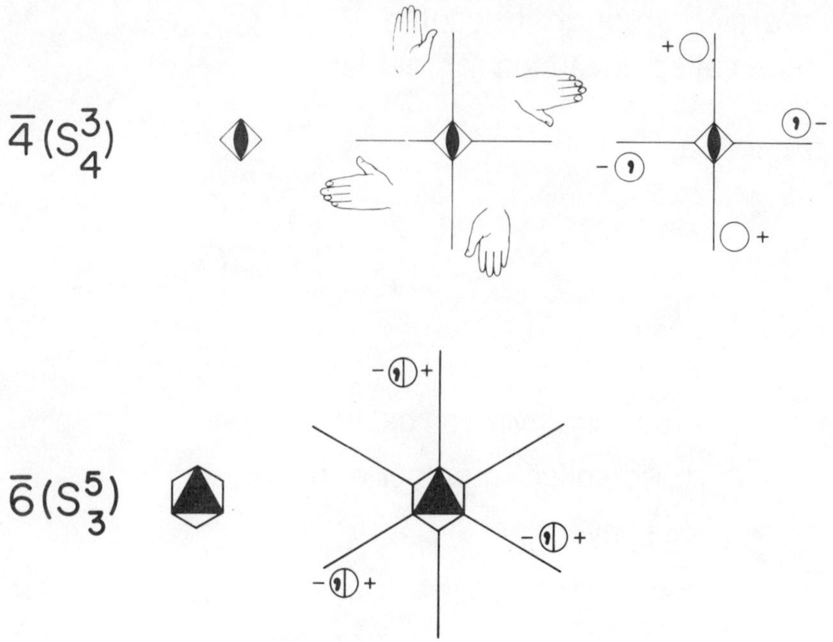


**Fig. 1-3** Point symmetry operations.

case. The line with the arrow is the International Tables convention for a 2-fold axis lying in the plane of the paper. This and all of the other conventional diagrammatic symbols are listed in Appendix 6. As can be seen, now one of the circles is above the plane of the paper and one is below. The matrices describing the 2-fold symmetry operations about other principal directions are given in Appendix 1. Thus, for the symmetry operation 2[001] or $C_2$[001] operating on a general point at (x,y,z), we can write

$$\{2[001]\}\ (x,y,z) = \begin{bmatrix} -1 & 0 & 0 \\ 0 & -1 & 0 \\ 0 & 0 & 1 \end{bmatrix} \begin{bmatrix} x \\ y \\ z \end{bmatrix} = \begin{bmatrix} -x \\ -y \\ z \end{bmatrix} \qquad (1\text{-}3)$$

to obtain a new point at (−x,−y,z) which is in agreement with the diagram.

The next symmetry operation discussed is 3($C_3$) denoted by a triangle. As can be seen in Fig. 1-3b, the right hand with palm up pointing to the top of the page is rotated into the right hand with palm up pointing to the bottom left of the page. At the same time the other hands are rotated into each other. Thus, the operation $3(C_3)$ is a symmetry operation for the three hands separated by 120° or $2\pi/3$ and equidistant from the origin as shown. Note that we have picked a **right-hand** or **counter-clockwise convention for our rotations**, to which we shall adhere throughout. The diagram to the right of the three hands shows the three circles above the plane of the paper with $3(C_3)$ as the symmetry operation. It is important to realize that there is another symmetry operation closely related to $3(C_3)$. This is the operation 33 in the International notation or $C_3C_3$ in the Schoenflies notation. This is normally written as $3^2$ or $C_3{}^2$ where the squaring of a symbol has the usual meaning of multiplying the operator by itself. Thus $n^2 = nn$, and this defines the **product** of n times n. We can see that $3^2$ $(C_3{}^2)$ is a symmetry operation since it takes the right-hand palm up pointing to the top of the page into the right-hand palm up pointing to the bottom right of the page. Again we point out a **convention**: If two operations AB are applied to an object, the operation on the right B is considered to be applied first and A second. Clearly the order of operations is of no consequence when an operator is squared (operation applied twice). The matrices representing the two symmetry operations $3(C_3)$ and $3^2(C_3{}^2)$ are given in Appendix 1 and can be applied directly to the coordinates of any general point.

The symmetry operations $4(C_4)$ and $6(C_6)$ are also shown in Figs. 1-3c and 1-3d. We also note that $4^2(C_4{}^2) = 2(C_2)$, so that $4^2(C_4{}^2)$ is an operation that we have already discussed. This is a very simple example of the fact that the existence of certain symmetry operations implies the existence of other symmetry operations. Thus if $4(C_4)$ is a symmetry operation for a particular crystal or molecule, then it implies that $2(C_2)$ is also a symmetry operation, as is $4^3(C_4{}^3)$. Similarly $3(C_3)$ implies $3^2(C_3{}^2)$. From $6(C_6)$ we know that $6^m(C_6{}^m)$, where m = 1, 2, 3, 4, 5, 6, are also symmetry operations. For m = 2 we have $3(C_3)$, for m = 3 we have $2(C_2)$, and for m = 6 we have 1(E) or the identity operation. The matrices describing these symmetry operations are in Appendix 1.

We note that in all these pure rotations, $n(C_n)$, right hands are all that are required. At no time do these operations require any left hands. Shortly we shall see that other symmetry operations will indeed require both hands.

We also note that these rotation symmetry operations have been taken with respect to a line, namely, the axis of rotation. This axis of rotation is sometimes referred to as the **symmetry element**. The symmetry operation is accomplished by the movement of the object (hands or circles), the required amount, about the symmetry element. The hands or circles have always been placed at a **general position** — a position in space that is not situated directly on a symmetry element. The effect of the symmetry operator is to produce a set of hands or circles which all lie on general positions but which are symmetry-related to one another, thus resulting in a set of **general equivalent positions**.

**1-2c Inversion** The symmetry operation of inversion, which is sometimes called **inversion through a center, a center of symmetry**, or simply a **center**, is more involved than the rotation operations because it changes right hands to left hands. By the operation of inversion we mean that for every position in space given by the coordinates (x,y,z), we operate with the inversion operator $\bar{1}$(i) and go to the position (−x,−y,−z). (Note that the crystallographic **convention** is to put the minus signs above the coordinates, thus (x,y,z) → ($\bar{x}$,$\bar{y}$,$\bar{z}$) and this is said, bar x, bar y, bar z, or x bar, y bar, z bar.) This can be written as

$$\{\bar{1}(i)\}(x,y,z) = (-x,-y,-z) \qquad (1\text{-}4)$$

(see Appendix 1). In Fig. 1-3e we see the result of $\bar{1}$(i) operating on a right hand, palm up, above the plane of the paper and pointing to the top of the page. The result is a left hand, palm down (knuckles up), below the plane of the paper and pointing to the bottom of the page. Thus, if two hands are placed as shown, $\bar{1}$(i) is a symmetry operation linking them.

When circles are used to show the symmetry operations, the fact that the chirality or "handedness" changes is conventionally denoted by a comma drawn in the circle. The right hand is said to be **enantiomorphically** related to the left hand and the inversion operation is said to be an **enantiomorphous operation**. As we shall see later, a mirror image has this same property so that sometimes one says that two objects that are enantiomorphically related are mirror images of each other. One might equally well say one is a right-handed system and the other is a left-handed system. There is no way in which left- and right-handed systems can be made equivalent using ordinary rotation operations. One point of definition: if two objects have the same handedness, they are said to be **congruent** to each other.

Note that just as the symmetry element of a rotation is a line, so the symmetry element of an inversion is a point. Examination of the benzene molecule in Fig. 1-1 will reveal that there is a center of inversion situated at the molecular center.

**1-2d Reflection across a plane** The operation of reflection across a plane, sometimes called a **mirror reflection** and denoted by the symbol m in the International notation and $\sigma$ in the Schoenflies notation, is shown in Fig. 1-3f. The plane of reflection is the symmetry element of a mirror operation and is called a **mirror plane**. Given a point in space (x,y,z) and a mirror operation, one drops a perpendicular onto the mirror plane, and places a new point along this line an equal distance on the other side of the mirror; this is the mirror image of the point at (x,y,z). Thus, if the right hand is drawn palm up on the right side of the mirror, the mirror image is a left hand also palm up on the left side of the mirror as shown. For the coordinate system shown, we would have

$$\{m[010]\}\ (x,y,z) = (x,-y,z) \tag{1-5}$$

Note that in order to specify the orientation of the mirror plane we again use the symbol [uvw] which, in this case gives the direction of the line perpendicular to the mirror plane. In the accompanying diagram, the two circles also show the m($\sigma$) operation; here we use a comma to indicate that one is the enantiomorphic (mirror) image of the other. Clearly we could just as well have put the comma in the circle on the right and have left it out of the circle on the left. Appendix 1 gives the matrices for some special orientations of a mirror plane.

On the far right we have another diagram of a mirror plane, only this time, the mirror is in the plane of the paper. In this case one circle will be observed to be on top of the other. The convention used in the International Tables to denote this is −, + with the circle divided into two halves, one with and one without a comma.

The Schoenflies symbol for a mirror plane, $\sigma$, usually has a subscript. If we define the **c**-axis as the **principal axis**, then $\sigma_h$ is a mirror perpendicular to this axis (the "h" comes from the word horizontal assuming that the principal axis is vertical). Mirror planes that contain the principal axis are either $\sigma_v$ or $\sigma_d$ (vertical or diagonal). $\sigma_v$ contains the principal axis and the **a**-axis, while $\sigma_d$ generally contains an axis that bisects the angle between the **a**- and **b**-axes. The benzene molecule, Fig. 1-1, has these three mirror planes. $\sigma_h$ passes through all of the atoms in the molecular plane, $\sigma_v$ passes through opposite pairs of atoms, and $\sigma_d$ passes through the midpoints of opposite C-C bonds.

**1-2e Rotation-inversion axes (improper rotation)** This last type of symmetry operation is the most complicated to understand for two entirely separate reasons. First, the approach taken in the International system is different from that taken by the Schoenflies system and so the symmetry operations are given different names. In the International system we talk about **rotation-inversion axes**, and in the Schoenflies system, **improper rotation axes**. In this book we shall, for brevity, often refer to both types of operations as improper rotations. The second complication is that this symmetry operation is a **compound operation**, that is, it is the product of two other operations. In general each of these other operations will not by itself be a symmetry operation for a particular crystal or molecule but the product of the two will be a symmetry operation. We shall deal with the two approaches separately.

**International approach** Let us first take the International approach and obtain the rotation-inversion symmetry operations. However, we shall continue to put the Schoenflies symbol in brackets following the International symbol since there is a one-to-one correspondence; the explanation of the Schoenflies symbol will be made clear later.

In the International approach we first perform a rotation operation $n(C_n)$ and then follow it immediately with an inversion operation. Writing this as a product, we have $\bar{1}n(iC_n)$. The short-hand International symbol used instead of $\bar{1}n$ is $\bar{n}$. (The short-hand Schoenflies symbol will be explained below.) First consider $\bar{4}(S_4{}^3)$ since it is probably the easiest to visualize (Fig. 1-3h). Start with a right hand, palm up, pointing to the top of the page and rotate it through $2\pi/4$ and immediately invert it through the origin. The result is a left hand, palm down, pointing to the right. To complete the diagram, reapply this operation to the hand just obtained. The result is a right hand, palm up, pointing to the bottom of the page. This shows that $\bar{4}^2 = 2$ (or $S_4{}^6 = S_4{}^2 = C_2$). Now apply the operation again to this last hand. The result is a left hand, palm down, pointing to the left, corresponding to the operation $\bar{4}^3(S_4)$. Applying the operation yet again to this last hand brings us back to the hand pointing to the top of the page in its original orientation, so that $\bar{4}^4 = 1$, the identity operation. Clearly the $\bar{4}$ operation is a symmetry operation. The conventional diagram with circles, heights (+ and −), and commas is also shown. Thus for an arrangement of atoms with positions represented by these circles we can state that $\bar{4}(S_4{}^3)$ and $\bar{4}^3(S_4)$ and $2(C_2)$ are all symmetry operations. Again notice how the symmetry operation $\bar{4}(S_4{}^3)$ implies the existence of a 2-fold rotation symmetry operation. Also note that for this system of hands or circles neither $4(C_4)$ nor $\bar{1}(i)$ by itself constitutes a symmetry operation. For example, $4(C_4)$ operating on the first hand would result in a second hand, palm up, pointing to the left. The hand pointing to the left in the diagram is, however, palm down. Therefore the compound operation $\bar{4}(S_4{}^3)$ is indeed a new type of symmetry operation whose component operations are not symmetry operations. This is an important point to grasp. The matrices for these various symmetry operations are given in Appendix 1.

Consider the operation $\bar{3}(S_6{}^5)$: if we start with the circle at the top of the page above the plane of the paper and apply $\bar{1}3 = \bar{3}(S_6{}^5)$, we rotate through $2\pi/3$ to a position toward the bottom left and immediately invert through the center to obtain the circle toward the top right. This circle lies below the plane of the paper and is enantiomorphically related to the circle that we started with. After doing this six times we come back to the circle that we started with. Therefore if a crystal or molecule has this arrangement of atoms, $\bar{3}(S_6{}^5)$ is a symmetry operation for this crystal or molecule.

The $\bar{6}(S_3{}^5)$ symmetry operation can be carried out easily and is left for the reader to complete. When you do this you will notice that for some n in $\bar{6}^n$ new operations are obtained, while for other n, operations that we have discussed previously are obtained.

We can also note, that $\bar{1}(i)$ is clearly the inversion operation and need not be discussed again. Furthermore, it is clear that the operation $\bar{2}$ is simply a mirror operation, $\bar{2} = m(\sigma)$. You can now see why we choose to specify the orientation of a mirror plane by the direction of a line perpendicular to it. This line is parallel to the $\bar{2}$ axis so that our use of a direction normal for the mirror plane is analogous to that used for proper rotations.

**Schoenflies approach**. In this approach the improper rotations are obtained in the following manner: first rotate by the appropriate amount and then immediately reflect across a plane perpendicular to the axis of rotation. The Schoenflies notation for this is $S_n = \sigma C_n$, but in order to make it perfectly clear that the mirror plane is perpendicular to the rotation axis we give the plane a subscript and write $S_n = \sigma_h C_n$. The "h" stands for a horizontal plane, naturally assuming that the axis of rotation is vertical and $S_n{}^m = (\sigma_h C_n)(\sigma_h C_n) \ldots = (\sigma_h C_n)^m$ as always.

Now apply this approach to the $\bar{4}(S_4{}^3)$ diagram. Start from the hand pointing to the top of the page and apply $S_4$. (Remember when $\bar{4}$ was applied, the hand pointing to the right was obtained.) Rotate by 90° ($2\pi/4$) and reflect. The hand pointing to the left is obtained. We see, then, that $S_4$ is equivalent to $\bar{4}^3$. In order to obtain the hand pointing to the right $S_4$ must be applied three times, i.e., $\bar{4}$ is equivalent to $S_4{}^3$. Thus, we obtain the hands or circles counterclockwise by the operations

$$E,\ S_4,\ S_4{}^2 = C_2,\ S_4{}^3,\ S_4{}^4 = E$$

We can see that the Schoenflies approach obtains the positions in a slightly more systematic order. For example the positions in the $\overline{3}(S_6^5)$ diagram are obtained successively in a counterclockwise order if one repeatedly applies $S_6$. In the International approach the positions are obtained successively in a clockwise manner but the rotational parts of the symmetry operation must be applied counterclockwise (i.e., our right-handed convention). Below, we list the corresponding symbols that are used to obtain the circles in the $\overline{3}(S_6^5)$ diagram in a counterclockwise manner.

| | | | | | |
|---|---|---|---|---|---|
| $S_6$ | $S_6^2 = C_3$ | $S_6^3 = i$ | $S_6^4 = C_3^2$ | $S_6^5$ | $S_6^6 = E$ |
| $\overline{3}^5$ | $\overline{3}^4 = 3$ | $\overline{3}^3 = \overline{1}$ | $\overline{3}^2 = 3^2$ | $\overline{3}$ | $\overline{3}^6 = 1$ |

The same list for the $\overline{6}(S_3^5)$ diagram, again in a counterclockwise manner is

| | | | | | |
|---|---|---|---|---|---|
| $S_3$ | $S_3^2 = C_3^2$ | $S_3^3 = \sigma_h$ | $S_3^4 = C_3$ | $S_3^5$ | $S_3^6 = E$ |
| $\overline{6}^5$ | $\overline{6}^4 = 6^4$ | $\overline{6}^3 = m$ | $\overline{6}^2 = 6^2$ | $\overline{6}$ | $\overline{6}^6 = 1$ |

Before we leave the subject of symmetry operations we should note, that from the definition of the term, the inverse of every symmetry operation must also be a symmetry operation. By the term inverse we mean another operation such that the product of the two is the identity. (If A, B, C,... are symmetry operations and if AC = E, the identity, then A is the inverse of C, or vice versa, because one may prove that a left inverse is equal to a right inverse.) We list below the inverse operation of each symmetry operation in Schoenflies notation.

| Symmetry Operation | Inverse | |
|---|---|---|
| $C_n^m$ | $C_n^{n-m}$ | |
| $S_n^m$ | $S_n^{n-m}$ | all m, n even |
| $S_n^m$ | $S_n^{2n-m}$ | m odd, n odd |

$S_n^m = C_n^m$ for n odd and m even; E, i, and $\sigma$ are their own inverses.

In Appendix 1 the improper operations are listed side by side with their proper partners. You will notice that the determinant of any matrix of a symmetry operation is always $\pm 1$, an important characteristic of orthogonal transformations. Moreover, the proper rotations all have determinant $+1$, whereas the improper rotations have determinant $-1$, a consequence of whether or not the operation is enantiomorphic. It is therefore a very simple matter to determine whether a particular matrix operation is proper or improper.

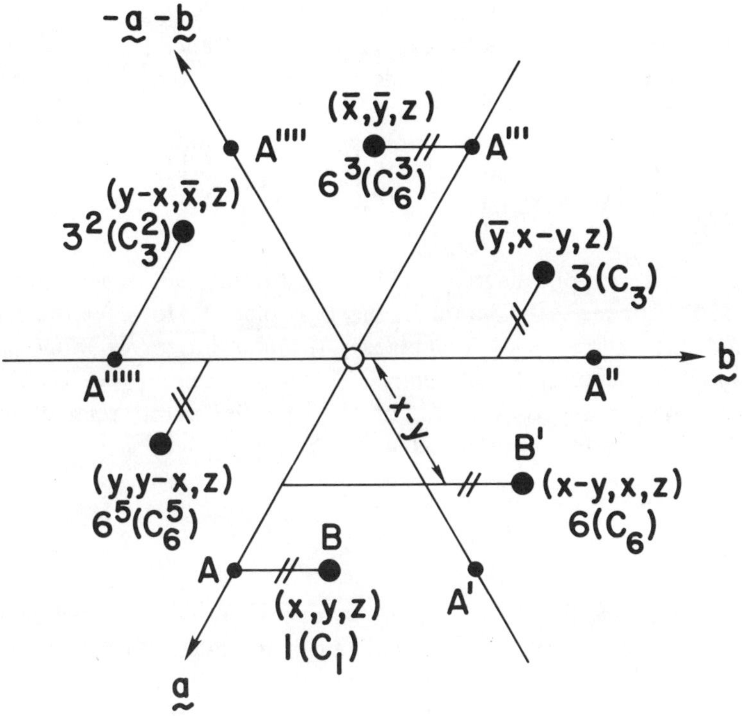


**Fig. 1-4** General equivalent positions on hexagonal axes.

## 1-3 Hexagonal Coordinates

Figure 1-4 shows the effect of operating on a point with coordinates (x,y,z) with the operation $6^m(C_6{}^m)$ for m=1,2,3,4,5,6; the coordinates are specified with respect to hexagonal axes of reference. The object of this figure is to show very clearly the coordinates of the resulting points and how they are obtained with respect to the hexagonal axes, **a** and **b**, which are at an angle of 120° to one another. Using this diagram, we can see how the coordinates are obtained for these symmetry operations as well as for all the $3^m$ and $6^m$ operations. The figure shows that when the operation $6(C_6)$ is applied to the point B at (x,y,z), a new point B′ at (x−y,x,z) is obtained. Careful study of this diagram should make this clear. We see that the position of B′ measured parallel to the **a**-axis is equal to A′ A″ minus A′B′. A′A″ is equal to x, and by the geometry of equilateral triangles, A′ B′ is equal to AB and hence equal to y. Therefore, the coordinate distance of B′ measured along **a** is x−y. Similarly, we find that the distance of B′ measured parallel to **b** is equal to the distance of A measured parallel to **a**, i.e., it is equal to x. Hence B′ is at (x−y,x,z). An alternative way of obtaining this result is to use the matrices given in Appendix 1. Thus we have

$$\{6\}(x,y,z) = \begin{bmatrix} 1 & -1 & 0 \\ 1 & 0 & 0 \\ 0 & 0 & 1 \end{bmatrix} \begin{bmatrix} x \\ y \\ z \end{bmatrix} = \begin{bmatrix} x-y \\ x \\ z \end{bmatrix} \tag{1-6}$$

in agreement with our diagram. This is hardly surprising since the matrix was derived from the diagram in the first place. However the matrix method does allow us to find quickly the coordinates of other points generated by successive operations. The reader should now be able to understand how the coordinates of all the other points related by the $6^m(C_6{}^m)$ operations are obtained.

## Problems

**1.** With reference to the list of improper operations given in Section 1-2e, verify for yourself that there is complete correspondence between the two sets of symbols (International and Schoenflies).

**2.** Using the matrix multiplication method, find which operation is equivalent to the product {2[100]} {4[001]} or $\{C_2[100]\}\ \{C_4[001]\}$. Also to {4[001]}{2[100]} or $\{C_4[001]\}\{C_2[100]\}$. What do the two results illustrate?

**3.** Show that the matrices used in the active approach are related to those in the passive approach by $R_{active} = (R_{passive})^{-1}$. Also show that if the order of operations is reversed, i.e., if $R_{active}\ S_{active} = T_{active}$, then $S_{passive}\ R_{passive} = T_{passive}$.

**4.** If in Fig. 1-4 the **a**- and **b**-axes are rotated counterclockwise through 30° about **c**, what are the coordinates of the general points with respect to this new orientation? You should be able to work this out both graphically and by multiplying by the appropriate rotation matrix.

**5.** Prove: (a) $S_n{}^{n/2} = i$ for n/2 odd; (b) the existence of an $S_n$ axis of even order always implies the existence of a $C_{n/2}$ axis.

**6.** How many independent operations are generated by the following: (a) $S_n$ with n odd; (b) $S_n$ with n even?

**7.** Verify that the determinants of the rotation matrices in Appendix 1 are always $\pm 1$. Note that the product of two improper rotations is a proper rotation. The reverse is not true.

**8.** What are the four symmetry operations in an $H_2O$ molecule? What are the eight symmetry operations in an Egyptian pyramid?

# Chapter 2

# CRYSTAL SYSTEMS

*This is not, however, the place to lament the misery of our century, but to rejoice with you over such beautiful ideas for proving the truth.*

*Letter from Galileo to Kepler, August 4, 1597.*

Having established the various symmetry operations that are important in crystalline materials, we must ask the question: how do these symmetry operations allow us to classify and characterize crystals? (We should add that we really refer to "fully ordered" crystals. In practice, however, there are thermal vibrations and other forms of disorder, such as those found in alloys, which give rise to an average structure. It is nevertheless possible to assign a particular symmetry to the crystal, so long as we do not deal with it at a local level.) In this chapter the basic symmetry operations are applied to a lattice and impose certain restrictions on the unit cell lengths and interaxial angles, giving rise to **7 crystal systems**. The seven crystal systems form the coarsest classification of crystals. In the following chapters we discuss the 14 Bravais lattices, then 32 point groups, and then the 230 space groups. In a certain sense each of these classifications successively describes the crystal in more detail.

## 2-1 Lattice

A **lattice** is defined as an infinite array of points in space, in which each point has identical surroundings to all other such points. The simplest way of generating such an array is by invoking the property of

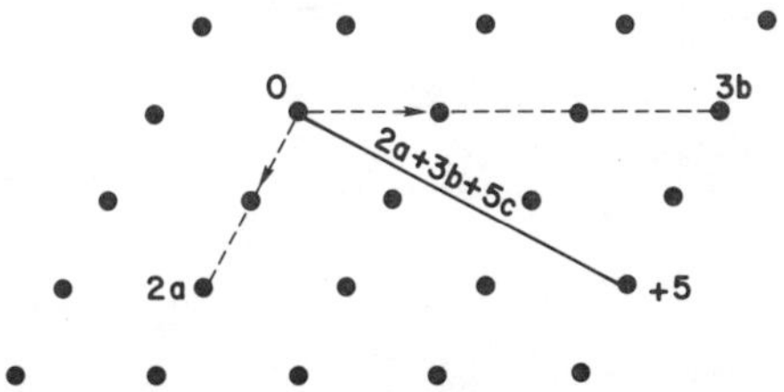


**Fig. 2-1** A lattice of points in projection.

**translational invariance**, which is the most fundamental feature of all crystals. This property can be conveniently represented by the **primitive translation vector**

$$\mathbf{t}_n = n_1\mathbf{a} + n_2\mathbf{b} + n_3\mathbf{c} \tag{2-1}$$

where $n_i$ is any integer and **a**, **b**, **c** are vectors along appropriately chosen axes such that **a** and **b** are not collinear and vector **c** is not coplanar with the **ab**-plane: all vectors **a**, **b** and **c** start from the same origin and serve as **axes of reference**.

Figure 2-1 shows an array of points obtained by considering the end points of the infinite number of vectors given by Eq. (2-1) as points in the array. For simplicity, we have drawn a projection of a 3-dimensional lattice. If we choose a particular point in this array and consider the other points with respect to it, then, Eq. (2-1) gives us the vectors to these points. For example, the point two units in the **a**-direction, three in the **b**-direction, and five in the **c**-direction is given by 2**a** + 3**b** + 5**c** from our observation point. We can see, then, that by taking integral amounts of the basic vectors, **a**, **b**, and **c**, and compounding them, an array of points is generated, with the points lying at the ends of the translation vectors given by Eq. (2-1). Furthermore, we can see that no matter which lattice point we choose, the array always looks the same when viewed from it.

Notice that we have not said anything about the angles between the vectors **a**, **b**, and **c**. In fact, if there is no special relationship between the interaxial angles, the resulting lattice forms an oblique net of points (Fig. 2-1 shows such an oblique lattice). If the interaxial angles are 90°, that is, the axes are orthogonal, either square or rectangular arrays are formed, depending on whether or not the vectors **a**, **b**, or **c** are equal in length.

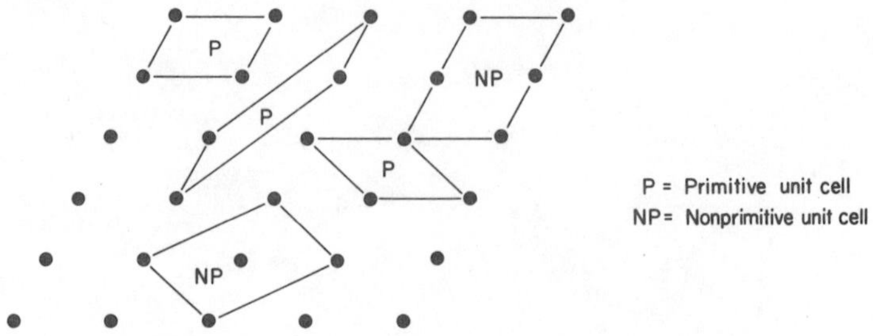


**Fig. 2-2** Some examples of primitive and non-primitive unit cells.

## 2-2 Primitive Unit Cell

By completing the parallelepiped formed by the axes **a**, **b**, and **c**, we enclose a volume in space, $\mathbf{a}\cdot(\mathbf{b}\times\mathbf{c})$, which, if translated parallel to itself by the translation vector in Eq. (2-1), would fill up all space and generate the lattice. If this volume in space only contains one lattice point (as it does in Fig. 2-2), we call it the **primitive unit cell**. (We should explain, here, what we mean when we say a primitive unit cell contains one lattice point. If a unit cell origin is chosen on a lattice point, then there are eight lattice points at each corner of the unit cell; however, because each is shared between eight unit cells only, there are $8 \times 1/8$ lattice points associated with any one primitive unit cell. An even easier way of seeing this is to imagine the unit cell slightly displaced so that its origin is away from a lattice point. Then, if the unit cell is primitive only one lattice point will be observed inside it.)

A primitive unit cell is not the only type of cell which is used in describing a lattice. We may define the more general term **unit cell** as one being formed by three vectors in much the same manner as before, i.e., when translated throughout space by all multiples of these three vectors, it will fill all space with a lattice in the same way as a primitive unit cell. The difference is that a unit cell need not contain only one lattice point. A unit cell that contains more than one lattice point is called a **non-primitive** or **multiply-primitive unit cell**. Figure 2-2 shows some examples of primitive and non-primitive unit cells.

Note that the volume (area in this figure) of all the primitive unit cells is the same. Clearly there is an infinite number of primitive and non-primitive unit cells that can be chosen. However, some restrictions on our choice can be made if we observe certain conventions. Nevertheless, it is very important to realize that no matter how we choose the axes, the lattice is the same. But the choice of a different unit cell may result in

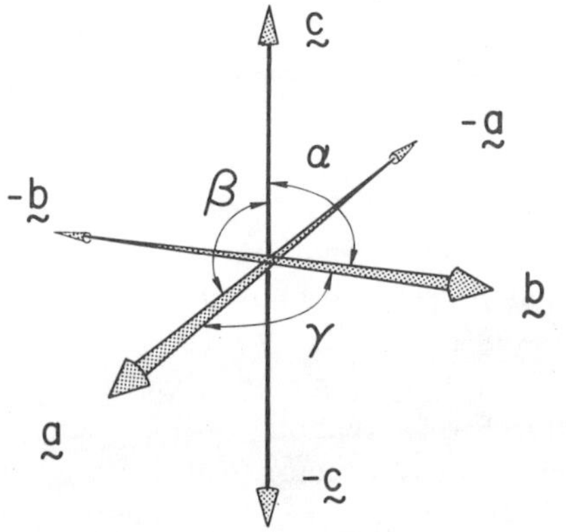


**Fig. 2-3** This figure shows how the angles are defined.

the lattice being given a different name or symbol. (Note: as we have defined the unit cell, it is not necessary for its origin to be at a lattice point. What we require is that the unit cell after repeated translation through all space should produce the lattice. Clearly this is possible even when the origin is picked at a point in space which is not a lattice point.)

We should also like to define the term crystal structure. By **crystal structure** we mean the periodic arrangement of atoms in the crystal. The crystal structure can be described by associating with each lattice point a group of atoms. This group of atoms is called the **basis**, or **lattice complex**, of the structure. Thus, a crystal structure is made up of a lattice and a basis. The crystal structure is also obtained by repeating, throughout space, a unit cell and the atoms within. A primitive unit cell is the smallest unit cell that will give the crystal structure. However, sometimes it is best to choose a unit cell that is larger and more clearly displays the lattice symmetry. This will be discussed fully in later chapters.

Whether the unit cell is primitive or not, it is important to remember that in a crystal structure we are dealing with the symmetry of the cell and its contents, and not just with the bare unit cell shape as determined by the lattice points.

## 2-3 Crystal Systems

Before we go ahead and derive the crystal systems, it is worthwhile mentioning a **convention**. For our unit cell we use the customary right-handed set of axes, labelled **a**, **b**, and **c** with interaxial angles $\alpha$, $\beta$, and $\gamma$. Figure 2-3 shows the axes together with the interaxial angles.

In our treatment of the crystal systems we shall start by considering the effect of the lowest-order symmetry operation on a unit cell and then, with the exception of 3-fold and 6-fold axes, work our way up progressively to the highest symmetry (we shall leave the 3- and 6-fold operations till last since a number of complications arise which make their associated crystal systems rather special). The seven crystal systems arise from applying various proper and improper rotations to the unit-cell axes or translation vectors of the lattice. We can deal with this mathematically in general terms in the following manner. Consider the effect of applying a symmetry operation R on a general position vector **r** as we did in Chapter 1. This position vector is a vector from the origin of a unit cell, which we may take at a lattice point, to some general position within the unit cell, and can be expressed in terms of components taken along the **a**-, **b**-, and **c**-axes. These components are usually expressed in the form of coordinates measured as fractions of the unit-cell axial lengths. This means that a point in the unit cell which is specified by (x,y,z) lies at a distance from the unit-cell origin with vector components x**a**, y**b**, z**c**. The fractional coordinates are often known as the **atomic position parameters** since we normally use them to represent atomic positions of a crystal structure. The position vector **r** joining the origin to the point (x,y,z) is given by

$$\mathbf{r} = x\mathbf{a} + y\mathbf{b} + z\mathbf{c} \tag{2-2}$$

After applying the operation R, a new point at (x′, y′, z′) is obtained which is related to the first point at (x,y,z) by

$$\begin{bmatrix} x' \\ y' \\ z' \end{bmatrix} = \begin{bmatrix} a_{11} & a_{12} & a_{13} \\ a_{21} & a_{22} & a_{23} \\ a_{31} & a_{32} & a_{33} \end{bmatrix} \begin{bmatrix} x \\ y \\ z \end{bmatrix} \tag{2-3}$$

This is the same relationship given in Eq. (1-1a) (only here, because we are considering unit cells, the coordinates are fractional). The new point is specified by the vector **r**′ which is

$$\mathbf{r}' = R\mathbf{r} = x'\mathbf{a} + y'\mathbf{b} + z'\mathbf{c} \tag{2-4}$$

Since we take R as a symmetry operation, when we compare the vector components along the axes before and after applying this operation, we obtain the relationship between the unit-cell axes. We shall see that the symmetry operations impose certain restrictions on the unit-cell geometry, in that there will be relationships between the axial lengths and interaxial angles. In what follows, notice that the only rotation operations that are

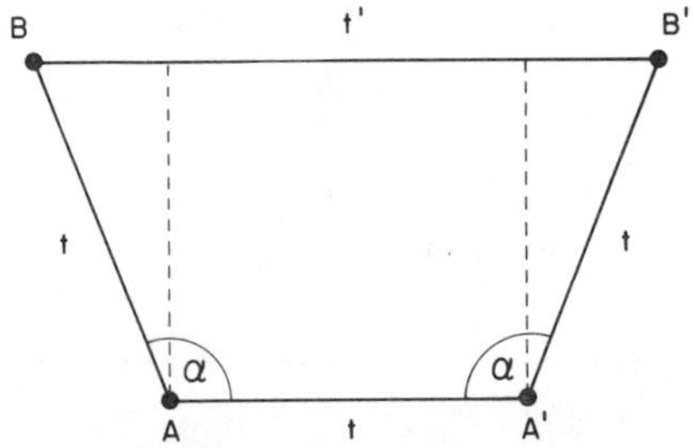


**Fig. 2-4** Points in a lattice.

used in defining the crystal systems are the proper and improper rotations $n(C_n)$ and $(S_n)$ with n = 1, 2, 3, 4, and 6. The reason for this is that it is not possible with other values of n to construct unit cells which when joined together fill all space. This can be demonstrated simply as follows.

Consider two lattice points A and A′ separated by a unit translation t as in Fig. 2-4. A particular rotation operator R or its inverse $R^{-1}$ acting at these points, respectively, will give rise to new points B and B′ by rotation of the vector AA′ through an angle $\alpha$. (The inverse of every symmetry operation is also a symmetry operation as discussed in Section 1-2.) The condition for B and B′ to be lattice points is that the distance between them, t′, must be an integral number of basic translation units t. Therefore, we can write

$$t' = mt \qquad \text{where m is some integer} \tag{2-5}$$

and from the diagram

$$t' = -2t\cos\alpha + t \tag{2-6}$$

Combining these two equations, we get

$$\cos\alpha = (1-m)/2 \tag{2-7}$$

Now if m is an integer, then $1-m = M$ where M is an integer. Furthermore, $\alpha$ must lie between 0 and 180° in order to obtain closure under the particular operation R, i.e., $\cos\alpha$ lies between +1 and −1.

$$|\cos\alpha| \leq 1 \tag{2-8a}$$

therefore

$$|M| \leq 2 \tag{2-8b}$$

and then

$$M = -2, -1, 0, 1, \text{ or } 2 \tag{2-8c}$$

This means that the only acceptable values of $\alpha$ are

$$\pi, \quad 2\pi/3, \quad \pi/2, \quad \pi/3, \quad \text{or } 0 \tag{2-8d}$$

And hence the only allowed rotations $2\pi/n$ are $n = 2, 3, 4, 6$, or 1, respectively. The same restrictions apply when considering improper rotations.

An alternative proof is as follows. Any proper rotation through an angle $\theta$ about the **c**-axis, say, is given with respect to orthogonal Cartesian axes by a matrix

$$\begin{bmatrix} \cos\theta & -\sin\theta & 0 \\ \sin\theta & \cos\theta & 0 \\ 0 & 0 & 1 \end{bmatrix}$$

As is well known from group-theoretical considerations, the trace of such a matrix (sum of diagonal elements) must be equal to an integer provided we are dealing with a symmetry operation of a crystal. (See for example Streitwolf page 60.) Since $|\cos\theta|$ can at most be equal to 1, the trace must lie between $+3$ and $-1$, i.e.,

$$1 + 2\cos\theta = 3, 2, 1, 0, -1$$

Therefore

$$\cos\theta = 1, 1/2, 0, -1/2, -1$$

These five solutions give rotations with $n = 1, 6, 4, 3$, and 2, respectively, as we expect.

We shall now develop the seven crystal systems one by one so that the effect of the progressive addition of higher symmetry can be seen.

**2-3a Triclinic** In this trivial case the unit cell has no rotational symmetry other than 1(E) or $\bar{1}$(i). Using the former we may write, according to Eq. (2-4),

$$\mathbf{r}' = \{1\}\mathbf{r} = \begin{bmatrix} 1 & 0 & 0 \\ 0 & 1 & 0 \\ 0 & 0 & 1 \end{bmatrix} \mathbf{r} = x'\mathbf{a} + y'\mathbf{b} + z'\mathbf{c} \tag{2-9a}$$

where

$$\begin{aligned} x' &= 1x + 0y + 0z \\ y' &= 0x + 1y + 0z \\ z' &= 0x + 0y + 1z \end{aligned} \tag{2-9b}$$

The matrix is obtained from Appendix 1 for the 1(E) operation. Since we demand that this operation be a symmetry operation, we find that

$$\mathbf{r}' = x\mathbf{a} + y\mathbf{b} + z\mathbf{c} \qquad (2\text{-}9c)$$

as expected for the identity operation.

In this trivial example the fractional coordinates are unchanged. If we proceed in a similar way with the $\bar{1}$(i) operation, we obtain

$$\mathbf{r}' = \{\bar{1}\}\mathbf{r} = -x\mathbf{a} - y\mathbf{b} - z\mathbf{c} \qquad (2\text{-}10)$$

In this case, all the signs have been reversed. Note that in both cases the coordinates x, y, and z remain "attached" to their axes **a**, **b**, and **c**. This is simply another way of saying that there are no impositions placed on the axes by this symmetry; the axes do not bear any relationship to one another, and therefore no special restrictions are put on the unit cell geometry. Therefore, the symmetry operations 1(E) or $\bar{1}$(i) define a unit cell, which we call triclinic, with geometry given by

$$a \neq b \neq c \qquad \alpha \neq \beta \neq \gamma$$

We add an important cautionary note. The $\neq$ signs imply that symmetry does not require the various quantities to be equal. It is quite possible that an experimental determination of the unit cell might lead to some or all axes being equal within the experimental precision. This does not mean that the crystal necessarily has high symmetry. In many cases the true symmetry may only become clear when the symmetry of the atomic arrangements in the unit cell or of certain physical properties are considered. For example, from the unit cell geometry of $PbZrO_3$, the crystal appears to be tetragonal (see Section 2-3d); however, the atomic arrangement displays a symmetry which is far from tetragonal. Sometimes changes in temperature may allow the unit cell to distort sufficiently to make the true symmetry more obvious. However, remember that it is the symmetry that puts restrictions on the axes and interaxial angles, and not the other way around.

**2-3b Monoclinic** In this crystal system the important symmetry elements are the 2-fold rotation $2(C_2)$ and/or the mirror $m(\sigma)$. Let the 2-fold axis lie along **c**. This is called the **first setting** and is the convention often used by most solid state scientists. (However, note that the **second setting**, where the 2-fold axis lies along **b**, is usually chosen by crystallographers.) Now consider the restrictions that a 2-fold rotation imposes on a unit cell. Clearly, in order to relate **a** to **−a** by rotation through 180°, the **a**-axis must be perpendicular to the rotation axis, **c**, for if it were not, the

2-fold rotation acting on **a** would result in yet another axis at some angle from −**a**. This situation can be seen in Fig. 2-5a, where the new axis is labelled **a**′. Similarly, the **b** axis must be perpendicular to the **c** axis, but not necessarily to **a**. Using the matrices in Appendix 1, we can write that the effect of the 2-fold operation is

$$\mathbf{r}' = \{2[001]\}\mathbf{r} = -x\mathbf{a} - y\mathbf{b} + z\mathbf{c} \qquad (2\text{-}11)$$

and the effect of the m(σ) operation (m is perpendicular to **c**) is

$$\mathbf{r}' = \{m[001]\}\mathbf{r} = x\mathbf{a} + y\mathbf{b} - z\mathbf{c} \qquad (2\text{-}12)$$

The differences in sign in Eq. (2-11) between the components along **c** and those along **a** and **b** imply perpendicularity as can be seen by taking the scalar product of these components before and after the transformation. Before the transformation for the **a**- and **c**-axes, we have

$$x\mathbf{a} \bullet z\mathbf{c} \qquad (2\text{-}13a)$$

After the transformation

$$x'\mathbf{a} \bullet z'\mathbf{c} = -\, x\mathbf{a} \bullet z\mathbf{c} \qquad (2\text{-}13b)$$

where the right side of Eq. (2-13b) is obtained by applying the result from Eq. (2-11) that $x' = -x$ and $z' = z$. Equations (2-13a) and (2-13b) must be equal by definition since we demand that the $2(C_2)$ operation be a symmetry operation, i.e., the crystal is unchanged. Thus we obtain

$$xz\,|\mathbf{a}|\,|\mathbf{c}|\cos\beta = -xz\,|\mathbf{a}|\,|\mathbf{c}|\cos\beta \qquad (2\text{-}14a)$$

$$\cos\beta = -\cos\beta \qquad \text{or} \qquad \beta = 90^\circ \qquad (2\text{-}14b)$$

$\beta = 90^\circ$ means that **a**- and **c** are perpendicular. In the same manner **b** and **c** are found to be perpendicular ($\alpha = 90^\circ$). The same dot product for the **a** and **b**-directions yields an identity. The result is

$$x'y'\,|\mathbf{a}|\,|\mathbf{b}|\cos\gamma = xy\,|\mathbf{a}|\,|\mathbf{b}|\cos\gamma \qquad (2\text{-}15)$$

which, when Eq. (2-11) is used, tells us nothing. Hence $\gamma$ is indeterminate. The fact that we have not interchanged the magnitudes of the axes under these operations means that no restrictions are placed on their lengths. Therefore, for the "first setting" the monoclinic system has

$$a \neq b \neq c \qquad \alpha = \beta = 90^\circ \qquad \gamma \neq 90^\circ$$

It should be noted that we normally choose the cell so that $\gamma$ is greater than 90°; this is only a matter of **convention** and is not applied strictly,

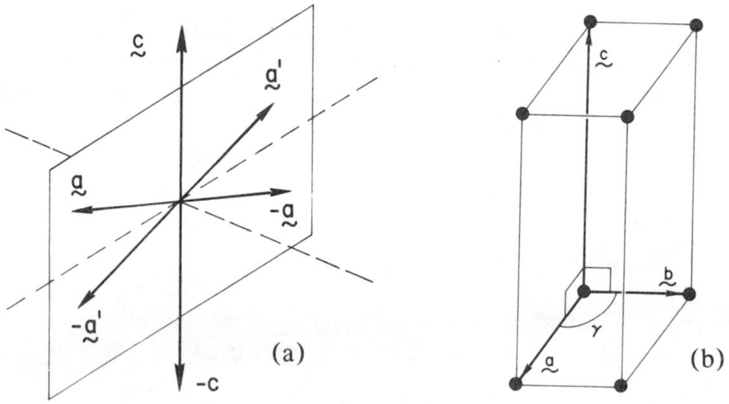


**Fig. 2-5** (a)The result of a 2-fold symmetry operation about the c-axis. (b)A monoclinic unit cell.

except in descriptions of crystal structures where confusion would otherwise occur. The use of a mirror plane, Eq. (2-12), instead of a 2-fold axis of rotation gives identical conditions for the axes and angles. Figure 2-5b shows a monoclinic unit cell.

Naturally, if one chooses the "second setting" where the 2-fold axis is the **b**-axis or the mirror plane is perpendicular to the **b**-axis, then one obtains

$$a \neq b \neq c \qquad \alpha = \gamma = 90^\circ \qquad \beta \neq 90^\circ$$

This is the setting usually preferred by crystallographers.

**2-3c Orthorhombic** In this system we consider the effect of having two or more 2-fold or $\bar{2}$ axes ($\equiv$ mirror planes). Suppose, that there are 2-fold axes along **a**(or [100]) and **b**(or [010]). Then we can write

$$\{2[100]\}\mathbf{r} = x\mathbf{a} - y\mathbf{b} - z\mathbf{c} \tag{2-16a}$$

and

$$\{2[010]\}\mathbf{r} = -x\mathbf{a} + y\mathbf{b} - z\mathbf{c} \tag{2-16b}$$

If we take the product of these two operations, we find

$$\{2[100]\}\ \{2[010]\}\mathbf{r} = -x\mathbf{a} - y\mathbf{b} + z\mathbf{c} \tag{2-16c}$$

which is the same as a 2-fold rotation about **c**(or [001]). This means that if we have two 2-fold axes, we automatically have a third. Moreover, the change in signs tells us about perpendicularity. Equation (2-16a) tells us that **a** is perpendicular to **b** and **c**, and Eq. (2-16b) tells us that **b** is perpendicular to **a** and **c**, just as we found in the monoclinic system using Eq. (2-13) and (2-14). Therefore, the three resulting axes are mutually perpendicular. Since the coordinates have not been interchanged with respect to the axes there are no restrictions placed on the axial lengths. Therefore, two 2-fold axes yield a crystal system which is called orthorhombic and has

$$a \neq b \neq c \qquad \alpha = \beta = \gamma = 90^\circ$$

We leave it as an exercise for the reader to show that appropriate combinations of mirror planes and 2-fold axes also lead to the orthorhombic system.

**2-3d Tetragonal** In this case, we consider the restriction put on the unit cell by one 4-fold $4(C_4)$ or one $\overline{4}(S_4{}^3)$ operation. By the same reasoning that we applied to the monoclinic system, Eqs. (2-13) and (2-14), we can see that if $4(C_4)$ is taken along the **c**-axis (the conventional choice), **a** and **b** must be perpendicular to **c**. The 4-fold operation, moreover, means that **+a** must move to **+b**, **+b** to **−a**, **−a** to **−b** and **−b** to **+a**, in order that we do not produce a surplus of axes. This can be written mathematically as

$$\mathbf{r}' = \{4[001]\}\mathbf{r} = -y\mathbf{a} + x\mathbf{b} + z\mathbf{c} \tag{2-17a}$$

Similarly, we find that

$$\mathbf{r}' = \{4^3[001]\}\mathbf{r} = y\mathbf{a} - x\mathbf{b} + z\mathbf{c} \tag{2-17b}$$

with similar relations for $\overline{4}(S_4{}^3)$ and $\overline{4}^3(S_4)$. Again, the opposite signs show that **a**, **b**, and **c** are perpendicular. Notice that there is now an interchange of x and y which means that **a** and **b** must have identical length. Therefore, the operation $4(C_4)$ or the operation $\overline{4}(S_4{}^3)$ results in a new crystal system which we call the tetragonal system

$$a = b \neq c \qquad \alpha = \beta = \gamma = 90^\circ$$

Of course, **c** can be greater or smaller than **a** = **b**.

**2-3e Cubic** This crystal system is very familiar to solid state physicists and chemists, and it is the system with the highest symmetry. However, despite its familiarity we need to be rather careful about how we define it; it is not sufficient to use the criterion that all axes are equal and all angles 90°. As we continue to emphasize, the symmetry is the important thing in determining the crystal system. The symmetry condi-

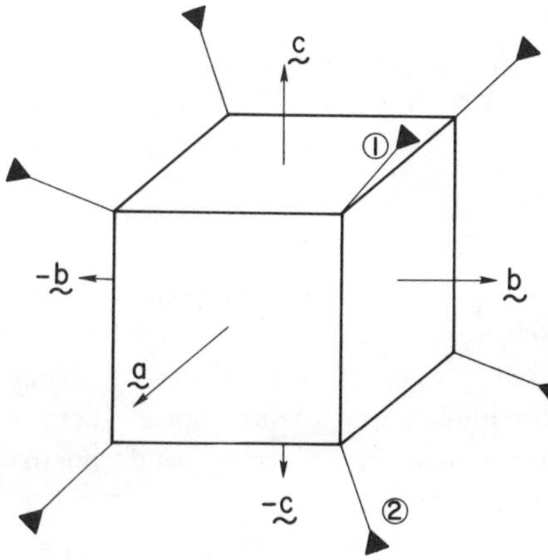


**Fig. 2-6** The four 3-fold symmetry axes of a cube.

tions our choice of axes, not the other way round. What, then, are the important symmetry elements in the cubic system? Perhaps surprisingly, they are not the three mutually perpendicular 4-fold axes so readily observed in a cube, but rather, the four 3-fold rotation axes corresponding to the body-diagonals, <111>, of the cubic unit cell. (Note that **angular brackets** signify the set of symmetry-equivalent directions. In this case <111> means the set [111], $[11\bar{1}]$, $[1\bar{1}1]$, $[\bar{1}11]$, $[1\bar{1}\bar{1}]$, $[\bar{1}1\bar{1}]$, $[\bar{1}\bar{1}1]$, and $[\bar{1}\bar{1}\bar{1}]$.) As we shall see in Chapters 4 and 5, it is perfectly possible to have a cubic crystal without any 4-fold axes of symmetry. It is possible to prove either by group theory or by spherical trigonometry that if a crystal contains more than one 3-fold ($C_3$) axis, then it must contain four altogether, each one making an angle of 109°28′ with any other.

We shall now show that the four 3-fold axes give rise to a cubic unit cell. Refer to Fig. 2-6. The 3-fold axis along [111] (number 1 on the diagram) operating on the vector **r** once or twice gives

$$\{3[111]\}\mathbf{r} = z\mathbf{a} + x\mathbf{b} + y\mathbf{c} \tag{2-18a}$$

$$\{3^2[111]\}\mathbf{r} = y\mathbf{a} + z\mathbf{b} + x\mathbf{c} \tag{2-18b}$$

Since the components have been freely interchanged, this implies that all axes are interchangeable and hence equal in length.

The 3-fold axis along $[11\bar{1}]$, marked (2), gives

$$\{3[11\bar{1}]\}\mathbf{r} = y\mathbf{a} - z\mathbf{b} - x\mathbf{c} \tag{2-19a}$$

$$\{3^2[11\bar{1}]\}\mathbf{r} = -z\mathbf{a} + x\mathbf{b} - y\mathbf{c} \tag{2-19b}$$

with similar relations for the remaining 3-fold axes. We see then that in addition to equality of axes the signs themselves permute, implying orthogonality of all the axes. Therefore our choice of four 3-fold axes gives a new crystal system, called the cubic crystal system, which has

$$a = b = c \qquad \alpha = \beta = \gamma = 90^\circ$$

**2-3f Trigonal and Hexagonal** We have deliberately left the trigonal and hexagonal systems till last because they both present special problems which in some respects render them different from the other crystal systems. Considerable confusion about these systems is found in the literature; we hope that the following and the discussion in Section 3-3f on centering will clarify the problem. Perhaps it is best to reread this section after reading Section 3-3f.

Let us first deal with the **hexagonal** system. This crystal system can be defined as one possessing a single $6(C_6)$ or $\bar{6}(S_3{}^5)$ axis. Note that we immediately encounter a conceptual difficulty in that the $\bar{6}$ axis is equivalent to an improper 3-fold rotation axis of the Schoenflies-type $S_3{}^5$, or alternatively to a proper 3-fold axis with a mirror plane perpendicular (3/m in International notation); this relationship will be discussed in Chapter 4. Either way it can be confusing that the hexagonal system may be described both by 6-fold as well as 3-fold axes in conjunction with other operations. The 6 or $\bar{6}$ symmetry leads by similar considerations to those used in the other crystal systems to the **a**- and **b**-axes being at 120° to each other. For example, we may write using Fig. 1-4 or the matrices in Appendix 1

$$\mathbf{r}' = \{6[001]\}\mathbf{r} = \begin{bmatrix} 1 & -1 & 0 \\ 1 & 0 & 0 \\ 0 & 0 & 1 \end{bmatrix} \mathbf{r} = x'\mathbf{a} + y'\mathbf{b} + z'\mathbf{c} \tag{2-20a}$$

where

$$\begin{aligned} x' &= 1x - 1y + 0z \\ y' &= 1x + 0y + 0z \\ z' &= 0x + 0y + 1z \end{aligned} \tag{2-20b}$$

Therefore, we can write

$$\{6[001]\}\mathbf{r} = x(\mathbf{a} + \mathbf{b}) - y\mathbf{a} + z\mathbf{c} \tag{2-20c}$$

Similarly, we find that

$$\mathbf{r}' = \{6^2[001]\}\mathbf{r} = x\mathbf{b} + y(-\mathbf{a} - \mathbf{b}) + z\mathbf{c} \tag{2-21}$$

and so on.

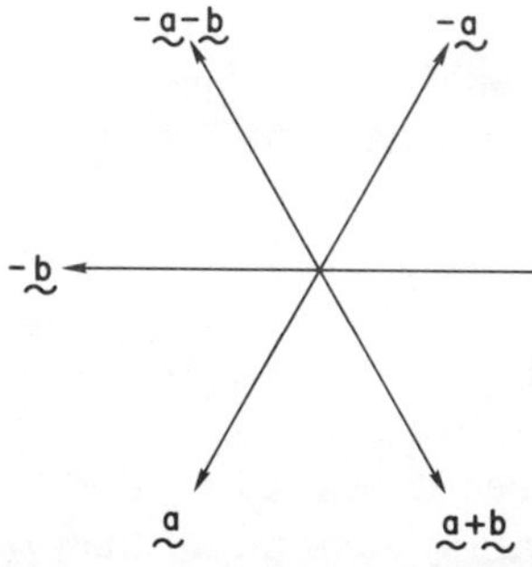


**Fig. 2-7** The hexagonal system of axes.

The free interchange of coordinates x and y, with respect to the **a**- and **b**-axes, indicates that **a** and **b** are equal in length. Furthermore it is a very simple matter to show that these equations are consistent with the **a**- and **b**-axes being at 120° to one another. The scalar product of the components along the **a**- and **b**-axes before transformation can be related to the product after transformation. For {6[001]}**r** this is

$$x\mathbf{a} \cdot y\mathbf{b} = x(\mathbf{a} + \mathbf{b}) \cdot -y\mathbf{a} \tag{2-22}$$

Therefore, we obtain

$$x\,y\,|\mathbf{a}|\,|\mathbf{b}|\cos\gamma = x\,y\,[-|\mathbf{a}|\,|\mathbf{b}|\cos\gamma - |\mathbf{a}|^2] \tag{2-23}$$

from which, since $|\mathbf{a}| = |\mathbf{b}|$, we get

$$\cos\gamma = -1/2 \tag{2-24}$$

We see that the **a**- and **b**-axes are at 120° to each another. (Of course this is not surprising since the rotation matrices in Chapter 1 were derived on the assumption that the axes of reference are placed at 120° to each other; it is nice, however, to see that when applied to the unit cell the interaxial relationships are preserved.) In a similar manner we can show that **c** is perpendicular to **a** and **b**. The 6-fold symmetry therefore implies that

$$a = b \neq c \qquad \alpha = \beta = 90^\circ \qquad \gamma = 120^\circ$$

It should be realized that in addition to the **a**- and **b**-axes, there is another direction **−a−b**, which is equivalent in magnitude to and 120° from **a** and **b** (see Fig. 2-7). Naturally, we could equally well choose this as an axis, so that there are four possible axes in this system. Such an arrangement of four axes is sometimes used, particularly when dealing with crystal morphology. However, we shall continue to use the three-axis notation. Another point that you should note is that sometimes you will see in books that the unit cell of a hexagonal lattice is drawn as a hexagonal prism. This is incorrect. A hexagonal prism is made up from three unit cells. The conventional hexagonal unit cell, like all others used in defining crystal systems, is a parallelepiped. (See Fig. 2-8a for example.)

We define a **trigonal** crystal system as possessing a single $3(C_3)$ or $\overline{3}(S_6{}^5)$ axis. Again note the conceptual difficulty with $\overline{3}$ and $S_6{}^5$. Nowadays some authors consider it best to treat the trigonal system as a special case of the hexagonal system, rather than treat it separately (see for example the book by Megaw), since both have the same relationships between the unit-cell axes.

The problem is the following: there are basically two ways of defining **crystal systems**. One is to use the symmetry of the crystal (as we do here, see end of Section 2-2), the other is to use the symmetry of the lattice. In the latter case we have a hexagonal lattice (denoted by the symbol P), with 6-fold symmetry, and this leads to the **hexagonal crystal system**. The other system in this scheme is the so-called **rhombohedral crystal system** (denoted by R) in which there is 3-fold symmetry but no 6-fold symmetry (see below). In this approach there is no trigonal system, as such, although the total number of crystal systems remains seven. While there are certainly merits to this approach, we shall adhere to the usage of the present International Tables, which is familiar to most people, i.e., to have a separate hexagonal and a separate trigonal system, with the rhombohedral system as a special case of the trigonal system.

We shall therefore now discuss this special case by describing the **rhombohedral unit cell**. The conditions on the axes and angles are

$$a = b = c \qquad \alpha = \beta = \gamma$$

where the $3(C_3)$ or $\overline{3}(S_6{}^5)$ axis makes an equal angle with **a**, **b**, and **c**. Figure 2-8 shows this unit cell and how it is constructed from a centered trigonal lattice. The traditional and simple way that the rhombohedral crystal system is developed is to take the trigonal crystal system, i.e., with a single $3(C_3)$ or $\overline{3}(S_6{}^5)$ axis, and consider the condition on the axes and angles. This results in a lattice identical with that of the hexagonal crystal system, as discussed above. This lattice is then centered (i.e. points are added in special places in the cells) in a manner consistent with the trigonal condition. Once this is done, the rhombohedral cell can be chosen as in Fig. 2-8. Centering in all the crystal systems is dicussed completely in the next chapter and so we leave the details of the discussion till Section 3-3f. However, notice that the rhombohedral unit cell shown in Fig. 2-8

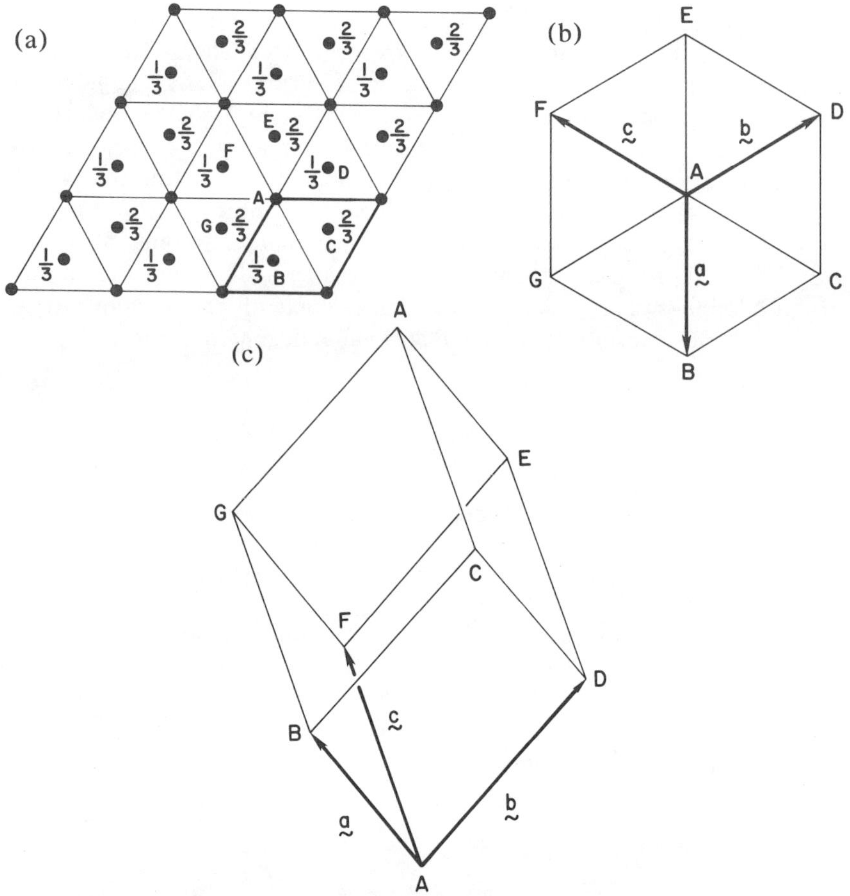


**Fig. 2-8** A centered trigonal lattice resulting in a primitive rhombohedral unit cell.

is primitive and is consistent with the symmetry of the trigonal crystal system but not with that of the hexagonal crystal system, since it does not possess $6(C_6)$ or $\overline{6}(S_3{}^5)$ symmetry.

## 2-4 Summary

In Appendix 2 the seven crystal systems are summarized in a convenient form. The axial lengths and interaxial angles for the seven crystal systems are determined by the symmetry conditions. The results are summarized below.

Here again we must emphasize that the inequality symbol means that the symmetry conditions do not impose an equality. However, as noted previously, within experimental error certain axes or angles may appear to be equal. In that case careful experimental observation of the arrangement of the atoms may show the true symmetry. For example, by an observation of the unit cell parameters alone one may find that a = b = c and $\alpha = \beta = \gamma = 90°$ within experimental accuracy. However, by a more complete analysis it might become clear that the atoms in the cell are arranged so that there are only axes of 2-fold symmetry (orthorhombic crystal system). This is an example of what in conventional group theory terminology is called accidental degeneracy.

| | | |
|---|---|---|
| 1(E) or $\bar{1}$(i) | Triclinic | $a \neq b \neq c$<br>$\alpha \neq \beta \neq \gamma$ |
| $2(C_2)$ or $\bar{2}(\sigma)$ | Monoclinic | $a \neq b \neq c$<br>$\alpha = \beta = 90° \neq \gamma$<br>(1st setting)<br>$\alpha = \gamma = 90° \neq \beta$<br>(2nd setting) |
| two 2-fold or $\bar{2}$ axes | Orthorhombic | $a \neq b \neq c$<br>$\alpha = \beta = \gamma = 90°$ |
| $4(C_4)$ or $\bar{4}(S_4^3)$ | Tetragonal | $a = b \neq c$<br>$\alpha = \beta = \gamma = 90°$ |
| four 3-fold or $\bar{3}$ axes | Cubic | $a = b = c$<br>$\alpha = \beta = \gamma = 90°$ |
| $6(C_6)$ or $\bar{6}(S_3^5)$ | Hexagonal | $a = b \neq c$<br>$\alpha = \beta = 90°; \gamma = 120°$ |
| $3(C_3)$ or $\bar{3}(S_6^5)$ | Trigonal<br>(Rhombohedral) | same as hexagonal<br>($a = b = c$; $\alpha = \beta = \gamma$) |

## Problems

**1.** (a) Show that the volume of a unit cell is given by

$$abc\,(1 - \cos^2\alpha - \cos^2\beta - \cos^2\gamma + 2\cos\alpha\cos\beta\cos\gamma)^{1/2}$$

(b) Prove that in a given lattice all primitive unit cells are equal in volume irrespective of the choice of axes. (c) Show that the distance between two points at $\mathbf{r}_1$ and $\mathbf{r}_2$ is

$$[(x_1-x_2)^2 a^2 + (y_1-y_2)^2 b^2 + (z_1-z_2)^2 c^2 + 2(x_1-x_2)(y_1-y_2)\,ab\cos\gamma + 2(y_1-y_2)(z_1-z_2)bc\cos\alpha + 2(z_1-z_2)(x_1-x_2)ca\cos\beta]^{1/2}.$$

**2.** Assuming the presence of a single $\bar{4}(S_4{}^3)$ axis prove, using the matrices in Appendix 1, that $a = b \neq c$ and that $\alpha = \beta = \gamma = 90°$. Find the relationship between the axes and angles when a unit cell has a mirror plane $m(\sigma)$ containing a $2(C_2)$ axis.

**3.** Prove that in a crystal if there is more than one 3-fold axis there are four in total.

**4.** Sketch any object which has cubic symmetry but does not contain a $4(C_4)$ axis.

**5.** Show that using the three operations i, $C_4$<001>, and $C_3$<111> in the cubic system will result in a total of 48 operations.

# Chapter 3

## THE 14 BRAVAIS LATTICES

*Neither the labor which the hand does nor that of the foot is contrary to nature, so long as the foot does the foot's work and the hand the hand's.*

*Marcus Aurelius, "To Himself"*

### 3-1 Introduction

The object of this chapter is to show that there are only 14 distinct lattices that fill all space. These lattices are called the **14 space lattices**, or more often, the **14 Bravais lattices**.

As we have already seen in the previous chapter, there are seven crystal systems. It might be thought that by combining the seven crystal systems with the idea of a primitive lattice a total of seven distinct Bravais lattices would be obtained, one for each crystal system. However, it turns out that the trigonal and hexagonal lattices so constructed are equivalent, and therefore only six are, in fact, formed in this way. These lattices, to which we give the label **P**, define **primitive unit cells** or **P-cells** in each case.

The other eight Bravais lattices arise by taking each of the six P-lattices and considering what happens when other lattice points are added, related by certain centering conditions. The first question is, after centering, is the new arrangement still a lattice? The second question is, does it form a new lattice? This results in eight centered lattices, seven of which are given a name (body-centered, all-face-centered, one-face-centered) and a new symbol (I, F, and A, B, or C). The last new lattice is a specially centered hexagonal lattice which, as we shall see in Section 3-3f, can be regarded after appropriate redefinition of axes of reference as a primitive rhombohedral lattice.

As we shall see, one crystal system can have all four space lattices (P, I, F, and C) while some crystal systems can have only the P-lattice. For each crystal system, it is clear that the I-, F-, or C-lattice has a unit cell that contains more then one lattice point since we have added lattice points in various centered positions. Cells with more than one lattice point are sometimes known as **multiply-primitive unit cells** as described in Section 2-2. It is convenient, and conventional, to use these multiply-primitive unit cells formed in this manner when dealing with Bravais lattices. These so-called **centered unit cells** are discussed in detail in Section 3-2. Using this convention, all the space lattices in a given crystal system will be referred to the same axes. Thus, all of these conventional, centered unit cells will display exactly the same rotational symmetry as the corresponding P-cell in a given crystal system. However, it is important to realize that for any of these new I-, F- or C-lattices it is always possible to choose a smaller unit cell that has only one lattice point in it. This primitive unit cell of an I-, F-, or C-lattice is a perfectly acceptable unit cell since by translation of its lattice vectors the entire space lattice will be reproduced. The disadvantage is that such a unit cell by itself does not neatly, in a clear manner, display the full rotational symmetry of the crystal system. Thus, primitive cells of I-, F-, or C-lattices are not conventionally used by crystallographers. On the other hand, solid state scientists often use such a primitive unit cell for problems concerning electronic band theory and lattice vibrations or in any counting problem (the number of allowed electronic or vibrational states). This is possible because a primitive unit cell still has the full translational symmetry of the lattice and thus has the full translational symmetry of the Hamiltonian. These remarks will become clearer when these primitive cells are discussed in Section 3-4.

## 3-2 Centering of Lattices

As we have mentioned in Section 3-1, the assignation of axes of reference in relation to the rotational symmetry of the crystal systems defines six lattices which, by definition, are primitive or P-lattices. For these lattices we should like to determine if more points can be added in such a way that the lattice condition is still maintained. At the same time, this addition of points must not alter the crystal system. These are the two conditions which are necessary if we wish to form a new space or Bravais lattice. For example, if we start with a simple cubic primitive lattice and add some other lattice points in such a way that we still have a

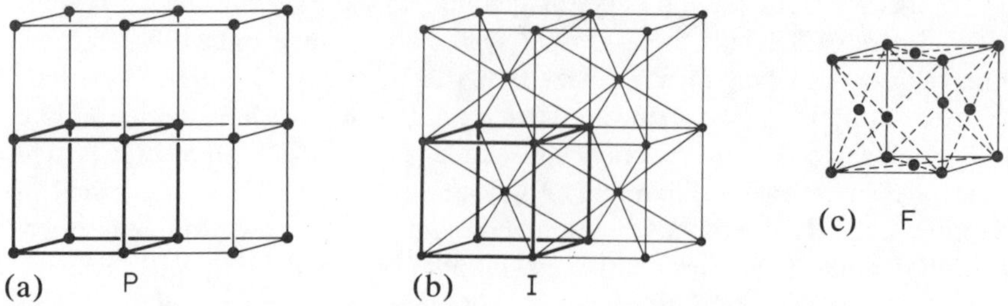


**Fig. 3-1** Two types of centering are shown. (a)Four unit cells (not necessarily cubic). (b)Body centering — all four unit cells are shown. (c)All-face centering — only one unit cell is shown for clarity.

lattice, we also want to make sure that the lattice still possesses cubic symmetry.

We shall discuss the addition of lattice points in general in this section and the specific results for each crystal system in the next section. Since the lattice condition must be maintained when these new points are added, the points must be added to highly symmetric positions of the P-lattice. These types of positions are: a single point at the body center of each unit cell; a point at the center of each independent face of the unit cell; a point at the center of one face of the unit cell (points at the centers of two independent faces of the unit cell do not permit a lattice to be formed, as we shall see later); and the special centering positions in the trigonal system that give a rhombohedral lattice (see Section 2-3f). We shall discuss each type of centering separately. Then in Section 3-3 we consider each crystal system separately and determine if within the crystal system the various kinds of centering maintain the lattice condition and form a new kind of lattice.

**3-2a Body centering (I)** To have this kind of centering, an additional point must be placed at the end of the vector $(\mathbf{a}/2+\mathbf{b}/2+\mathbf{c}/2)$. The result is shown in Fig. 3-1b, which indicates a point in the body center of the unit cell. The result is a lattice, given the symbol I (from the German Innenzentrierung). Notice that this unit cell (always provided that a lattice is formed) will now contain two lattice points, one at the origin of the unit cell (0,0,0), and one at the body center (1/2, 1/2, 1/2). The other lattice points in the diagram belong to neighboring unit cells. Or alternatively, one may say that 1/8 of a lattice point is at each of the eight corners of the unit cell and one lattice point is at the body-center position, although there is no intrinsic difference between the lattice points at the corner or at the body center. (A better way of looking at this is to displace the origin of the unit cell away from a lattice point, remembering that the choice of origin is entirely arbitrary, in which case both lattice points are seen to be contained completely within the unit cell.)

**3-2b Face centering (F)** For this type of centering three new points are added to the initial primitive unit cell. They are placed at the centers of each of the faces of the unit cell or at positions described by the end points of vectors (**a**/2+**b**/2), (**a**/2+**c**/2) and (**b**/2+**c**/2). The lattice so obtained is given the symbol F. The conventional unit cell shown in Fig. 3-1c contains four lattice points, which at (0,0,0), (1/2, 1/2, 0), (1/2, 0, 1/2), and (0, 1/2, 1/2). Alternatively, one may say that this unit cell contains 1/8 of a lattice point at each of the eight corners and 1/2 of a lattice point at each of the six faces.

**3-2c One-face centering (base centering)** In this centering only one face is centered, not all three. If the centering is in the **ab**-plane (at **a**/2+**b**/2), the lattice which results is given the symbol C. Similarly the lattice is given the symbol A if the centering is on the **bc**-plane and B, if the centering is on the **ac**-plane. In each case there are two lattice points per unit cell. These are

| | |
|---|---|
| for A centering: | (0,0,0) and (0, 1/2, 1/2) |
| for B centering: | (0,0,0) and (1/2, 0, 1/2) |
| for C centering: | (0,0,0) and (1/2, 1/2, 0) |

Examples of B- and C-centering will be shown later in Fig. 3-4.

**3-2d Two-face centering** Figure 3-2 shows that the centering of two independent faces can never form a lattice, since the environment of all the points (as indicated, for example, by the dashed lines) is not the same no matter how one picks the translation vectors.

**3-2e Special centering R** We have already mentioned in the last chapter that a trigonal unit cell can be centered in a very special manner to give a rhombohedral cell. There are two possible rhombohedral centering positions, at ±(2/3, 1/3, 1/3) and ±(1/3, 2/3, 1/3), as described in Section 2-3f. The resulting lattice is given the symbol R. There is a good deal of confusion with respect to the rhombohedral lattice and it is best to consult Section 3-3f. Part of this confusion results from the fact that the rhombohedral lattice can be referred to rhombohedral axes, thus resulting

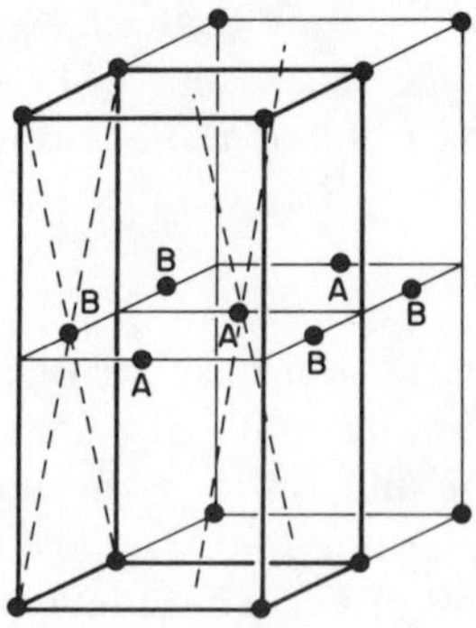


**Fig. 3-2** An impossible way to center a lattice.

in a rhombohedral unit cell with one lattice point, or the lattice can be referred to hexagonal axes with a unit cell that looks hexagonal and has three lattice points per cell.

It is possible to body-center or face-center the rhombohedral lattice. However such lattices are not new lattices since an R-lattice can still be formed, but with different angles between the axes and with only one lattice point per cell. Examples of this are shown in Fig. 3-3.

## 3-3 The 14 Bravais Lattices

In order to discuss the 14 Bravais lattices, we shall consider the seven crystal systems in turn and show what sort of unique space lattices can be formed in each case. As in the previous chapter, we shall start with the lowest symmetry, triclinic, and progressively go on to crystal systems of higher symmetry. As before, however, we shall leave the trigonal and hexagonal systems till last. Figure 3-4 shows the 14 Bravais lattices.

**3-3a Triclinic** In this system there are no restrictions on the magnitudes of the translation vectors, i.e., the lengths of the unit cell axes, nor on their directions, i.e., the interaxial angles. Therefore, we can always take a triclinic lattice and center it and a lattice will, indeed, be formed compatible with the conditions of the triclinic crystal system. However, there is nothing new about this lattice. A smaller primitive cell can be determined with the same complete arbitrariness of the cell edges and

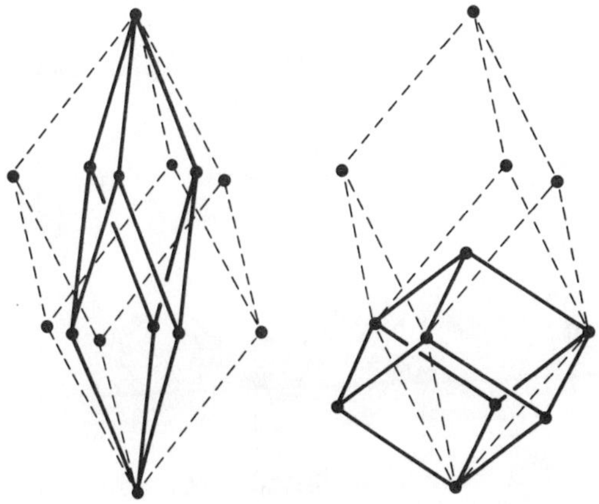

**Fig. 3-3** A rhombohedral unit cell shown face centered and body centered.

angles. Thus, for the triclinic crystal system there is only one Bravais lattice, the primitive or P-lattice.

**3-3b Monoclinic** Figure 3-5 shows several aspects of centering of a monoclinic unit cell. In this paragraph we use the "1st setting" which takes the unique 2-fold axis as the **c**-axis. As can be seen in Fig. 3-5b, if one attempts to center the C-face (**ab**-plane) nothing new is obtained. The lattice can still be described as a P-lattice with a different value of **a** and $\gamma$ but the fundamental monoclinic conditions, **c** perpendicular to both **a** and **b**, $\gamma \neq 90°$, and all axes with unequal lengths, are retained. Thus, we say P = C for the monoclinic crystal system. However, a new lattice is obtained if the B-face is centered as shown in Fig. 3-5c. This is because it is not possible to maintain the fundamental monoclinic conditions and yet describe this lattice as a P-lattice. An attempt at this is shown in Fig. 3-5c (dashed cell), where with regard to this P-cell the 2-fold symmetry appears to be absent. Of course we know that the lattice still possesses a 2-fold axis. The multiply-primitive unit cell outlined with a full line in Fig. 3-5c displays the 2-fold axis and this is the conventional unit cell. A lattice centered in this way is called a B-lattice and it is also shown in Fig. 3-4 where all the 14 Bravais lattices are shown. In an identical manner the **bc**-plane can be centered to give rise to an A-lattice. It is usual, if one is dealing with a crystal not previously described, to choose the axes to give a B-lattice rather than the equivalent A-lattice (B = A), although there is no strict rule about this. One can also show that by appropriate choice of the **a**- and **b**-axes, monoclinic F- and I-lattices can

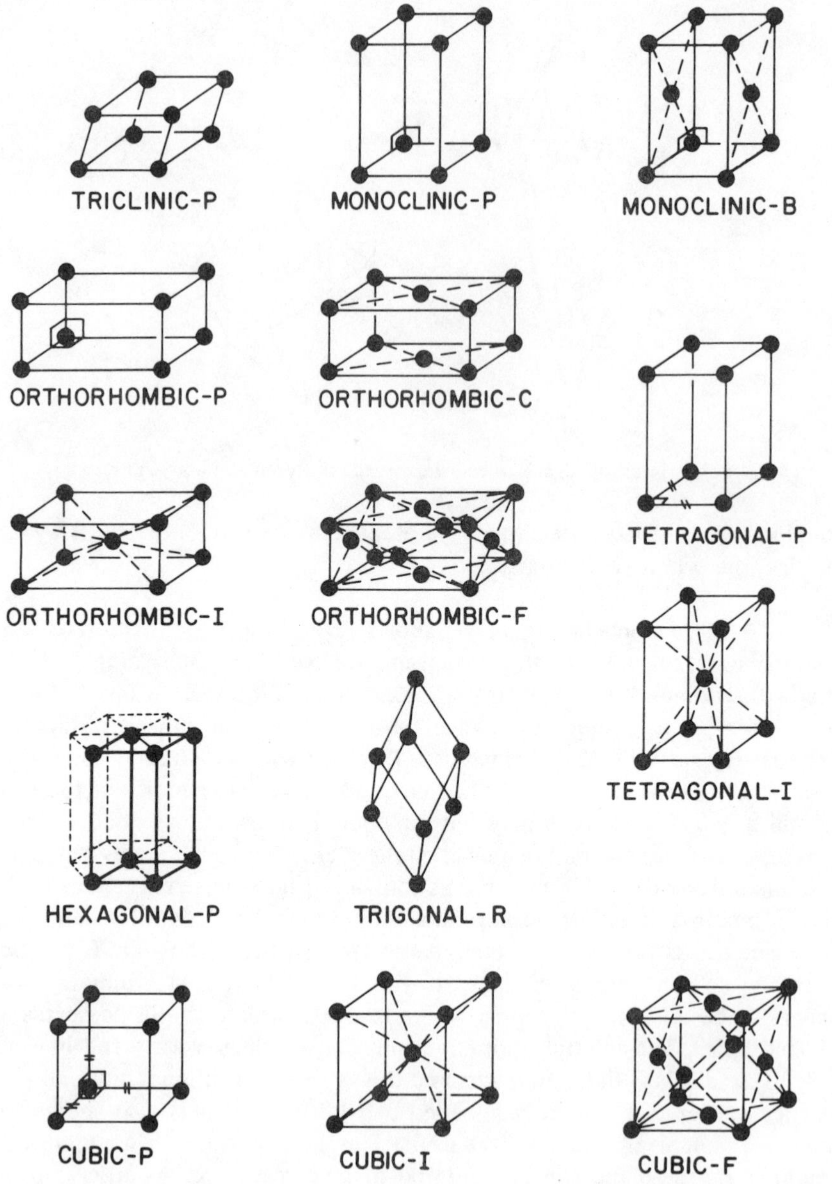


**Fig. 3-4** The conventional unit cell for each of the 14 Bravais lattices. (The hexagonal unit cell is outlined in black. The dashed prism shown only serves to help indicate the angles of the unit cell.)

also be described by a B-centered lattice (B = F = I = A). It is conventional, but not strictly so, to use B-centering in preference to the others. There are therefore two unique monoclinic Bravais lattices, P and B (see Fig. 3-4).

The "2nd setting," the convention preferred by crystallographers, takes the unique 2-fold axis as the **b**-axis. In this case, the above discussion is still appropriate except for the interchange of axes. Thus, in this setting the P-lattice and C-lattice are unique monoclinic Bravais lattices and C = F = I = A, C being the usual choice.

**3-3c Orthorhombic** We may consider a primitive orthorhombic lattice to arise from a primitive monoclinic lattice with the added restriction that the third angle must also be 90°. Then all the unit cell translation vectors are 90° to one another but with different lengths. As in the case of the monoclinic crystal system, an orthorhombic base-centered lattice is a new lattice that cannot be described as a P-lattice and yet retain orthorhombic symmetry. However, in the orthorhombic crystal system any one face may be centered, but if we try to construct a primitive unit cell from it, in just the same way as we did for the monoclinic C-centered cell in Fig. 3-5b, we would find that the axes so obtained are not orthogonal. Thus, we have a C-centered lattice which can also be described as an A- or B-lattice by an interchange of the orthogonal axes. In this crystal system the all-face-centered F-lattice and the body-centered I-lattice are also distinct from the P- or C-lattices. Thus, for the orthorhombic crystal system there are four unique Bravais lattices, P, I, F, and C. All four are illustrated in Fig. 3-4. (Again we note that C-, A-, and B-face centering form identical lattices but with a redefinition of the axes.)

**3-3d Tetragonal** We already know that a lattice is not obtained if two faces, the A- and B-faces, are centered as discussed in Section 3-2d. Furthermore, the tetragonal condition of 4-fold symmetry is not maintained if only one of these two faces is centered. Thus, for one-face centering, only the C-face centering need be considered. Centering this face does result in a lattice, but as can be seen in Fig. 3-6a, the lattice is the same as a P-lattice rotated by 45° about the **c**-axis. Thus, in the tetragonal crystal system, P = C. Since the primitive cell is the smaller of the two cells (one lattice point per cell compared with two), the P-cell is usually chosen.

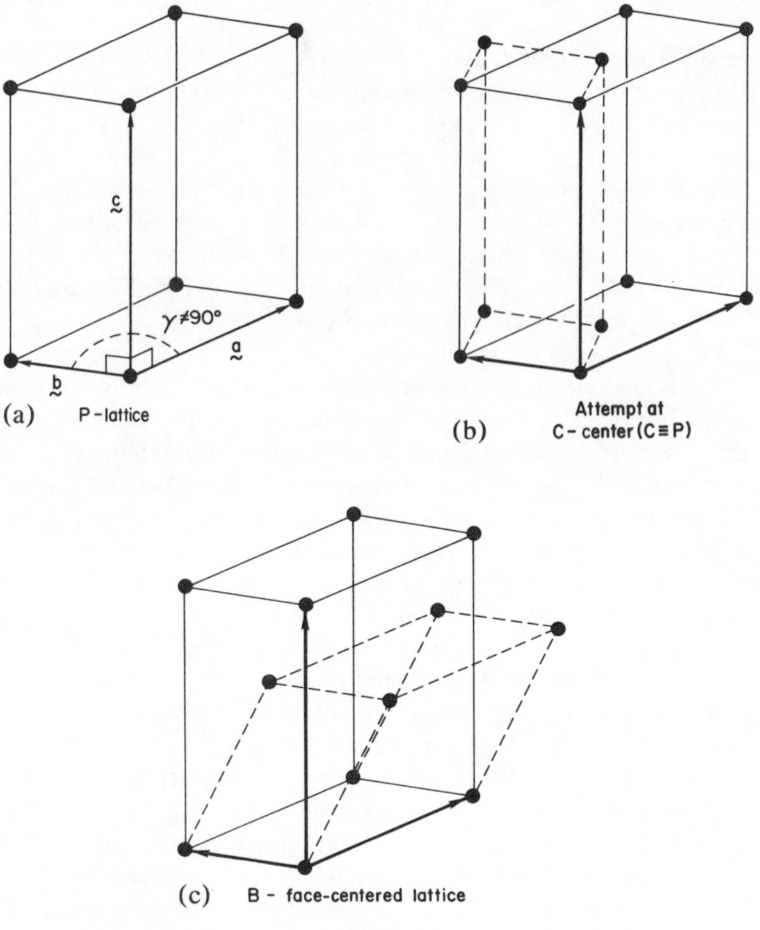


**Fig. 3-5** Several aspects of centering a monoclinic lattice.

Now consider the effect of body-centering. As in the orthorhombic lattice, body-centering of a tetragonal lattice still gives us a lattice. The surroundings of every point are still identical, with each point having eight nearest neighbors at the same distance and in the same directions. The 4-fold symmetry is maintained. Thus, the I-lattice is a new lattice in the tetragonal crystal system.

Face-centering also gives a lattice in the tetragonal crystal system. However, just as a P-lattice can be obtained from a C-lattice by new tetragonal axes rotated 45° to the old ones, an I-lattice can be obtained from the F-lattice. This is shown in Fig. 3-6b. Thus, F = I in the tetrago-

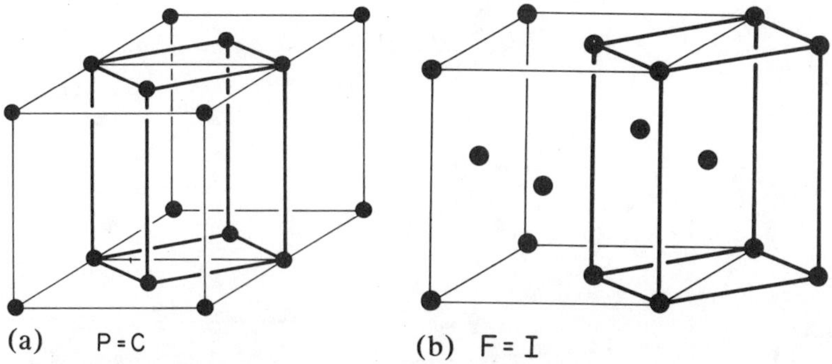


**Fig. 3-6** Several aspects of centering a tetragonal lattice.

nal system and since the I-cell is smaller than the F-cell, the I-cell is usually preferred.

Therefore, we see that for the tetragonal crystal system there are only two distinct Bravais lattices, the P-lattice and the I-lattice (and C = P and F = I).

**3-3e Cubic** Figure 3-1b effectively shows a primitive cubic lattice that has been centered by placing a lattice point at the body-center position. It is clear that a new lattice is formed. Each point is surrounded by eight other nearest-neighbor points, all in the same relative positions no matter from which point one observes. In addition the four 3-fold axes are preserved and so the system remains cubic. Therefore the cubic crystal system can have an I-lattice, sometimes denoted **bcc (body-centered cubic)**. Figure 3-1c shows the result when extra points are added at the face centers of the primitive cubic unit cell. Close observation will reveal that a lattice is again formed. Every lattice point is surrounded by twelve nearest-neighbor points. Once more it is obvious that the four 3-fold axes remain. This F-lattice is sometimes denoted **fcc (face-centered cubic)**. It is clear that the cubic crystal system cannot have a base-centered lattice because centering only one face would destroy the four 3-fold axes of symmetry. Thus we conclude that there are three cubic Bravais lattices, P, I, and F. These are shown in Fig. 3-4.

**3-3f Hexagonal, Trigonal (and Rhombohedral)** As we have already seen in Section 2-3f, there are some complications and confusing points that crop up when dealing with these systems. In this section, we shall go into detail about the centering of trigonal and hexagonal lattices.

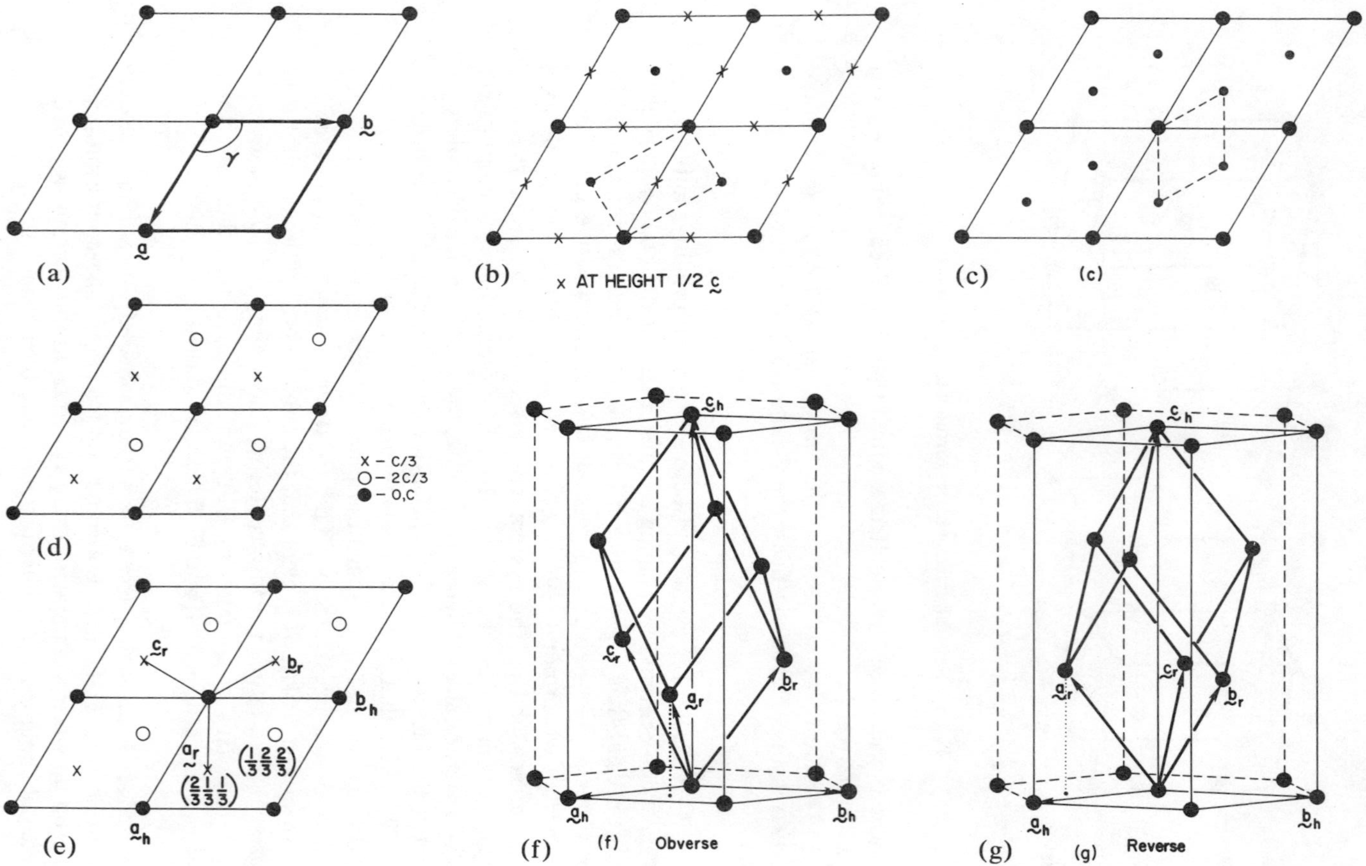


**Fig. 3-7** Various aspects of the hexagonal, trigonal and rhombohedral lattices.

In Fig. 3-7a we have drawn four primitive unit cells with hexagonal axes, one of which is outlined more heavily than the rest. Now let us try to center it in the same way as we have been centering cells for the other crystal systems. In Fig. 3-7b we have shown how this grouping of four primitive cells can be centered in several ways. First, consider the solid circles at the base center of each primitive cell [at the position ($\mathbf{a}/2+\mathbf{b}/2$)]. It is clear that a hexagonal or trigonal lattice is not formed since the 6, $\bar{6}$, 3, or $\bar{3}$ symmetry is not retained. In fact the crystal system is orthorhombic as shown by the dashed lines in the figure. If, on the other hand, the solid circles are placed at the body-centered position [at ($\mathbf{a}/2+\mathbf{b}/2+\mathbf{c}/2$)] a hexagonal or trigonal lattice is again not formed. Now consider face centering. Centering on the side faces is represented by the x's in Fig. 3-7b. Consideration of the environments of these points again shows that a hexagonal or trigonal lattice is not formed. Figure 3-7c shows the same four primitive cells as in Fig. 3-7a but centered at positions (1/3, 2/3, 0) and (2/3, 1/3, 0). A lattice is now formed, and the symmetry elements are maintained. However, this lattice is really still primitive, as can be seen from the dashed lines in Fig. 3-7c; these form a hexagonal primitive unit cell but in a different orientation and with different axial lengths from the original cell.

On the other hand, by centering the primitive lattice at the two positions (1/3, 2/3, 2/3) and (2/3, 1/3, 1/3), which is the same as $\pm$(1/3, 2/3, 2/3), we produce a new lattice, as shown in Fig. 3-7d where the heights along the $\mathbf{c}$-axis are indicated by the key. It is fairly clear that the surroundings of every point are identical and so a lattice is formed. Notice, however, that the lattice no longer has 6 or $\bar{6}$ symmetry but has $\bar{3}$ symmetry. As explained in Chapter 2 it is now possible to define a new cell which is a rhombohedron. Its edges, shown in Figs. 3-7e and 2-8, are the basic translation vectors of a new lattice, the rhombohedral lattice. It is evident from the figure that the rhombohedral unit cell is primitive. (The rhombohedral cell so obtained is in the obverse setting with respect to the hexagonal axes; the meaning of obverse and reverse will be explained shortly.) Thus we have seen that by centering the cell shown in Fig. 3-7a in this special way, a new lattice can be formed, the rhombohedral lattice. We have also seen that this Bravais lattice can always be referred to the hexagonal axes shown in Fig. 3-7a, in which case there are three lattice points per unit cell. Thus, we have two choices with which to describe the unit cell of this rhombohedral R-lattice. We may pick the primitive unit cell which has a = b = c and $\alpha = \beta = \gamma$ with the 3-fold axis making equal angles with the three axes, or we may take the 3-fold axis as a principal axis **c**. The latter is conventionally referred to as the rhombohedral unit cell specified with **hexagonal axes of reference**, with $a = b \neq c$, $\alpha = \beta = 90°$, $\gamma = 120°$. The symbol **R** is used for rhombohedral lattice no matter whether specified on hexagonal or rhombohedral axes of reference. As we shall see in the next chapter, the Schoenflies symbol also makes no distinction between the two sets of axes of reference.

Note a last point of confusion: we have centered a trigonal cell to give a rhombohedral unit cell and then we go ahead and describe the rhombohedral unit cell in terms of what we call, by convention, "hexagonal axes of reference," even though it is impossible to obtain a rhombohedral unit cell from a true hexagonal unit cell where 6 or $\bar{6}$ symmetry is maintained. Strictly speaking, therefore, we should say "trigonal" rather than "hexagonal." However, "hexagonal" is the common usage and it would cause even more confusion to alter it now. The reason for its use is that as far as the primitive lattice, Fig. 3-7a, is concerned there is no distinction between hexagonal and trigonal (see Section 2-3f); only when we consider the centering of the unit cell can we make any distinction. Although the primitive rhombohedral unit cell has the advantage of containing only one lattice point, it is frequently simpler to consider the unit cell with hexagonal axes of reference. This is because hexagonal coodinates are considerably easier to deal with than rhombohedral coordinates, especially when one is trying to visualize the crystal structure.

Note that the rhombohedral axes can be orientated in two ways relative to the set of hexagonal axes. Instead of choosing our centering at $\pm(2/3, 1/3, 1/3)$, we could have chosen $\pm(1/3, 2/3, 1/3)$. The rhombohedron, thus constructed, would be turned through 180° with respect to the previous one. The two settings are given the names **obverse** for the first centering and **reverse** for the second. These are shown in Figs. 3-7f and 3-7g with respect to a fixed set of hexagonal axes. It is generally considered best, in order to avoid confusion, to keep to the obverse setting wherever possible; and this is the usage we shall keep to here.

For convenience, it is worthwhile writing the relationships connecting the rhombohedral and hexagonal coordinate systems. The axes are defined in Figs. 3-7e and 3-7f, where the subscript r refers to rhombohedral and h to hexagonal. In order to convert from hexagonal to rhombohedral axes, we have

$$\begin{bmatrix} a_r \\ b_r \\ c_r \end{bmatrix} = \begin{bmatrix} 2/3 & 1/3 & 1/3 \\ -1/3 & 1/3 & 1/3 \\ -1/3 & -2/3 & 1/3 \end{bmatrix} \begin{bmatrix} a_h \\ b_h \\ c_h \end{bmatrix} \qquad (3\text{-}1a)$$

From this we can write

$$\mathbf{a}_r = (2/3)\mathbf{a}_h + (1/3)\mathbf{b}_h + (1/3)\mathbf{c}_h \tag{3-1b}$$

If we take the scalar product of $\mathbf{a}_r$ with itself, we find

$$\mathbf{a}_r\bullet\mathbf{a}_r = a_r^2 = (4/9)a_h^2 + (1/9)b_h^2 + (1/9)c_h^2 + (4/9)a_h b_h \cos 120^\circ \tag{3-1c}$$

which simplifies to

$$a_r = (1/3)(3a_h^2 + c_h^2)^{1/2} = (a_h/3)(3 + c_h^2/a_h^2)^{1/2} \tag{3-1d}$$

The rhombohedral angle can be found by proceeding in a similar way. We take the scalar product of $\mathbf{a}_r$ and $\mathbf{b}_r$:

$$\begin{aligned}\mathbf{a}_r\bullet\mathbf{b}_r &= [(2/3)\mathbf{a}_h+(1/3)\mathbf{b}_h+(1/3)\mathbf{c}_h]\bullet[-(1/3)\mathbf{a}_h+(1/3)\mathbf{b}_h+(1/3)\mathbf{c}_h] \\ &= -(2/9)a_h^2 + (1/9)b_h^2 + (1/9)c_h^2 + (1/9)a_h\, b_h \cos 120^\circ\end{aligned} \tag{3-2a}$$

But

$$\mathbf{a}_r\bullet\mathbf{b}_r = a_r^2 \cos \gamma_r \tag{3-2b}$$

and therefore we can write that

$$\begin{aligned}\cos \alpha_r &= \cos \beta_r = \cos \gamma_r \\ &= [(1/3)(c_h/a_h)^2 - (1/2)]/[(1/3)(c_h/a_h)^2 + 1]\end{aligned} \tag{3-2c}$$

If we wish to transform from rhombohedral to hexagonal axes of reference, we have

$$\begin{bmatrix} a_h \\ b_h \\ c_h \end{bmatrix} = \begin{bmatrix} 1 & -1 & 0 \\ 0 & 1 & -1 \\ 1 & 1 & 1 \end{bmatrix} \begin{bmatrix} a_r \\ b_r \\ c_r \end{bmatrix} \tag{3-3a}$$

This tranformation matrix is simply the inverse of the preceding one, and yields

$$c_h/a_h = 3[1 - (4/3)\sin^2 (\alpha_r/2)]^{1/2}/[2 \sin (\alpha_r/2)] \tag{3-3b}$$

$$a_h = 2a_r \sin (\alpha_r/2) \tag{3-3c}$$

Note that if we wish to transform coordinates from one orientation to the other, the transformation matrices are the transposed inverses of the preceding ones. That is, if the matrix A converts unit cell axes from orientation 1 to orientation 2, and matrix B converts coordinates from orientation 1 to orientation 2, $B = (\widetilde{A^{-1}})$.

This can be proved quite simply as follows. Matrix B converts coordinates $(x_o,y_o,z_o)$ to $(x_n,y_n,z_n)$ and matrix A converts unit cell axes $\mathbf{a}_o$, $\mathbf{b}_o$, $\mathbf{c}_o$ to $\mathbf{a}_n$, $\mathbf{b}_n$, $\mathbf{c}_n$. That is

$$\begin{bmatrix} a_n \\ b_n \\ c_n \end{bmatrix} = A \begin{bmatrix} a_o \\ b_o \\ c_o \end{bmatrix} \quad \text{and} \quad \begin{bmatrix} x_n \\ y_n \\ z_n \end{bmatrix} = B \begin{bmatrix} x_o \\ y_o \\ z_o \end{bmatrix} \tag{3-4}$$

Now, the vector $x_o\mathbf{a}_o + y_o\mathbf{b}_o + z_o\mathbf{c}_o$ must be invariant under the transformation (passive operation) of the unit cell axes and we can write

$$x_n\mathbf{a}_n + y_n\mathbf{b}_n + z_n\mathbf{c}_n = x_o\mathbf{a}_o + y_o\mathbf{b}_o + z_o\mathbf{c}_o \tag{3-5}$$

This is

$$(a_nb_nc_n) \begin{bmatrix} x_n \\ y_n \\ z_n \end{bmatrix} = (a_ob_oc_o) \begin{bmatrix} x_o \\ y_o \\ z_o \end{bmatrix} = (a_ob_oc_o)B^{-1} \begin{bmatrix} x_n \\ y_n \\ z_n \end{bmatrix} \tag{3-6}$$

Therefore

$$(a_nb_nc_n) = (a_ob_oc_o)B^{-1} \tag{3-7}$$

Now, in order to form column vectors as in Eq. 3-4, we must write

$$\begin{bmatrix} a_n \\ b_n \\ c_n \end{bmatrix} = (\widetilde{B^{-1}}) \begin{bmatrix} a_o \\ b_o \\ c_o \end{bmatrix} \tag{3-8}$$

But this matrix $(\widetilde{B^{-1}})$ is clearly the same as A from Eq. 3-4.

In this case, in order to transform hexagonal coordinates to rhombohedral coordinates, we use

$$\begin{bmatrix} x_r \\ y_r \\ z_r \end{bmatrix} = \begin{bmatrix} 1 & 0 & 1 \\ -1 & 1 & 1 \\ 0 & -1 & 1 \end{bmatrix} \begin{bmatrix} x_h \\ y_h \\ z_h \end{bmatrix} \tag{3-9a}$$

and for conversion in the opposite direction:

$$\begin{bmatrix} x_h \\ y_h \\ z_h \end{bmatrix} = \begin{bmatrix} 2/3 & -1/3 & -1/3 \\ 1/3 & 1/3 & -2/3 \\ 1/3 & 1/3 & 1/3 \end{bmatrix} \begin{bmatrix} x_r \\ y_r \\ z_r \end{bmatrix} \tag{3-9b}$$

## 3-4 Primitive Cells of the 14 Bravais Lattices

For each of the I, F, or C Bravais lattices we have 2, 4, and 2 lattice points, respectively, in the conventionally chosen unit cells shown in Fig. 3-4. As mentioned in Section 3-1, for each of these lattices it is possible to pick unit cells that are smaller by factors of 2, 4, and 2, respectively, so that each of these new unit cells will contain just one lattice point. Thus, for each of the centered unit cells it is always possible to find a primitive cell. As we shall see, these primitive cells by themselves (when isolated from the lattice) do not display the full symmetry of the particular system. However, they are unit cells, since when translated parallel to themselves by their translation vectors they will fill all space and result in the original lattice. The examples will make this clear.

Figure 3-8a shows a primitive cell constructed from an F-lattice. As can be seen, there is only one lattice point in this unit cell. The basic translation vectors of the primitive cell of an F-lattice in terms of the translation vectors of the conventional F Bravais lattice are also shown. The basic translation vectors of a primitive cell as well as the primitive cells of the I and C Bravais lattices are also given in Figs. 3-8b and 3-8c.

From the primitive cell of a cubic F Bravais lattice one can no longer find four 3-fold axes. Thus the isolated primitive cell of a cubic F-lattice does not have cubic symmetry. However, that is not a requirement of a unit cell. All that is required of it is that it generates the lattice by repeated translation. From a visual point of view, it is easier to think of the crystal structure when working with a unit cell that has the full symmetry of the lattice. Therefore, one can appreciate why the conventional unit cells of the Bravais lattices are usually used. The conventional unit cells of these 14 Bravais lattices display the full rotational symmetry of the various crystal systems in a clear manner, while the primitive cells of the F, I, and C Bravais lattices do not. It is worth repeating here that solid state physicists and chemists often prefer to work with the primitive cell, even though this means working with a cell of lower symmetry. This is because the primitive cell contains one lattice point per cell: thus it is the smallest cell that describes the full translational invariance of the Hamiltonian. For counting problems such as in the evaluation of normal modes of vibration or electronic states in band theory, working with the primitive cell will always give the correct number of states. One can use the ordinary Bravais cell for these problems, but one must take care to allow always for the effect of centering and divide the resulting number of modes or states by the number of lattice points in the cell. The conventional isolated primitive cells of the cubic F-lattice and cubic I-lattice shown in Fig. 3-8 are rhombohedral with rhombohedral angles $\alpha = 60°$ and $109°28'$, respectively.

Remember that the choice of primitive cell is not unique, as was shown in Fig. 2-2. However, the primitive cells shown in Fig. 3-8 are the conventional primitive cells used by most solid state scientists.

(a)      F-Lattice

$$\underset{\sim}{a}_1^P = (\underset{\sim}{a} + \underset{\sim}{c})/2$$

$$\underset{\sim}{a}_2^P = (\underset{\sim}{a} + \underset{\sim}{b})/2$$

$$\underset{\sim}{a}_3^P = (\underset{\sim}{b} + \underset{\sim}{c})/2$$

(b)      I-Lattice

$$\underset{\sim}{a}_1^P = (\underset{\sim}{a} + \underset{\sim}{b} - \underset{\sim}{c})/2$$

$$\underset{\sim}{a}_2^P = (-\underset{\sim}{a} + \underset{\sim}{b} + \underset{\sim}{c})/2$$

$$\underset{\sim}{a}_3^P = (\underset{\sim}{a} - \underset{\sim}{b} + \underset{\sim}{c})/2$$

(c)      C-Lattice

$$\underset{\sim}{a}_1^P = (\underset{\sim}{a} - \underset{\sim}{b})/2$$

$$\underset{\sim}{a}_2^P = (\underset{\sim}{a} + \underset{\sim}{b})/2$$

$$\underset{\sim}{a}_3^P = \underset{\sim}{c}$$

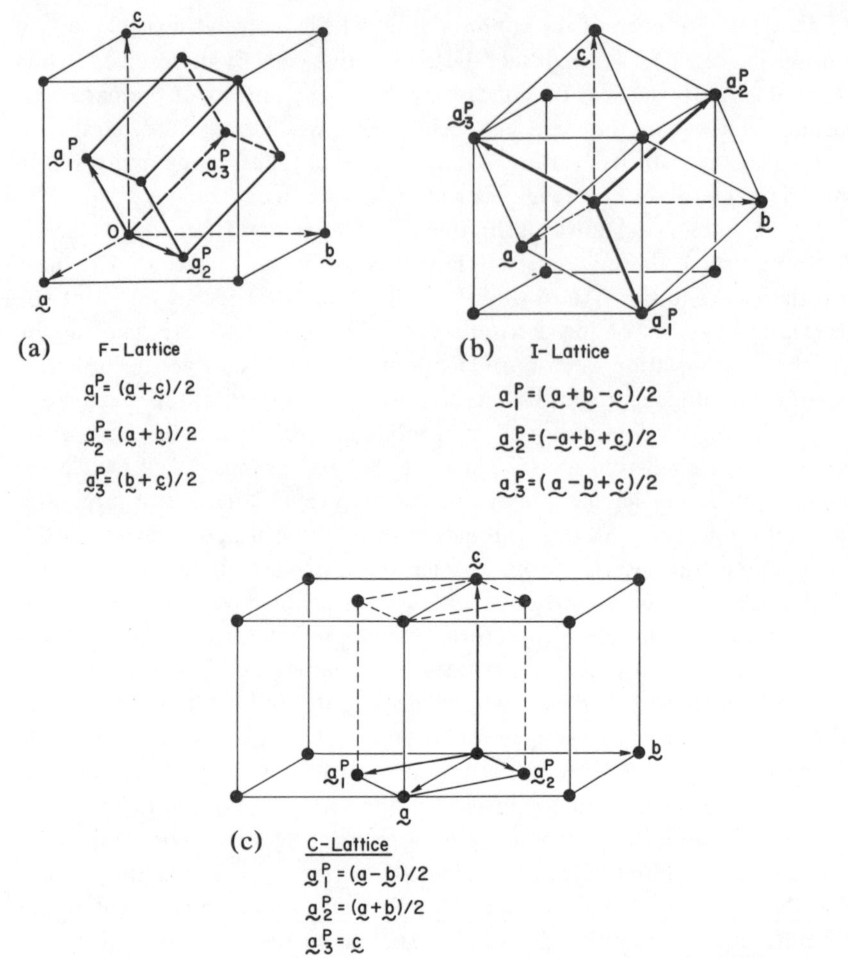

**Fig. 3-8** The conventional primitive cells of the F-, I-, and C-lattice.

### 3-5  The Wigner–Seitz Unit Cell (And Other Unit Cells)

We take this opportunity to emphasize that the conventional centered unit cells of the 14 Bravais lattices shown in Fig. 3-4 or their corresponding primitive cells shown in Fig. 3-8 are not the last word on unit cells.

Occasionally some special unit cell is chosen to emphasize certain special aspects of the crystal structure. For example, there might be a change of structure at some temperature (a phase transition) from a very

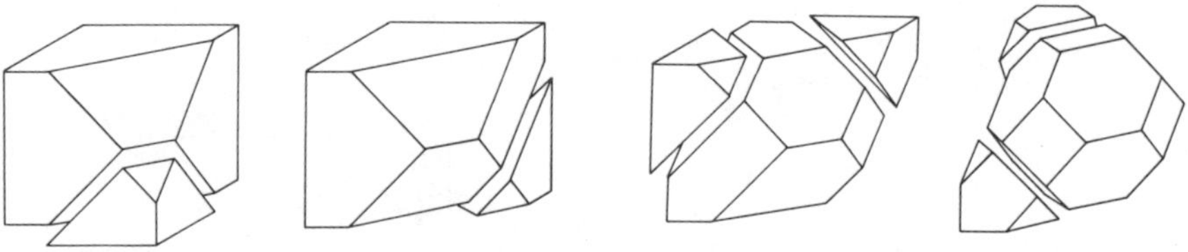

**Fig. 3-9** The construction of the Wigner–Seitz cell of a cubic I-lattice.

simple high-temperature structure to a much more complicated low-temperature structure. The unit cell chosen in the simple structure could be relatively complicated (contain many lattice points centered at various positions), but might be picked to show how the low-temperature structure follows in a natural manner from the high-temperature structure. Thus, the orientation of the axes in the high temperature structure might be chosen so that the same orientation of axes above and below the phase transition is maintained. Clearly this choice would make visualization of the phase transition easy although it may make the choice of the unit cell in the high-temperature structure unusual.

Besides this type of special choice of unit cell there is another primitive unit cell of more general use, particularly in electronic band theory. This is known as the **Wigner–Seitz cell** (sometimes called the **proximity cell** or **symmetrical unit cell**). This cell is obtained by starting at any lattice point, which we can call the origin, and drawing vectors to all neighboring lattice points. Planes are then constructed perpendicular to and passing through the midpoints of these vectors. The Wigner–Seitz cell is the cell with the smallest volume about the origin bounded by these planes.

Figure 3-9 shows a step-by-step construction of the Wigner–Seitz cell for an I-cubic lattice. Note that the Wigner–Seitz cell contains just one lattice point and yet it displays the full rotational symmetry of the crystal system as do the conventional unit cells of the 14 Bravais lattices in Fig. 3-4. Of course, the Wigner–Seitz cell does not form a parallelepiped but it is, nevertheless, a perfectly acceptable unit cell. Figures 3-10a and 10-b show the Wigner–Seitz cells for I- and F-cubic lattices, where the full cubic symmetry is again obvious. Figure 3-10c shows the Wigner–Seitz cell of an I-tetragonal Bravais lattice. The similarity to the I-cubic Wigner–Seitz cell is readily apparent especially for the case where $c < a$. Figure 3-10d shows the stacking of the Wigner–Seitz cells for an I-cubic lattice to form the complete lattice. It is

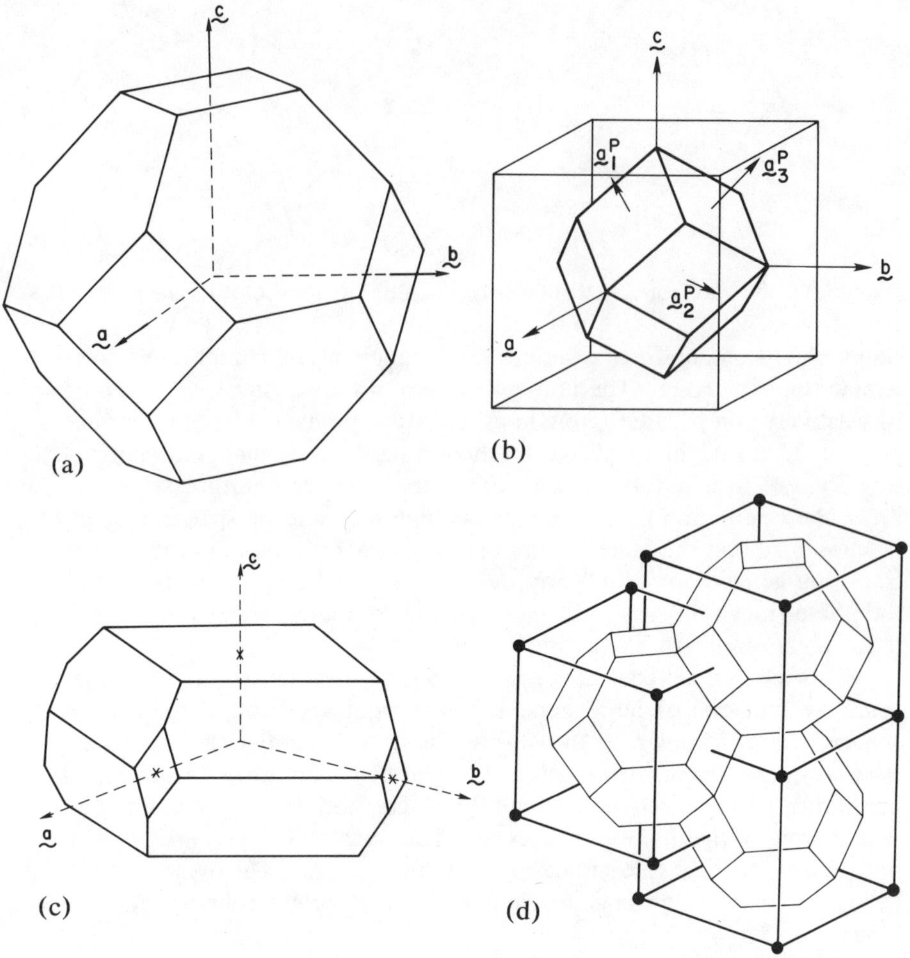


**Fig. 3-10** (a), (b), and (c) show the Wigner–Seitz cell of cubic I-lattice, a cubic F-lattice, and a tetragonal I-lattice respectively (c<a). (d) The stacking of Wigner–Seitz cells of a cubic I-lattice.

clear that translation vectors can be defined for this cell so that a true lattice will indeed be obtained.

A construction identical to the Wigner–Seitz cell construction is often used in solid state theory. This construction occurs in reciprocal space or **k**-space where the resulting cell is conventionally given the name, the **first Brillouin zone**. There are 14 first Brillouin zones corresponding to the 14 Bravais lattices. To those readers who are familiar with this we remind them that an I-lattice in space (direct space) has a reciprocal lattice that is an F-lattice. So the first Brillouin zone of an I-lattice looks like the Wigner-Seitz cell of an F-lattice and vice versa. The Brillouin zone is of great importance in lattice dynamics, where it is used in representing the phonon dispersion relations, and in band theory where it shows the allowed electron states. This aspect is discussed further in Chapter 7.

## 3-6 Two-Dimensional Lattices

It is a very simple matter to derive the 2-dimensional lattices by taking the 14 space lattices and collapsing them onto a plane. Clearly, all primitive lattices will remain primitive; in 2-dimensions they are given the symbol p. (For 2-dimensions small letters are used.) C-centered lattices when collapsed onto the **ab**-plane produce a centered 2-dimensional lattice, given the symbol c. A- and B-centered lattices when collapsed onto the **ab**-plane give halved unit cells which can be redefined as primitive; all-face-centered lattices do both. Note that in the case of the rhombohedral centering, collapsing onto a plane perpendicular to the **c**-axis produces, a primitive lattice with **a**- and **b**-axes redefined.

The 2-dimensional lattices can adopt four possible shapes, oblique (where there is no relationship between the **a**- and **b**-axes), rectangular, square, or hexagonal. Proceeding in the same way that we did for the 14 space lattices we find that there are five 2-dimensional space lattices in four crystal systems. The 2-dimensional space lattices are

| | |
|---|---|
| oblique | p |
| rectangular | p |
| rectangular | c |
| square | p |
| hexagonal | p |

All other combinations are equivalent to these five.

## Problems

**1.** (a) Show that every lattice point is at a center of inversion and that midway between neighboring lattice points there is another center of inversion. (b) By drawing a suitable diagram, show that halfway between neighboring lattice points that have a 2-fold axis, another 2-fold axis is generated. Do the same for mirror planes.

**2.** Consider cubic P-, I-, and F-lattices with the length of the conventional unit cell axis in each case given by **a**. Make a table for the three lattices showing the number of nearest neighbors for each lattice point, the distance to these neighbors, the number of second neighbors, and the distance to these second neighbors.

**3.** Again consider the cubic P-, I-, and F-lattices. Show that the maximum amount of volume that may be filled with hard spheres on the lattice points is, 0.52, 0.68, and 0.74, respectively, of the unit-cell volumes.

**4.** Work out the matrix relating hexagonal axes to reverse rhombohedral axes. A point in the hexagonal cell has coordinates $(-y, x-y, z)$. What are the coordinates of this point with respect to the reverse rhombohedral cell?

## Chapter 4

# THE 32 CRYSTALLOGRAPHIC POINT GROUPS

*In seeking wisdom, men's interests are not antagonistic. No person's gain in wisdom is diminished by anyone else's gain. Wisdom is the one commodity that is unlimited in supply.*

*Reich, "The Greening of America"*

## 4-1 Introduction

In Chapter 1 we discussed symmetry operations and their notation. In this chapter we shall consider what happens when several of these symmetry operations are combined. For example, what is the result when a rotation axis is combined with other rotation axes perpendicular to the first, or with mirror planes? These combinations of symmetry operations enable us to describe the symmetry of 3-dimensional objects.

In this chapter we shall show how the **32 crystallographic point groups** can be determined. The word "crystallographic" implies that we shall only allow rotations through $2\pi/n$ where $n = 1, 2, 3, 4,$ and 6. As discussed in Chapter 2, other rotations are not compatible with filling all space when periodic translation is considered; we only want to consider point groups that are allowed in crystals. This restriction, on allowed values of n, results in 32 point groups. Thus they are sometimes simply called the **32 point groups** since when we say "32," the word "crystallographic" becomes somewhat redundant. The word "point" means that we demand that all the symmetry elements have one point in common, which remains fixed throughout the application of all the symmetry operations. This point is called the origin. We can take the word "group" in a loose way to mean a collection or a set of symmetry operations. However, we hasten to add that the set of symmetry operations for every point group (crystallographic or not) really is a group in the mathematical sense. (Note that the concept of point groups is very important and useful for isolated molecules as well as for crystalline solids; the only difference is that for molecules there is no restriction on the allowed rotations.)

While we do not require group theoretical concepts to develop the 32 point groups, it is useful to appreciate the intimate connection between these point groups and mathematical groups. Thus, occasionally we shall point out the group theoretical aspects in this book, but even when we do not, the reader who is already acquainted with group theory will detect how the same concept can be dealt with from a group theory point of view. We take this opportunity to refresh the reader on certain elementary aspects of group theory.

A set of operations forms a **group** if and only if the following four conditions are met.

**(i)** The product of any two operations is also a member of the set (closure).

**(ii)** The set includes an identity 1(E). One can show that a right identity is also a left identity.

**(iii)** For each operation R there is an inverse $R^{-1}$, such that $RR^{-1} = 1(E)$, (e.g., $C_n^m C_n^{n-m} = E$, $\sigma\sigma = E$, $i\,i = E$, etc.).

**(iv)** The multiplication of operations is associative (this is axiomatic for symmetry operations).

The number of elements of the group is defined as the **order of the group**, which we shall denote by the letter h.

One other group concept will prove useful later in Section 4-4. Consider two groups $\{a_i\}$ and $\{b_j\}$ where $a_i$ (i = 1 to n) are the elements of one group and $b_j$ (j = 1 to m) are the elements of the other group. Further, these two groups have only the identity element in common and all the elements of $\{a_i\}$ commute with all the elements of $\{b_j\}$ i.e. $a_i b_j = b_j a_i$ for all i and j. The product of these two groups is defined as the set of nm elements

$$\{a_1b_1, a_1b_2, \ldots a_1b_m, a_2b_1, \ldots, a_2b_m, \ldots a_nb_m\}$$

or

$$\{a_ib_j\}, \quad i = 1 \text{ to } n \quad \text{and} \quad j = 1 \text{ to } m$$

One can show that the set of nm elements still forms a group and this group is of order h = nm. We should note that the set of symmetry operations forms a group in the mathematical sense as a consequence of our definition of a symmetry operation in Chapter 1. There we see that the set has closure because the product of any two symmetry operations always produces a third operation of the set. In addition there is an identity and an inverse for each operation. Finally, it is clear that associativity applies to symmetry operations.

There are several very important reasons why we should study point groups. First, it allows us to classify different crystals. Historically, the study of crystals began with the study of their external faces. By characterizing them with directions taken normal to each face and drawn through one point, it was found that all crystals could be classified as belonging to one of **32 crystal classes**. (That there are 32 was not actually established until around 1830.) Each one of these crystal classes corresponds to one of the 32 point groups. Second, finite objects that can be described by one of the 32 point groups can be added to the lattice points in order to derive space groups, as will be shown in the next two chapters. Or, to put it another way, the space groups may be built up from objects with different point symmetry by the addition of translation. Third, the symmetry operations possessed by an object, molecule, or crystal can be described simply by means of a symbol. From this symbol another solid state scientist will know the symmetry operations. Fourth, every space group has one of the 32 crystallographic point groups associated with it (the point group of the space group, usually just called the point group of the crystal). This is very important in many areas of solid state science. For example, most of the symmetry aspects of the physical properties of solids are related to the point group, as given by Neumann's principle, a subject that will be discussed in Section 6-6.

## 4-2 Procedure

There are several ways of developing the 32 crystallographic point groups. Perhaps the fastest and most elegant method is to find all the point groups that can be made from proper rotations only. There are 11 such **pure rotational crystallographic point groups**. After this, a further 11 point groups can be obtained by adding inversion as a symmetry operation to each of these. This results in 11 **centrosymmetric crystallographic point groups**. From the centrosymmetric point groups one can find 10 distinct noncentrosymmetric subgroups that are different from the 11 pure rotational point groups. This gives us the 32 crystallographic point groups and the procedure is outlined in Section 4-4. The second procedure for developing the point groups is to start with the five point groups 1($C_1$), 2($C_2$), 3($C_3$), 4($C_4$), and 6($C_6$), the so-called cyclic groups, and add various symmetry operations to each of them. For example, by adding 2-fold rotation axes perpendicular to the cyclic axis of symmetry new point groups result. Similarly, by adding a mirror plane perpendicular to the cyclic axis of symmetry five other point groups are formed. In general we can say that by adding planes perpendicular to, or containing the cyclic axis, by adding 2-fold rotations perpendicular to the cyclic axis, by substituting improper axes for proper axes, or by any combinations of these three, we obtain new point groups. This is the usual procedure that is used in many solid state or group theory courses and is outlined in Section 4-5. It has the advantage that a good deal of insight is developed into the symmetry operations of the different point groups. One disadvantage of determining the 32 point groups using either of these two general procedures is that after they are obtained we must then determine to which of the seven crystal systems each point group belongs. This is not difficult in practice, but conceptually the result is that the 32 crystallographic groups seem to be quite independent of the seven crystal systems. Actually the 32 point groups and the seven crystal systems can both be developed from the same very simple symmetry operations discussed in Chapter 1, and this is the approach that we shall take initially. Thus, the crystallographic point groups for each of the crystal systems are derived one at a time. For example, we shall take the tetragonal crystal system and determine what symmetry planes and axes can be added to the symmetry operations that define the system with the proviso that we remain within the tetragonal crystal system. This will be done for each crystal system and in this way we shall obtain all of the 32 crystallographic point groups. The advantage of this approach is that we can use a similar procedure to develop the space groups. However, one may proceed to either Section 4-4 or 4-5 before reading Section 4-3. This would be particularly advantageous if one of these procedures has been studied previously. Naturally, all of the procedures yield the same result.

Note that the 32 point groups are illustrated in Appendix 5 in two ways; first with diagrams similar to the ones we have used for the symmetry elements, except that for convenience we draw them in the more usual stereographic projections, and second as shapes in which you should be able to determine the symmetry elements. As we discuss each point group you should consult this appendix. A description of a stereogram and how it shows the point symmetry is given in this appendix and should be read at this point. It is a very simple and descriptive approach which we shall refer to in the following discussion.

## 4-3 The Crystallographic Point Groups for each Crystal System

**4-3a Triclinic** In Chapter 2 we showed that the symmetry operations 1(E) and $\overline{1}$(i) put no restrictions on the unit-cell axes and angles, leading to the triclinic crystal system. Any object, whether it be a crystal, or a molecule or even a set of "hands" as in Chapter 1, which only possesses the identity element is said to belong to point group 1 in the International notation or to point group $C_1$ in the Schoenflies notation. We shall continue to write the Schoenflies notation in parenthesis after the International notation. Thus the symbol for the point group will be $1(C_1)$.

If an object, crystal, set of "hands," molecule, or whatever, has the symmetry operation 1(E) as well as $\overline{1}$(i), then the point symmetry is called $\overline{1}(S_2)$. Thus, if we say an object has the point symmetry $\overline{1}(S_2)$ we mean that there are two symmetry operations that take the object into itself, namely: 1 and $\overline{1}$ or E and i. We may also say the point group of the object is $\overline{1}(S_2)$. Although we shall not dwell on the group theory aspect, this means that the point group $\overline{1}$ has the set of symmetry operations $\{1, \overline{1}\}$, or using the Schoenflies notation we say that the point group $S_2$ consists of $\{E, i\}$, and these two operations form a group of order 2 $(h = 2)$. Now, within a crystal system, the point group with the largest number of symmetry operations (we might loosely say it has the highest symmetry) is called the **holosymmetric point group**. As there are only two point groups belonging to the triclinic system, the holosymmetric point group here is $\overline{1}(S_2)$.

The notation for some of these point groups is very similar or even the same as for the symmetry operations. This can be troublesome, but we should bear in mind that a point group is a set, or collection, of symmetry operations obeying certain mathematical laws and that a symmetry operation is a single operation that takes the object into itself. As we encounter point groups with more symmetry operations, this will become less of a problem.

We cannot add any more symmetry operations and remain within the triclinic crystal system. The addition of a 2-fold axis of symmetry or a mirror plane, for instance, results in the monoclinic crystal system. Any other symmetry axes of rotation result in other crystal systems. Therefore we conclude that there are only two point groups compatible with triclinic symmetry. These are the point groups 1 and $\overline{1}$ in the International notation or $C_1$ and $S_2$ in the Schoenflies notation and we shall write these as $1(C_1)$ and $\overline{1}(S_2)$ to bring out both notations. The stereograms for these two point groups are shown in Appendix 5. For the point group $1(C_1)$, only a single point is shown; for point group $\overline{1}(S_2)$, there are two points corresponding to the two symmetry operations in the point group. These points are obtained in the following manner. We start with a general point above the plane of the paper, indicated by a dot at the bottom-right of the stereogram. Application of the identity operator naturally leaves it unchanged, but the inversion operator, on the other hand, moves it through the center of the stereogram. This means that the general point is taken to the top-left of the diagram but below the plane of the paper as represented by the open circle. Note that since we took a general point, i.e., a point <u>not</u> positioned directly on a symmetry element, there are as many points on the stereogram as there are symmetry operations in the point group.

**4-3b Monoclinic** In Chapter 2 we found that the symmetry operations $2(C_2)$ or $\overline{2}(\sigma_h)$ give rise to what is called the monoclinic set of axes and angles. (You will recall from Chapter 1, that $\overline{2}$ is the same as a mirror plane and so $\overline{2}$ can be written equally well as m.) Therefore, any object which possesses a single 2-fold symmetry element is compatible with monoclinic symmetry. It is then said to belong to point group 2 (or $C_2$), which is a group of order h = 2; the h symmetry operations are {1,2,} or {E, $C_2$}. In the same way, objects with just $\overline{2}$ or m symmetry belong to the point group m ($C_{1h}$) of order h = 2, whose symmetry operations are {1, m} or {E, $\sigma_h$}. The stereograms for these two point groups are shown in Appendix 5. As has been pointed out earlier, in the monoclinic crystal system we may take the unique axis to be the **c**-axis (the 1st setting) or we may take it to be the **b**-axis (the 2nd setting). In the appendix both settings are shown; they are merely different views of the same situation. In each case we see that the stereograms show two points corresponding to the two symmetry operations. It is also instructive to examine carefully the shapes having point symmetry $m(C_{1h})$ and $2(C_2)$. The presence and positions of the symmetry elements are fairly clear and one can see how these shapes and the stereograms display the same symmetry.

It is pertinent to ask whether we can have any other point groups that put no new restrictions on the monoclinic axes and angles. Clearly, if we have more 2-fold axes or more mirror planes we shall have the necessary conditions for the orthorhombic system. However, if we have a mirror plane perpendicular to the 2-fold axis, no new conditions on the crystal axes or angles will be imposed. This can be checked by the methods we used in Chapter 2, but it is also intuitively clear: if the **c**-axis is a 2-fold axis perpendicular to the **ab**-plane, and if the **ab**-plane is a plane of mirror symmetry, then no new conditions can be put on the lengths of the **a**-, **b**-, or **c**-axes and no new condition can be put on the angle between the **a**- and **b**-axes. What is new is that the addition of the mirror-symmetry plane generates the symmetry operation of inversion $\bar{1}$(i). This can readily be seen by first applying the symmetry operation 2($C_2$) followed by the mirror-symmetry operation m($\sigma_h$) perpendicular to the 2-fold axis. To show this explicitly, we can write, using the matrices in Appendix 1

$$\{m[001]\}\ \{2[001]\} = \begin{bmatrix} 1 & 0 & 0 \\ 0 & 1 & 0 \\ 0 & 0 & -1 \end{bmatrix}\begin{bmatrix} -1 & 0 & 0 \\ 0 & -1 & 0 \\ 0 & 0 & 1 \end{bmatrix} = \begin{bmatrix} -1 & 0 & 0 \\ 0 & -1 & 0 \\ 0 & 0 & -1 \end{bmatrix} = \{\bar{1}\} \tag{4-1}$$

and so we find that $\{m[001]\}\{2[001]\} = \{\bar{1}\}$ (or $\sigma_h C_2 = i$). In the International notation the point group is written as 2/m and has symmetry operations {1, 2, $\bar{1}$, m} or in the Schoenflies notation the point group is $C_{2h}$ and has symmetry operations {E, $C_2$, i, $\sigma_h$}. The stereogram for 2/m ($C_{2h}$) shows these symmetry operations. Start with the dot at the bottom-right. This is the starting point and represents the effect of the identity operation 1(E). Now operate on this point with 2($C_2$) and the dot at the top-left is obtained. Then, operate on the starting point with $\bar{1}$(i) and the circle at the top-left is obtained. (Remember, the circle indicates that the general point now lies below the plane of the paper.) Finally, operate on the starting point with m($\sigma_h$) and the circle at the bottom-right is obtained. Thus we have four points on the stereogram corresponding to the four symmetry operations of the point group. If we operate on any point of the stereogram with any of these four symmetry operations or products of these operations, then one of the other four points on the stereogram will be obtained. This is a consequence of the fact that these four operations form a group.

The **notation** is now becoming clear for the monoclinic as well as for the other point groups. In the International notation n/m means a mirror plane perpendicular to the n-fold rotation axis, while nm means a mirror plane (or really n such mirror planes) containing the n-fold axis. In the Schoenflies notation $C_n$ is a point group which contains the symmetry operation $C_n$, $C_n^2$, etc. The symbol $C_{nh}$ means that the point group also contains a mirror plane perpendicular to the $C_n$-axis. Because of operations such as in Eq. (4-1), the point group $C_{nh}$ will have twice as many symmetry operations as the point group $C_n$. The symbol $C_{nv}$ means that the mirror plane contains the $C_n$ axis (as opposed to being perpendicular to it as in $C_{nh}$) and, again, there will be twice as many symmetry operations in the point group $C_{nv}$ as in $C_n$. Recall, from Chapter 1, that in the Schoenflies notation the mirror plane $\sigma_h$ is perpendicular to the rotation axis while $\sigma_v$ contains it (h, horizontal and v, vertical.)

Appendix 4 has all the point groups listed in the International and Schoenflies notations together with the symmetry operations for each point group. **Note** that in the International notation we can define a **full symbol** and a **short symbol**. In the monoclinic point groups the full symbols are never necessary. For the three point groups the symbols are as follows:

| Full symbol (1st setting) | Short symbol | Schoenflies |
|---|---|---|
| 1 1 2 | 2 | $C_2$ |
| 1 1 m | m | $C_{1h}(C_s)$ |
| 1 1 2/m | 2/m | $C_{2h}$ |

Here $2/m(C_{2h})$ is centrosymmetric and holosymmetric; the other point groups in the crystal system are subgroups of the holosymmetric group. Within a crystal system this must always be true. In the full symbols, the symmetry elements are indicated with respect to the crystallographic axes, **a**, **b**, and **c**, in turn. Thus we see that there is no symmetry element along **a** and **b** (except for 1), while the important symmetry elements 2 and m respectively lie along or perpendicular to **c**. For the second setting, where the **b**-axis is the 2-fold axis, the full symbol is 1 2/m 1.

We shall see that in some of the other crystal systems, particularly the orthorhombic system, the full symbol is more important. Normally, however, the full symbol contains redundant information. The short symbol has sufficient information to enable us to construct all of the symmetry operations of the point group. The same general comments about full and short symbols will apply to the space group symbols. Finally, examine the shape with point symmetry 2/m ($C_{2h}$) given in Appendix 5. It is apparent that the addition of a mirror plane to the $2(C_2)$ shape creates the 2/m ($C_{2h}$) shape. It is also apparent that the addition of a 2-fold axis to the $m(C_{1h})$ shape again creates the 2/m ($C_{2h}$) shape.

**4-3c Orthorhombic**. For this crystal system two 2-fold axes, or two mirror planes, perpendicular to each other determine the characteristic restrictions on the unit-cell axes and angles as shown in Chapter 2. The two 2-fold symmetry operations determine a third 2-fold axis, perpendicular to both, as can easily be shown by multiplying the appropriate matrices, as in Eq. (4-1) or by using stereograms. Thus the point group is 222 with symmetry operations {1, 2[100], 2[010], 2[001]} or in the Schoenflies notation $D_2$ with symmetry operations {E, $C_2$[100], $C_2$[010], $C_2$[001]}, and is of order h = 4.

Similarly, two perpendicular mirror planes determine the presence of a 2-fold axis along the intersection of the two planes; if we call the axes perpendicular to the mirror planes **a** and **b**, the 2-fold axis is along **c** and the point group is mm2 with operations {1, 2[001], m[010], m[100]}, or $C_{2v}$ with operations {E, $C_2$[001], $\sigma_v$[010], $\sigma_v$[100]}. The symbol mm2 is the **standard form** by which this point group is denoted in the International Tables. This, however, is only a matter of convenience, since the choice of axes in a crystal may be dictated by other considerations apart from the types of symmetry elements and may necessitate referring to the crystal by a nonstandard symbol. If the **a**-axis is the 2-fold axis, the symbol is 2mm and if the **b**-axis is the 2-fold axis, the symbol is m2m.

Again we ask if there are any other combinations of symmetry operations that will not impose new restrictions on the unit-cell axes and angles of the orthorhombic system. It is clear that we can place a mirror plane normal to any of the three mutually perpendicular 2-fold axes without affecting the unit-cell geometry. If we try this we find that there must be mirror planes perpendicular to all of the 2-fold axes and not to just one or two. The point group thus generated can be given the symbol 2/m 2/m 2/m, for which the short symbol mmm can be used, or $D_{2h}$ in the Schoenflies notation. In the Schoenflies notation the point group $C_2$ means the principal axis has 2-fold symmetry and if there are 2-fold axes perpendicular to the principal axes, then the symbol becomes $D_2$ as above. The h in $D_{2h}$ refers to $\sigma_h$, a mirror plane perpendicular to the n-fold axis. The point group $D_{2h}$ has eight symmetry operations, the six operations in the full symbol plus the identity operation and a generated center of inversion. That the center of inversion is generated can be seen simply by multiplying the matrices for the three mutually perpendicular mirror operations:

{m[100]} {m[010]} {m[001]} =

$$\begin{bmatrix} -1 & 0 & 0 \\ 0 & 1 & 0 \\ 0 & 0 & 1 \end{bmatrix}\begin{bmatrix} 1 & 0 & 0 \\ 0 & -1 & 0 \\ 0 & 0 & 1 \end{bmatrix}\begin{bmatrix} 1 & 0 & 0 \\ 0 & 1 & 0 \\ 0 & 0 & -1 \end{bmatrix} = \begin{bmatrix} -1 & 0 & 0 \\ 0 & -1 & 0 \\ 0 & 0 & -1 \end{bmatrix} = \{\bar{1}\} \tag{4-2}$$

Another way of seeing this is by means of a stereogram as shown in Appendix 5. The general point is taken by the three mirror planes to form seven other points, making four enantiomorphic pairs. Inspection of the stereogram reveals the presence of a center of inversion.

The orthorhombic point groups are summarized below: of these, mmm($D_{2h}$) is centrosymmetric and holosymmetric. Appendix 5 shows stereograms for these three point groups as well as three shapes having these symmetry operations.

| Full symbol | Short symbol | Schoenflies |
|---|---|---|
| 2 2 2 | 2 2 2 | $D_2$ |
| m m 2 | m m 2 | $C_{2v}$ |
| $\frac{2}{m}\ \frac{2}{m}\ \frac{2}{m}$ | m m m | $D_{2h}$ |

**4-3d Tetragonal** This crystal system is defined by the presence of a single 4 or $\bar{4}$ axis in the crystal. This results in point groups 4($C_4$) and $\bar{4}$($S_4$) both of which are of order h = 4 (see Appendix 4).

Which symmetry elements can we add and still remain within the crystal system? The obvious choices are mirror planes and 2-fold axes placed in strategic positions. For example, if we place a 2-fold axis perpendicular to the 4-fold axis, let us say along **a**, consider what other symmetry elements, if any, will be generated. We can find this out by multiplying the appropriate matrices:

{4[001]} {2[100]} =

$$\begin{bmatrix} 0 & -1 & 0 \\ 1 & 0 & 0 \\ 0 & 0 & 1 \end{bmatrix}\begin{bmatrix} 1 & 0 & 0 \\ 0 & -1 & 0 \\ 0 & 0 & -1 \end{bmatrix} = \begin{bmatrix} 0 & 1 & 0 \\ 1 & 0 & 0 \\ 0 & 0 & -1 \end{bmatrix} = \{2[110]\} \tag{4-3}$$

This shows us that another 2-fold axis is produced, this time along the face-diagonal of the **ab**-plane. For this reason the resulting point group is called 422($D_4$). Notice that because the 4-fold direction is such an important direction (it is the principal axis or unique direction in the tetragonal crystal), it is conventional to place the symbol "4" first, unlike the procedure used in the orthorhombic system where there is no unique direction. In the International notation the first "2" after the "4" refers to the 2-fold axis along **a** (and to an equivalent 2-fold axis along **b** as a consequence of the 4-fold axis) while the second "2" refers to the diagonal 2-fold axis along [110] (and another equivalent 2-fold axis along $[1\bar{1}0]$). As before, in the Schoenflies notation the "D" implies that perpendicular to the principal axis there are 2-fold axes. The occurrence of these symmetry elements can be seen by reference to the stereogram of point group $422(D_4)$ given in Appendix 5.

There are other ways of adding symmetry elements to point groups 4 and $\bar{4}$. For example, a mirror plane placed normal to the 4-fold axis results in point group $4/m(C_{4h})$ which is centrosymmetric, as can be seen from Appendix 5. You should now be able to show this for yourself by multiplying the relevant matrices. Another thing that we can do is to place a mirror plane parallel to the 4-fold axis and lying in the **ac**-plane. By similar arguments as those used above, we find another mirror plane diagonally between the **a** and **b**-axes (see Appendix 5) giving the point group $4mm(C_{4v})$. Also we can now add a mirror plane or 2-fold axes perpendicular to **c**. The result is another centrosymmetric point group 4/m 2/m 2/m, or 4/mmm for short, $(D_{4h})$. Finally, to point group $\bar{4}(S_4)$ we can add a 2-fold axis perpendicular to **c**, say along **a**. If we multiply the appropriate matrices:

$\{\bar{4}[001]\}\ \{2[100]\} =$

$$\begin{bmatrix} 0 & 1 & 0 \\ -1 & 0 & 0 \\ 0 & 0 & -1 \end{bmatrix} \begin{bmatrix} 1 & 0 & 0 \\ 0 & -1 & 0 \\ 0 & 0 & -1 \end{bmatrix} = \begin{bmatrix} 0 & -1 & 0 \\ -1 & 0 & 0 \\ 0 & 0 & 1 \end{bmatrix} = \{m[110]\} \qquad (4\text{-}4)$$

we obtain a mirror plane along a diagonal of the **ab**-face. The point group is therefore $\bar{4}2m\ (D_{2d})$. For convenience we summarize the tetragonal point groups in the table below. The point group $4/m(C_{4h})$ is centrosymmetric and $4/mmm(D_{4h})$ is both centrosymmetric and holosymmetric. [The point group $\bar{4}(S_4)$ is a subgroup of the point group $\bar{4}2m(D_{2d})$ and naturally all these point groups are subgroups of $4/mmm(D_{4h})$.]

| Full symbol | Short symbol | Schoenflies |
|---|---|---|
| 4 | 4 | $C_4$ |
| 422 | 422 | $D_4$ |
| 4/m | 4/m | $C_{4h}$ |
| 4mm | 4mm | $C_{4v}$ |
| $\frac{4}{m}\frac{2}{m}\frac{2}{m}$ | 4/mmm | $D_{4h}$ |
| $\bar{4}$ | $\bar{4}$ | $S_4$ |
| $\bar{4}2m$ | $\bar{4}2m$ | $D_{2d}$ |

**4-3e Trigonal** For this crystal system we require a 3- or $\bar{3}$-axis. Again, we successively add other symmetry elements in the same way that we did for the tetragonal system and arrive at five possibilities listed below. $\bar{3}(S_6)$ is centrosymmetric and $\bar{3}m(D_{3d})$ is both centrosymmetric and holosymmetric. Note that by placing a plane of symmetry perpendicular to the 3-fold axis we do not remain within this crystal system, since $3/m = \bar{6}$, which belongs in the hexagonal system.

| Full symbol | Short symbol | Schoenflies |
|---|---|---|
| 3 | 3 | $C_3$ |
| 32 | 32 | $D_3$ |
| 3m | 3m | $C_{3v}$ |
| $\bar{3}$ | $\bar{3}$ | $S_6$ or $C_{3i}$ |
| $\bar{3}\,\frac{2}{m}$ | $\bar{3}m$ | $D_{3d}$ |

**4-3f Hexagonal** This crystal system requires a 6 or $\bar{6}$-axis as discussed in Chapter 2. The resulting seven point groups are quite analogous to the tetragonal case, and so we simply list them below.

| Full symbol | Short symbol | Schoenflies |
|---|---|---|
| 6 | 6 | $C_6$ |
| 622 | 622 | $D_6$ |
| 6/m | 6/m | $C_{6h}$ |
| 6mm | 6mm | $C_{6v}$ |
| $\frac{6}{m}\frac{2}{m}\frac{2}{m}$ | 6/mmm | $D_{6h}$ |
| $\bar{6}$ | $\bar{6}$ | $C_{3h}$ |
| $\bar{6}m2$ | $\bar{6}m2$ | $D_{3h}$ |

$6/m(C_{6h})$ is centrosymmetric and $6/mmm(D_{6h})$ is both centrosymmetric and holosymmetric. Note how the number 3 appears in the Schoenflies symbols for the $\bar{6}$ and $\bar{6}m2$ point groups (also recall that $S_6$ is the Schoenflies symbol for the $\bar{3}$ point group in the trigonal crystal system). Unfortunately these symbols can confuse the reader into placing these point groups in the incorrect crystal system. Appendix 5 shows some shapes and stereograms that display these various point symmetries.

**4-3g Cubic**. The cubic crystal system is a little more difficult to treat than the above systems because here we do not have a principal axis. The crystal system is defined by four 3-fold axes all making equal angles with one another (109°28′). We want to see which symmetry operations we may add to these four axes and still remain within the cubic crystal system. Remember that the 3-fold operation implies the symmetry operator $3(C_3)$ as well as $3^2(C_3{}^2)$.

The first question is: Do we have a point group using just 1(E) and the eight $3(C_3)$ and $3^2(C_3{}^2)$ operations about the four axes? We realize quickly that the answer is no. This is because for a point group we want to be able to repeat the operations of the set, in any order, and have the object in an equivalent position. However, we find

$$\{3[\bar{1}11]\}\,\{3[111]\} =$$

$$\begin{bmatrix} 0 & -1 & 0 \\ 0 & 0 & 1 \\ -1 & 0 & 0 \end{bmatrix} \begin{bmatrix} 0 & 0 & 1 \\ 1 & 0 & 0 \\ 0 & 1 & 0 \end{bmatrix} = \begin{bmatrix} -1 & 0 & 0 \\ 0 & 1 & 0 \\ 0 & 0 & -1 \end{bmatrix} = \{2[010]\} \qquad (4\text{-}5)$$

and so, at the very least, we must include in the set of operations comprising the point group, 2-fold rotations about the **a**-, **b**-, and **c**-axes. By repeated multiplications we find that there are no new operations that are required and that the 2-fold axes keep us within the cubic crystal system. This leads us to the cubic point group 23(T) which consists of $3(C_3)$ and $3^2(C_3{}^2)$ symmetry operations about the four $\langle 111 \rangle$ directions and $2(C_2)$ symmetry operations about the three $\langle 100 \rangle$ directions. Adding the identity operation, there is a total of 12 symmetry operations in this cubic point group (and note that none of them is a 4-fold operation). This and the other cubic point groups to follow can best be visualized by reference to the diagrams in Appendix 5. (However, do not confuse this point group with the trigonal point group which is 32 in the International notation.)

To the point group 23(T) we now try to add mirror planes perpendicular to the 2-fold axes. From these mirror planes and by taking various products, as in Eq. (4-5), we obtain a center of inversion $\bar{1}(i)$ as well as $\bar{3}(S_6{}^5)$ and $\bar{3}^5(S_6)$ about the four $\langle 111 \rangle$ directions. This cubic point group is called $2/m\ \bar{3}$ or m3 (or $T_h$) and has 24 symmetry operations.

Again note that there are no 4-fold axes in this cubic point group. (Do not confuse the cubic point group m3 with the trigonal point group 3m, in the International notation.)

Now we shall add mirror planes containing both the 3-fold and the 2-fold axes. For example, m[1$\bar{1}$0] contains the 2[001] axis and the 3[111] and 3[$\overline{11}$1] axes, while m[110] also contains the 2[001] axis and the other two 3<111> axes. There are three distinct pairs of such mirror planes, the line of intersection of each pair being coincident with the **a**-, **b**-, and **c**-axes. In the Schoenflies notation they are called diagonal planes $\sigma_d$ and are similar to $\sigma_v$ in that they contain the rotation axis, and yet are different in that they lie diagonally between the unit-cell axes. The inclusion of such planes gives rise to three axes of $\bar{4}(S_4^3)$ and $\bar{4}^3(S_4)$ symmetry about the **a**-, **b**-, and **c**-axes. The resulting cubic point group, called $\bar{4}$3m ($T_d$), has 24 symmetry operations. Again there are no proper 4-fold operations in this cubic point group.

If we take the cubic point group 23(T) and allow 4-fold, and $4^3(C_4^3)$, operations about the three 2-fold axes, then using techniques similar to those used in Eq. (4-5), we obtain six new 2-fold axes, i.e., 2[110], 2[1$\bar{1}$0], etc. This is the cubic point group 432(O) which again has 24 symmetry operations. Note that, as in the point group 23(T), in this point group there are only proper rotation operations and no inversions, mirrors, or improper rotations.

The last cubic point group is obtained by allowing mirror planes perpendicular to the 4-fold axes. The point group is 4/m $\bar{3}$ 2/m or m3m for short (or $O_h$) and has 48 symmetry operations. It can be seen from Appendix 5 that all the operations of the other cubic point groups are subgroups of this point group.

As we have already remarked, only two of the five cubic point groups have proper 4-fold symmetry operations. Also note that the cubic point group 23(T) has only 12 symmetry elements, not a very large number and that there are other point groups in the hexagonal, trigonal and tetragonal crystal systems which have the same or more symmetry elements. Therefore cubic point groups should not be associated, necessarily with a large number of symmetry operations. The cubic point groups can be summarized as shown below.

| Full symbol | Short symbol | Schoenflies |
|---|---|---|
| 23 | 23 | T |
| $\frac{2}{m}\bar{3}$ | m3 | $T_h$ |
| 432 | 432 | O |
| $\bar{4}3m$ | $\bar{4}3m$ | $T_d$ |
| $\frac{4}{m}\bar{3}\frac{2}{m}$ | m3m | $O_h$ |

where m3($T_h$) is centrosymmetric and m3m($O_h$) is both centrosymmetric and holosymmetric. Appendix 4 lists all the symmetry elements of the cubic point groups and Appendix 5 gives the point group diagrams. It is worthwhile spending some time testing the various symmetry operations on these diagrams.

## 4-4 The 32 Point Groups Derived from the Rotational Point Groups

We now develop the same 32 crystallographic point groups as in the last section, but from a different point of view. We shall use an approach that is slightly more group theoretical. The use of group theory is not vital here any more than in the last section, but group theory is very useful and really is the basis of much of what is said in this book. (As Dirac said, "I will explain everything without any previous knowledge of Group Theory.")

Consider the point groups that consist only of proper rotations about one or more axes. There are 11 such crystallographic point groups and it is possible to show that there are only 11 of these groups and to determine their symmetry by purely mathematical means. (See Bhagavantam in the Bibliography.) We, however, take a more physical approach with the hope that this will lead to better understanding of the various symmetry groups.

We have already mentioned some very simple group theoretical concepts in the introductory section of this chapter; note in particular the multiplication of two groups. This concept will prove useful in what follows.

**4-4a Cyclic Point Groups** We have five crystallographic point groups of the type of n($C_n$), where n = 1, 2, 3, 4, and 6, which are known as the **cyclic point groups** (hence the Schoenflies symbol "C"). The symmetry operations for any one of these are {n, $n^2$, $n^3$, etc., with $n^h = 1$} where the order of the point group, h, is the number of symmetry operations in the point group. For example, the point group $6(C_6)$ has six symmetry operations, 1, 6, $6^2$, $6^3$, $6^4$, $6^5$, $6^6 = 1$ (or $C_6{}^6 = E$). The axis of rotation is often called the **principal axis**; it is normally taken along **c** (except in the monoclinic system crystallographers will often, but not always, take the **b**-axis as the principal axis).

**4-4b Dihedral Point Groups** Now consider rotations perpendicular to the rotation axis of the cyclic group. It is clear that if we want the principal axis to remain a symmetry axis we may only add 2-fold axes parallel or perpendicular to this axis but not at other angles. To each of the five cyclic point groups we can add a 2-fold axis perpendicular to the principal axis and generate four new point groups. There are four, not five, because there is the trivial case of a 2-fold axis added to the point group $1(C_1)$, which gives us the cyclic point group $2(C_2)$. In the International notation these are given the symbol n22 or n2, where n = 2, 3, 4, or 6, or, alternatively, given the letter "D" (dihedral) in the Schoenflies notation and written $D_n$. The nine point groups obtained in this way, cyclic and dihedral are

International notation

| | | | | | | | | |
|---|---|---|---|---|---|---|---|---|
| 1 | 2 | 3 | 4 | 6 | 222 | 32 | 422 | 622 |

Schoenflies notation

| | | | | | | | | |
|---|---|---|---|---|---|---|---|---|
| $C_1$ | $C_2$ | $C_3$ | $C_4$ | $C_6$ | $D_2$ | $D_3$ | $D_4$ | $D_6$ |

The $D_n$ point groups can also be developed very easily from the $C_n$ point groups using simple group theory techniques. Consider the point group consisting of elements {E, $C_2$[100]}. These elements are just the identity and a 2-fold rotation about the **a**-axis. The group is simply the 2-fold cyclic group with the principal axis taken as the **a**-axis. The $D_n$ point groups can then be obtained by the direct product of this point group with the appropriate $C_n$ point group:

$$C_n \times \{E, C_2[100]\} = D_n \tag{4-6}$$

This group theoretical approach is very compact and simple and immediately shows that the $D_n$ point groups have twice as many elements as the corresponding $C_n$ point group. Recalling that the order of the group, h, is the number of symmetry operations or elements in the group, then the order of the point group $C_n$ is n and the order of the point group $D_n$ is twice as large (or 2n).

**4-4c Cubic Point Groups** In order to arrive at the rotation group 23(T), we must carry out multiplication of various operations, as was done in Section 4-3g.

If we now add $4(C_4)$ symmetry operations to point group 23(T), a new point group 432(O) is obtained. For example, the following give new symmetry elements which are contained in 432(O) (see Appendix 4).

{4[001]} {3[111]} =

$$\begin{bmatrix} 0 & -1 & 0 \\ 1 & 0 & 0 \\ 0 & 0 & 1 \end{bmatrix} \begin{bmatrix} 0 & 0 & 1 \\ 1 & 0 & 0 \\ 0 & 1 & 0 \end{bmatrix} = \begin{bmatrix} -1 & 0 & 0 \\ 0 & 0 & 1 \\ 0 & 1 & 0 \end{bmatrix} = \{2[011]\} \qquad \text{(4-7a)}$$

{3[111]} {4[001]} =

$$\begin{bmatrix} 0 & 0 & 1 \\ 1 & 0 & 0 \\ 0 & 1 & 0 \end{bmatrix} \begin{bmatrix} 0 & -1 & 0 \\ 1 & 0 & 0 \\ 0 & 0 & 1 \end{bmatrix} = \begin{bmatrix} 0 & 0 & 1 \\ 0 & -1 & 0 \\ 1 & 0 & 0 \end{bmatrix} = \{2[101]\} \qquad \text{(4-7b)}$$

By various combinations of $4(C_4)$ and $3(C_3)$, we obtain $2(C_2)$ operations with reference to the six face diagonals of a cube and thus obtain all the elements of the point group. The same result can be achieved by adding a 2[110] ($C_2$[110]) operation to the point group 23(T).

The cyclic, dihedral, and cubic rotation groups constitute the 11 pure rotational groups. The symmetry operations of these groups are pure rotations about various axes.

**4-4d 11 Centrosymmetric Point Groups** From the 11 pure rotational crystallographic point groups, 11 centrosymmetric crystallographic point groups can be obtained immediately. Take the elements of each of the 11 rotational point groups, multiply them by the inversion operator and add the resulting elements to the corresponding point groups. In group theoretical language, take the point group $S_2$ or $C_i$ = {E, i} and multiply each rotational point group by this group. Below we show the result of this directly beneath the corresponding rotational group.

International notation

| | | | | | | | | | | |
|---|---|---|---|---|---|---|---|---|---|---|
| 1 | 2 | 3 | 4 | 6 | 222 | 32 | 422 | 622 | 23 | 432 |
| $\bar{1}$ | 2/m | $\bar{3}$ | 4/m | 6/m | mmm | $\bar{3}$m | 4/mmm | 6/mmm | m3 | m3m |

Schoenflies notation

| | | | | | | | | | | |
|---|---|---|---|---|---|---|---|---|---|---|
| $C_1$ | $C_2$ | $C_3$ | $C_4$ | $C_6$ | $D_2$ | $D_3$ | $D_4$ | $D_6$ | T | O |
| $C_i$ | $C_{2h}$ | $S_6$ | $C_{4h}$ | $C_{6h}$ | $D_{2h}$ | $D_{3d}$ | $D_{4h}$ | $D_{6h}$ | $T_h$ | $O_h$ |

Obviously each of these 11 new point groups is centrosymmetric. It should be obvious that the order of the group obtained by multiplying each rotational point group by {E, i} is twice the order of the corresponding rotation group.

**4-4e 10 New Subgroups** From the 11 centrosymmetric point groups we can find 10 subgroups that do not have $\bar{1}$(i) as a symmetry operation yet have symmetry operations other than just pure rotations. These new groups have not been accounted for above. Naturally each of these new groups is a group in the mathematical sense. Appendix 4 shows the symmetry operations for each of these 10 point groups. Appendix 5 shows the stereogram for each of these point groups as well as a representative shape for each. Below we list these 10 new point groups and indicate the centrosymmetric point groups from which they are derived.

International notation

| | | | | | | | | | |
|---|---|---|---|---|---|---|---|---|---|
| 2/m | mmm | 4/m | 4/mmm | | $\bar{3}$m | 6/m | 6/mmm | | m3m |
| m | mm2 | $\bar{4}$ | $\bar{4}$2m | 4mm | 3m | $\bar{6}$ | $\bar{6}$m2 | 6mm | $\bar{4}$3m |

Schoenflies notation

| | | | | | | | | | |
|---|---|---|---|---|---|---|---|---|---|
| $C_{2h}$ | $D_{2h}$ | $C_{4h}$ | $D_{4h}$ | | $D_{3d}$ | $C_{6h}$ | $D_{6h}$ | | $O_h$ |
| $C_{1h}$ | $C_{2v}$ | $S_4$ | $D_{2d}$ | $C_{4v}$ | $C_{3v}$ | $C_{3h}$ | $D_{3h}$ | $C_{6v}$ | $T_d$ |

Note that when we remove the center of inversion from 4/mmm($D_{4h}$) and 6/mmm($D_{6h}$), there are, in each case, two different possibilities. Naturally none of these 10 new point groups can be centrosymmetric or holosymmetric.

## 4-5 Schoenflies Approach to the 32 Point Groups

We can obtain the 32 point groups in yet another way, namely by using mirror planes instead of a center of inversion. This difference between the Schoenflies and International approach was already pointed out in Chapter 1. We shall just briefly outline this approach using the Schoenflies notation alone.

We start again with the five cyclic point groups $C_n$ (n = 1, 2, 3, 4, 6). We shall use the usual notation $\sigma_h$ to represent a mirror plane perpendicular to the principal axis which by convention is the **c**-axis; the h means horizontal, taking the principal axis as vertical. Also, $\sigma_v$, means a mirror plane containing the principal axis (v, vertical) and the **a**- and/or **b**-directions, while $\sigma_d$ is a mirror plane containing the principal axis but bisecting the angle between the **a**- and **b**-directions.

From each of the $C_n$ point groups, new point groups can be obtained by adding a $\sigma_h$ plane. These are called $C_{nh}$. The order of the $C_{nh}$ group is twice the order of the corresponding $C_n$ group or $C_{nh} = C_n \times \{E,\sigma_h\}$ in group multiplication notation. For example, $C_{4h}$ has the point operations of $C_4$ plus $\sigma_h E = \sigma_h$, $\sigma_h C_4 = S_4$, $\sigma_h C_2 = i$, and $\sigma_h C_4^3 = S_4^3$. Thus we see that the center of inversion occurs in the same natural way as in Chapter 1.

Four new point groups can be obtained by adding a vertical plane $\sigma_v$ instead of a horizontal plane to the cyclic point groups. These are labelled $C_{nv}$, n = 2, 3, 4, 6, where $C_{nv} = C_n \times \{E,\sigma_v\}$. The case n=1 is the same as $C_{1h}$, and therefore it is not repeated here. Clearly the order of the $C_{nv}$ group is twice that of the corresponding $C_n$ group.

By allowing improper rotations $S_n$ about the principal axis as well as proper rotations, three new point groups are obtained. These are the point groups $S_n$, n = 2, 4, 6. The symmetry operations are $S_2\{E,i\}$; $S_4\{E, C_2, S_4, S_4^3\}$; $S_6\{E, C_3, C_3^2, S_6, i, S_6^5\}$. Again, we see how the center of inversion appears in some point groups and not in others of the same type, such as the $S_n$ point groups, when generated by the Schoenflies approach.

By taking the five $C_n$ cyclic point groups and adding a 2-fold symmetry operation perpendicular to the principal axis, one obtains four new point groups $D_n$ (n = 2, 3, 4, 6) with twice as many symmetry operations as the corresponding cyclic point groups; $D_n = C_n \times \{E, C_2[100]\}$.

Similarly, by placing a 2-fold rotation perpendicular to the principal axis in the point groups $C_{nh}$, four new groups $D_{nh}$ (n = 2, 3, 4, 6) will be generated; $D_{nh} = C_{nh} \times \{E, \sigma_d\}$.

By adding a diagonal mirror plane which contains the principal axis of the point groups $S_n$, two new point groups can be obtained, $D_{nd}$ ($n = 2, 3$); $D_{nd} = S_{2n} \times \{E, C_2[100]\}$.

All the above point groups have a principal axis. In addition to these there are five cubic point groups which are distinguished by not possessing a unique axis but having four 3-fold axes. The point group $T_h$ is obtained from the point group T by adding a mirror operation, and so the order of the $T_h$ group is twice that of T. $T_h = T \times \{E, \sigma_h\}$. $O_h$ is obtained from O in the same manner and $T_d$ is found to be a subgroup of $O_h$ when the center of inversion is removed; alternatively we may write $T_d = T \times \{E, \sigma_d\}$.

## 4-6 Laue Groups

It is a feature of X-ray diffraction from a single crystal that the coherent diffraction effects appear to be centrosymmetric, even when the crystal is noncentrosymmetric. Thus, if a series of X-ray diffraction photographs is taken in order to determine the symmetry of the crystal, it is not easily possible to determine whether a crystal is centrosymmetric or not, although anomalous dispersion and other considerations can be used to distinguish between the two cases. (See Lipson and Cochran.) X-ray diffraction, therefore, has the effect of adding a center of inversion to the point group of the crystal. This means that one can only distinguish directly between the 11 centrosymmetric groups which, for historical reasons, are also known as the **11 Laue groups** or the **11 Laue symmetry groups**. We may say, then, that the 32 point groups are associated with the 11 Laue groups. For instance, point groups $4(C_4)$ and $\bar{4}(S_4)$ are associated with Laue group $4/m(C_{4h})$, i.e., the X-ray diffraction pattern from a crystal having $4(C_4)$ or $\bar{4}(S_4)$ symmetry will look as if it had $4/m(C_{4h})$ symmetry. In Table 4-1 we list the 11 Laue groups with all the point groups associated with them; in each case the Laue group is the last point group in each box. Note that the definition of the term Laue groups in the 1965 edition of the International Tables is not strictly correct since it defines them as "groups of point groups that become identical when a center of symmetry is added to those that lack it." However, the collections of point groups associated with each Laue group do not constitute groups in the mathematical sense. The more recent 1969 edition of the International Tables does not, however, make this mistake since the term **Laue class** is used.

**Table 4-1** The 11 Laue-Symmetry Groups

**International notation**

| Triclinic | Monoclinic | Tetragonal | Trigonal | Hexagonal | Cubic |
|---|---|---|---|---|---|
| 1<br>$\bar{1}$ | 2<br>m<br>2/m | 4<br>$\bar{4}$<br>4/m | 3<br>$\bar{3}$ | 6<br>$\bar{6}$<br>6/m | 23<br>m3 |
| | Orthorhombic | | | | |
| | 222<br>mm2<br>mmm | 422<br>4mm<br>$\bar{4}$2m<br>4/mmm | 32<br>3m<br>$\bar{3}$m | 622<br>6mm<br>$\bar{6}$m2<br>6/mmm | 432<br>$\bar{4}$3m<br>m3m |

**Schoenflies notation**

| Triclinic | Monoclinic | Tetragonal | Trigonal | Hexagonal | Cubic |
|---|---|---|---|---|---|
| $C_1$<br>$C_i$ | $C_2$<br>$C_{1h}$<br>$C_{2h}$ | $C_4$<br>$S_4$<br>$C_{4h}$ | $C_3$<br>$S_6$ | $C_6$<br>$C_{3h}$<br>$C_{6h}$ | T<br>$T_h$ |
| | Orthorhombic | | | | |
| | $D_2$<br>$C_{2v}$<br>$D_{2h}$ | $D_4$<br>$C_{4v}$<br>$D_{2d}$<br>$D_{4h}$ | $D_3$<br>$C_{3v}$<br>$D_{3d}$ | $D_6$<br>$C_{6v}$<br>$D_{3h}$<br>$D_{6h}$ | O<br>$T_d$<br>$O_h$ |

In two dimensions the six Laue symmetry groups are associated with (1,2), (m,2mm), (4), (4mm), (3,6), (3m,6mm), the last group in parentheses is the symbol for the Laue group.

## 4-7 Point Group Notation

**4-7a Schoenflies Notation** We shall summarize the Schoenflies notation first since it is slightly more systematic. A cyclic point group is given the symbol $C_n$ with n = 1, 2, 3, 4, 6. If there are one or more 2-fold axes perpendicular to the principal axis (denoted $C_2'$), then the symbol $D_n$ is used. If there is a $\sigma_h$ plane, then the point group is $C_{nh}$ or $D_{nh}$. If there is no $\sigma_h$ plane but one or more $\sigma_v$ planes, then we have $C_{nv}$.

$D_n$ point groups can only have $\sigma_d$-planes and so the relevant point groups are called $D_{nd}$. The point groups $S_4$, $S_6$, and $C_i$ ($C_i$ is sometimes called $S_2$) have only symmetry operations of the $S_n$ type. The notation for the cubic point groups is somewhat specialized. The point group T has only symmetry operations of the type $C_2$ and $C_3$. The point group $T_h$ has twice the number of operations as T and is obtained by adding a center of inversion, as has already been explained ($T_h = T \times C_i$). The point group O has only $C_2$, $C_3$ and $C_4$ symmetry operations and $O_h$ is obtained by adding i ($O_h = O \times C_i$). $T_d$ is a subgroup of $O_h$ or $T_d = T \times \{E, \sigma_d\}$.

Figure 4-1a shows a flow chart method of determining the point group of any object. The cubic point groups should be determined separately by noting the existence of four 3-fold axes and then checking carefully all of the other symmetry operations.

**4-7b International Notation** The cyclic point groups are given the symbol n where n = 1, 2, 3, 4, and 6. If there is a 2-fold axis perpendicular to the principal axis, then the number 2 is added after n to give n2 or else n22 if a distinct diagonal 2-fold axis also occurs (e.g., 622, 32, 422, 222). If there is a mirror plane perpendicular to the principal axis, the symbol is written n/m (e.g., 2/m, 4/m, 6/m). If there is only one or more mirror planes containing the principal axis, the symbol is written nm or nmm if a distinct diagonal mirror also occurs (e.g., 4mm, 3m, 6mm). If there are vertical and horizontal planes, then there are also 2-fold axes and so the full symbol would be n/m 2/m 2/m (e.g., 4/m 2/m 2/m, 6/m 2/m 2/m). Usually, however, the short symbol n/mmm is used (e.g., 4/mmm, 6/mmm). The 32 crystallographic point groups are listed in Appendix 4 in the Schoenflies, International, and full International notations. From the symmetry operations given in the short symbol, one can derive the operations in the full symbol and this is why the full symbol is not used very often. The International notation for the point groups $\bar{4}$ and $\bar{6}$ is self-evident and $\bar{4}2m$ means a $\bar{4}$ axis with a 2-fold axis perpendicular and a mirror plane containing the principal axis. $\bar{6}m2$ has a similar meaning. For the cubic point groups, it is best to look at the full symbols before looking at the short symbols and to memorize them.

Figure 4-1b shows in flow chart form using the International notation, how to obtain the point group of an object. This is similar to Fig. 4-1a, although sometimes the International symbol may look slightly different for a particular point group from that given on the chart, because of contractions to the short forms and non-standard directions for the symmetry elements.

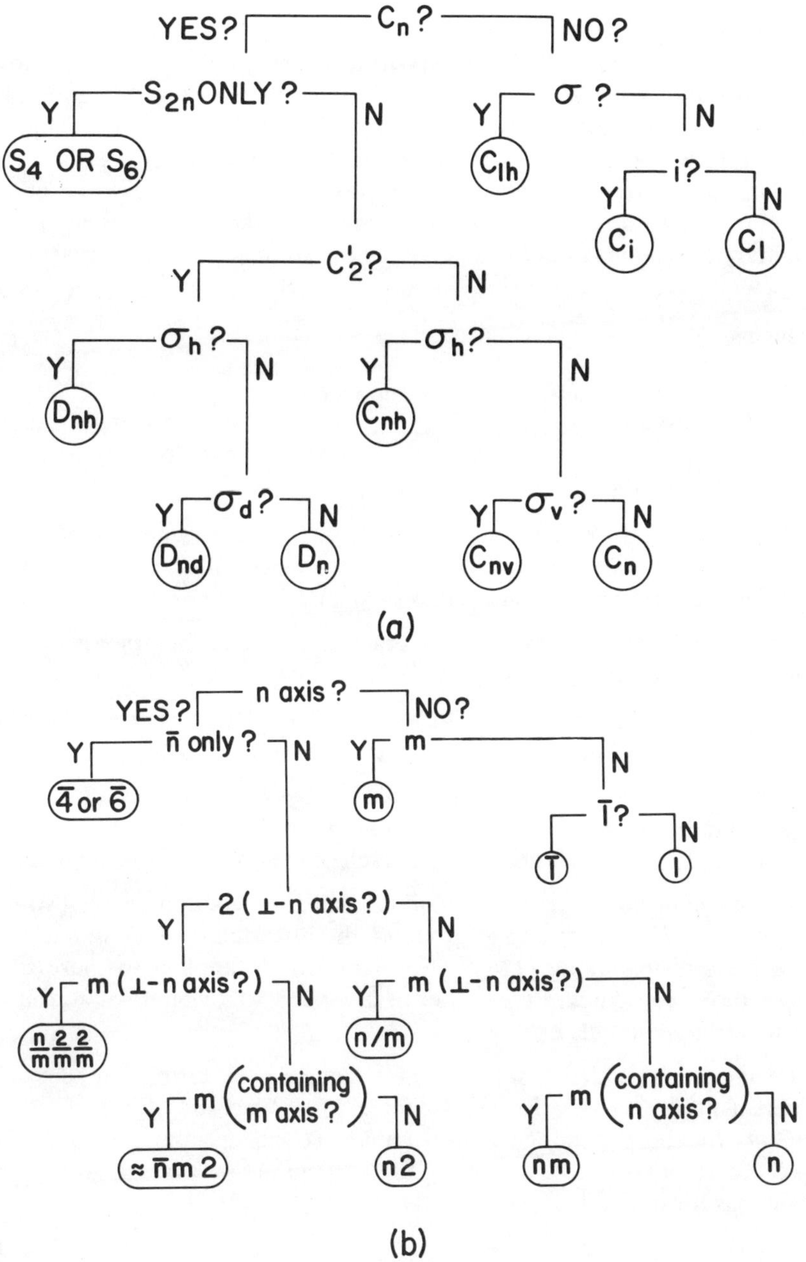


**Fig. 4-1** A chart showing a systematic way to determine the appropriate point group.

We should emphasize that given the point group symbol, one now knows the symmetry operations, i.e., the flow charts in Fig. 4-1 go either way. This is a nice aspect of the point group symbol, namely, the symmetry operations involved can be derived in an instant. (Drawing a stereogram of several of the symmetry operations will usually make the other symmetry operations clear. Do remember that there must be as many symmetry operations as general points on the stereogram.)

## Problems

**1.** Show that when the $C_{nh}$ point groups are obtained from the $C_n$ point groups, a center of inversion is produced when n is even. This is why only two new distinct point groups are obtained by $C_n \times \{E, i\}$. These result when n = 1 and 3 and are called $C_i$ and $S_6$ (or $\bar{1}$ and $\bar{3}$).

**2.** $2\bar{2}2$, $\bar{3}/m2$ and $43\bar{2}$ are unusual descriptions of the symmetry of three crystallographic point groups. What are the conventional symbols? What do these point groups have in common?

**3.** Show that the point group of a space lattice must be among the 11 centrosymmetric point groups, as in Section 4-4d.

**4.** For the point groups $\bar{4}2m$ ($D_{2d}$) and 622 ($D_6$) write out the coordinates of the general points.

**5.** To which point groups do the following belong? (a) a molecule of $H_2O$, (b) a brick, (c) an octahedron, (d) a tetrahedron, (e) a propeller, (f) this book (ignoring lettering), (g) each of the letters of the alphabet.

**6.** An object of point symmetry m3m ($O_h$) distorts under a uniaxial stress along [001]. What is the point group of the distorted object? What is it when the stress is along [111]? An electric field applied to these two distorted objects removes the center of inversion. To which point groups do the resulting objects belong?

**7.** Define precisely the term **cyclic** point group, i.e., in terms of a generating element (hint: see Burns, Chapter 1). What are the generating elements for the $C_n$ and $S_n$ point groups? To which point groups do $S_1$ and $S_3$ correspond? Note that in $S_n$ for n even the order of the group h is n, whereas for n odd, h = 2n.

# Chapter 5

# DEVELOPMENT OF SPACE GROUPS

*To be a philosopher is not to merely have subtle thoughts, or even to found a school, but so to love wisdom as to live according to its dictates, a life of simplicity, independence, magnanimity, and trust. It is to solve some of the problems of life, not only theoretically, but practically.*

*Thoreau, "Walden"*

## 5-1 Introduction

A crystal may be described in differing degrees of detail according to one's requirement. We might assign it to one of the seven crystal systems or to one of the 14 Bravais lattices, in which case we know the crystal system as well as the type of lattice. If we wish to go deeper we might then ask to which of the 32 point groups does the crystal belong; this tells us the crystal system and the relationship between the tensor components that describe the macroscopic behavior and properties of the crystal. We can go further than this by taking into account how the electron density (atoms) is distributed spatially. We have already dealt with the symmetry with respect to a fixed point in the crystal and with the symmetry of space or Bravais lattices. In order to describe the entire crystal (assuming it to be of infinite extent) we must combine the two and also allow for two new types of symmetry operation (which will be discussed below). A space group determined in this way describes the spatial symmetry of the crystal. Thus, a crystallographic **space group** is the set of geometrical symmetry operations that take a 3-dimensional periodic object (a crystal) into itself. The set of operations that make up the space group must form a group in the mathematical sense, and certainly must include the primitive lattice translations as well as other symmetry operations.

In order to discuss the set of symmetry operations more easily, consider the lattice to be finite with periodic boundary conditions. This is easily understood with reference to a finite 1-dimensional lattice of points labelled 1, 2, ..., n, n + 1, ..., N, in which case the translational symmetry operation takes each point n into point n + 1. We can write the periodic boundary condition as

$$t_1 = t_{N+1}$$

where t is a unit of translation. This is a useful trick for simulating an infinite lattice and can be applied to a 2-dimensional or 3-dimensional lattice equally well.

Let N be the number of symmetry operations in the finite lattice. Apart from the N operations that translate one primitive unit cell into every other one, there are h symmetry operations that transform the contents of the primitive unit cell into themselves and are symmetry operations of the entire crystal. Thus, the space group has hN symmetry operations in the set obtained by taking products of the h and N operations. It is very convenient to distinguish one product in particular, that is the product of the h symmetry operations with the identity of the translation group, namely, zero translation. These h symmetry operations we call **essential space group operations**. The other products of the h operations with primitive lattice translations we call **nonessential space group operations**. Operations obtained by the product of the identity of the h operations with the primitive lattice translations are simply the translation symmetry operations. These nonessential operations are perfectly acceptable symmetry operations and are included in the set of hN operations; it is just that they can always be obtained from products of the essential ones with the translations. These ideas will be discussed more fully below, where we shall see that exactly which operations we take as the essential ones can often vary.

All space group operations can be described conveniently by means of the **Seitz operator** $\{R \mid \mathbf{t}\}$ defined by a point operation R, followed by a translation $\mathbf{t}$. The operator operates on a general position vector $\mathbf{r}$ and can be written as

$$\{R \mid \mathbf{t}\}\, \mathbf{r} = R\mathbf{r} + \mathbf{t} \qquad (5\text{-}1)$$

As in previous chapters, R can refer to either proper or improper rotations or reflection planes and it operates directly on the position vector. When $\mathbf{t}$ is any translation, not necessarily one associated with a periodic crystal, the set of operations defined by Eq. (5-1) forms a group known as the **real affine group**, of which space groups are subgroups. We can easily check, in the following way, that the set of operations defined by Eq. (5-1) forms a group. (See Section 4-1 for the definition of a group.)

(i) Consider multiplication of any two operations $\{R \mid \mathbf{t}\}$ and $\{S \mid \mathbf{u}\}$ where both operations are in the set.

$$\{R \mid \mathbf{t}\}\{S \mid \mathbf{u}\}\mathbf{r}=\{R \mid \mathbf{t}\}(S\mathbf{r}+\mathbf{u})=RS\mathbf{r}+R\mathbf{u}+\mathbf{t}=\{RS \mid R\mathbf{u}+\mathbf{t}\}\mathbf{r} \quad (5\text{-}2)$$

We can see then that, since $R\mathbf{u}$ is still a translation, the product of any two operators is another operator that is also a member of the set.

(ii) There is obviously an identity element, $\{1 \mid \mathbf{0}\}$ or $\{E \mid \mathbf{0}\}$, in the International and Schoenflies notation respectively.

(iii) The inverse operator $\{R \mid \mathbf{t}\}^{-1}$ is $\{R^{-1} \mid -R^{-1}\mathbf{t}\}$ since

$$\{R \mid \mathbf{t}\}\{R^{-1} \mid -R^{-1}\mathbf{t}\} = \{1 \mid \mathbf{0}\} \quad (5\text{-}3)$$

as can be checked by using Eq. (5-2).

(iv) From the law of combination in Eq. (5-2), associativity is obeyed.

These four results show that Eq. (5-1) defines a group. We shall find that Eq. (5-1) will prove very useful in studying the different space groups. However, remember that for crystals the lattice can be described by the Seitz operator $\{1 \mid \mathbf{t}_n\}$, or $\{E \mid \mathbf{t}_n\}$ in the Schoenflies notation, where $\mathbf{t}_n = n_1\mathbf{a} + n_2\mathbf{b} + n_3\mathbf{c}$ with **a**, **b**, and **c** as the primitive lattice translation vectors of Eq. (2-1).

As we shall see, space group symmetry operations may involve a translation, $\boldsymbol{\tau}$, smaller than a primitive lattice translation coupled with a rotation or reflection. These symmetry operations are known as glide or screw operations. This leads to an important classification of space groups into two types – symmorphic and nonsymmorphic space groups. A **symmorphic space group** is one which may be entirely specified by symmetry operations all acting at a common point and which do not involve one of these translations $\boldsymbol{\tau}$. When it is necessary to specify a space group, with respect to any choice of origin, by at least one operation involving a translation $\boldsymbol{\tau}$, the space group is said to be **nonsymmorphic**. Certain of these latter types of operations are conventionally known as screw or glide operations (also see the discussion at the end of section describing the $P2_12_12_1(D_2{}^4)$ space group). As we shall see in Sections 5-2 and 5-5, screw or glide operations can be symmetry operations in symmorphic space groups; it is just that they can be generated by appropriate combinations of symmorphic operations with translation operations.

## 5-2 The Symmorphic Space Groups

We may think that in order to obtain the space groups we simply combine the 32 point groups with the 14 Bravais lattices. That is, each point group can be combined with the types of Bravais lattices allowed for the crystal class, i.e., P, I, F, and/or C. Let us examine this idea more closely and see how a large number of space groups can be generated. As we shall see, this generates the symmorphic space groups which account for 73 out of a total of 230. These symmorphic space groups also serve as a useful starting point when generating the nonsymmorphic space groups. We shall see why and how this is done when we come to the various symmetry operations in Sections 5-4 and 5-5 and again in Section 5-6, where a method for deriving all the space groups is outlined.

As an example of how a symmorphic space group is developed, consider the case of an orthorhombic P-lattice (see Appendix 3). Now, take any object whose symmetry belongs to one of the orthorhombic point groups and with the appropriate orientation attach it to a lattice point (actually to every lattice point by translational symmetry). For example, suppose we start with an object having point symmetry mm2($C_{2v}$). It might be one of the special shapes drawn in Appendix 5 or a collection of atoms arranged as in the mm2($C_{2v}$) stereogram of Appendix 5. If the object consists of an arrangement of atoms or of a molecule, then the result of adding it to the lattice is to produce what is commonly called a **crystal structure**. We have to be careful how we attach our mm2($C_{2v}$) object to the lattice. Obviously, if we wish to preserve the orthorhombic symmetry at each lattice point the object must be placed so that its mirror-planes and 2-fold axis are lined up with the unit-cell axes. The resulting crystal structure has translational symmetry and, in addition, about <u>any</u> lattice point it has point symmetry mm2($C_{2v}$). These two types of symmetry operation are all that are essential for describing the symmetry of the entire structure.

In Fig. 5-1a we show an example of how the space groups can be described diagrammatically. The unit cell is outlined with the origin taken, arbitrarily, at the upper left-hand corner. As usual we use a **right-hand convention** for the axes with **a** drawn down the page, **b** to the right, and **c** out of the page (the same convention as that used throughout the

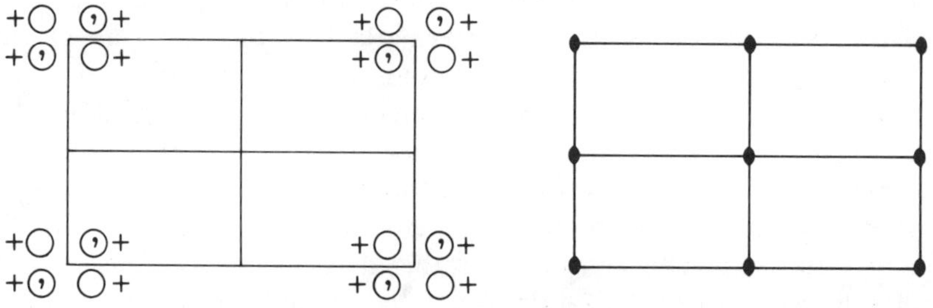

(a) $Pmm2(C_{2v}^{I})$

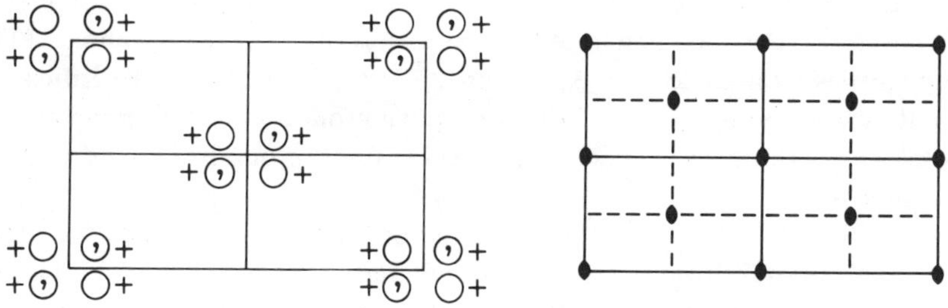

(b) $Cmm2(C_{2v}^{II})$

International Tables). The effect of the symmetry at each lattice point is shown in the left-hand diagram by the arrangement of circles drawn in the same way as we have discussed in Chapter 1 and it can be seen in our example that this arrangement has symmetry mm2($C_{2v}$), produced as a result of four operations 1, 2 [001], m[100], m[010] (E, $C_2$, $\sigma_v$, $\sigma_v'$). The circles on this diagram represent the effect of the symmetry operations on any general point at (x,y,z), the point specified by vector **r** of Eq. (5-1). The symmetry-equivalent positions thus obtained are known as the **general equivalent positions**. We emphasize once again that, in a crystal, each circle may represent a single atom or a collection of atoms. The diagram on the right-hand side shows the symmetry elements themselves; these are indicated by conventional symbols which are explained in Appendix 6.

We see here that the 2-fold axis is shown to be along **c** at the origin together with the two mirror planes (marked by the heavy lines). By translational symmetry {1 | **a**}, {1 | **b**}, and {1 | **a**+**b**}, we obtain the same arrangement of circles and symmetry elements about positions other than the origin, as shown in the figure. One of the interesting aspects of combining the point symmetry operations with translational symmetry is that many new, but nonessential, symmetry operations are generated. We shall see throughout this chapter that this always happens. Here we find that halfway between the 2-fold axes, other 2-fold axes occur; and likewise in the case of mirror planes (see Problem 1 in Chapter 3). We can describe the symmetry of this space group in International notation by the symbol Pmm2. The P stands for the primitive lattice and the mm2 describes the other symmetry operations that are **essential** to the space group. By this we mean that the point group symbol mm2 allows us to work out the four (in this case) essential symmetry elements mentioned above. The nonessential operations, extra 2-fold axes and mirror planes in this case, that are generated are not described in the symbol. (The Schoenflies symbol for this space group is $C_{2v}^{1}$; it clearly describes the point symmetry used in obtaining the space group but it does not explicitly tell us anything else, since the particular space group is denoted only by the superscript.)

Returning for the moment to the orthorhombic P-lattice we could add appropriately orientated objects having point symmetry 222($D_2$) or point symmetry mmm($D_{2h}$). If we do this, two different space groups will result whose symmetry operations can be completely described by the space group symbols P222 or Pmmm, respectively. Diagrams for these two space groups can be drawn as in Fig. 5-1a. We see that some space groups can be generated without difficulty.

In the same way, we may consider an orthorhombic base-centered C-lattice and add an appropriately orientated object with point symmetry mm2($C_{2v}$). Again, about any lattice point the point symmetry of the entire crystal structure is mm2($C_{2v}$). Thus the space group is labelled Cmm2, where the C serves to denote the lattice type and the other symbols describe the remaining essential symmetry operations, which are, naturally, the same as in Pmm2. Figure 5-1b shows this space group in diagrammatic form. The C-centering at position (**a**+**b**)/2 is readily apparent. In fact, without this centering the space group Cmm2 reverts to Pmm2. It can be seen that other nonessential symmetry operations are generated, including glide planes, marked by the dashed lines. These will be discussed later in this chapter but note that they have been generated by the combination of point symmetry mm2($C_{2v}$) with translational symmetry. They are not essential in describing the space group.

We see immediately how to go about generating space groups C222 and Cmmm and in the same way, we can form other orthorhombic space groups with I and F-lattices taken together with the three orthorhombic point groups. The result is that, for the orthorhombic system, when we combine mm2, 222, and mmm with the four Bravais arrays, P, C, I, and F, $3 \times 4 = 12$ distinct space groups are obtained. The same process can be generalized for many other unique space groups in other crystal systems. Thus, in the triclinic system we have one Bravais lattice P and two point groups 1($C_1$) and $\bar{1}$($C_i$) giving two space groups. These we label P1 and P$\bar{1}$. Similarly, in the monoclinic system there are two Bravais lattices P and B and three point groups 2($C_2$), m($C_{1h}$), and 2/m($C_{2h}$), giving rise to six space groups labelled P2, Pm, P2/m, B2, Bm, and B2/m. Proceeding in this way for all seven crystal systems a total of 66 space groups can be found. However, other space groups are obtained when we take account of the orientation of the point group elements with respect to the Bravais lattice. For example, in the orthorhombic crystal system, A-, B-, and C-centered Bravais lattices are equivalent. However, when we combine these lattices with point groups mm2($C_{2v}$) we can either have the 2-fold axis, which we take along **c**, perpendicular to the centered face or parallel to it. In the former case we shall have C-centering, in the latter A- or B- centering. The cases where the 2-fold axis is either perpendicular or parallel to the centered face are physically distinct from each other and lead to space groups Cmm2 and Amm2. It turns out that by considering the orientation of the point symmetry elements with respect to the Bravais array a further seven space groups are obtained giving the **73 symmorphic space groups**. These 73 space groups are listed in Table 5-1 using the International notation for each space group. The exact meaning of this notation will be made clearer at a later stage; however, from this discussion the notation is fairly apparent. The asterisks in Table 5-1 mark the seven extra space groups which are generated when the orientation of the point group elements with respect to the Bravais cell is taken into account.

Before we go on, a subtle but important point should be brought up. In the development at the beginning of this section we were careful to place objects belonging to one of the orthorhombic point groups at the lattice points of an orthorhombic lattice. Both the object and the lattice had the symmetry of the same crystal system. This procedure is correct but we should like to question it and see why it is justified. For example, can we put an object with just 1($C_1$) point symmetry on a cubic Bravais

**Table 5-1** The 73 symmorphic space groups.

| Crystal system | Bravais lattice | Space group |
|---|---|---|
| Triclinic | P | P1, $P\bar{1}$ |
| Monoclinic | P | P2, Pm, P2/m |
| | B or C | B2, Bm, B2/m (1st setting) |
| Orthorhombic | P | P222, Pmm2, Pmmm |
| | C, A or B | C222, Cmm2, Amm2*, Cmmm |
| | I | I222, Imm2, Immm |
| | F | F222, Fmm2, Fmmm |
| Tetragonal | P | P4, $P\bar{4}$, P4/m, P422, P4mm, $P\bar{4}2m$, $P\bar{4}m2$*, P4/mmm. |
| | I | I4, $I\bar{4}$, I4/m, I422, I4mm, $I\bar{4}2m$, $I\bar{4}m2$*, I4/mmm. |
| Cubic | P | P23, Pm3, P432, $P\bar{4}3m$, Pm3m |
| | I | I23, Im3, I432, $I\bar{4}3m$, Im3m |
| | F | F23, Fm3, F432, $F\bar{4}3m$, Fm3m |
| Trigonal | P | P3, $P\bar{3}$, P312, P321*, P3m1, P31m*, $P\bar{3}1m$, $P\bar{3}m1$* |
| (Rhombohedral) | R | R3, $R\bar{3}$, R32, R3m, $R\bar{3}m$ |
| Hexagonal | P | P6, $P\bar{6}$, P6/m, P622, P6mm, $P\bar{6}m2$, $P\bar{6}2m$*, P6/mmm |

lattice? Conversely, can we put an object with m3m($O_h$) point symmetry on a triclinic Bravais lattice?

The answer to both these questions is no. The reason is that, physically, the forces compatible with a cubic Bravais lattice can be expanded about a lattice point in combinations of spherical harmonics that have cubic symmetry. There are no combinations that have lower symmetry. Thus, on a cubic Bravais lattice, the object must have one of the cubic point symmetries. Similarly, for a triclinic Bravais lattice the forces expanded about a lattice point have triclinic symmetry and so these forces would tend to distort the object of higher symmetry and make it adopt triclinic point symmetry. (However, always remember that the distortion may be very small and difficult to observe experimentally.)

## 5-3 Nonsymmorphic Operations

We briefly mentioned before that space groups which must be specified by at least one operation which involves a non-primitive translation, $\tau$, are called nonsymmorphic space groups. Now, if we take such operations into account, it is found that there is a total of 157 nonsymmorphic space groups. These taken together with the 73 symmorphic space groups produce 230 in all.

We now consider in some detail what happens when we combine rotations and reflections with nonprimitive translations to produce the so-called screw and glide operations. The symmetry elements are known as **screw axes** and **glide planes**, respectively.

The nonsymmorphic operations can conveniently be represented about some origin by the Seitz operator $\{R \mid \tau\}$ as

$$\{R \mid \tau\}\mathbf{r} = R\mathbf{r} + \tau \tag{5-4}$$

The matrix of the operation R operates first on the position vector **r** and is then followed by the nonsymmorphic translation $\tau$, where $\tau$ is a translation by a fraction of a unit cell. $\tau = 0$ for the symmorphic operations.

Let us now deal with these two nonsymmorphic symmetry operations in turn.

### 5-3a Screw operation

**5-3a Screw operation** The **screw operation** is a symmetry operation derived from the coupling of a proper rotation with a nonprimitive translation parallel to the axis of rotation, which is called the screw axis. The order in which the two operations are performed is unimportant, as R**r** and $\tau$ are commutative under addition.

Consider the rotational part of the screw operation. The rotation R operates on the general vector **r** separately from the translation. Since vectors have magnitude and direction but do not have different origins, for crystals the only allowed proper rotations associated with nonsymmorphic operations are the same as in the symmorphic operations, namely, 1, 2, 3, 4, and 6. This is a very important point and so we explain it more fully.

(i) With reference to Fig. 5-2 consider the point A. At this point there is a screw axis perpendicular to the plane of the page that takes the

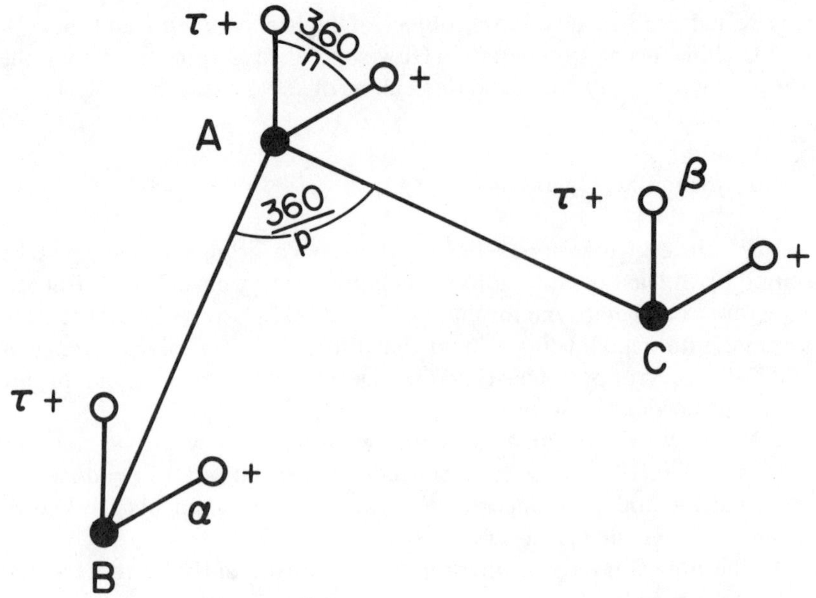


**Fig. 5-2** The effect of a general screw operation.

circle marked with a + into the one marked $\tau+$. The symmetry operation is $\{n \mid \tau\}$ and so the projected angle between the circles is 360/n as shown in the diagram.

(ii) Now consider the effects of the lattice. By translational symmetry, we obtain the same arrangement about lattice points, B and C and this is shown in the figure. These points are chosen so that they are equidistant from the lattice point A, something that can always be done in every crystal system. Now for a particular crystal class there are restrictions placed on the angle BAC as discussed in Section 2-3. These conditions can be expressed in terms of the symmetry operations for the lattice $\{p \mid \mathbf{0}\}$, with p = 1, 2, 3, 4, or 6, which implies that angle BAC = 360/p. This is indicated in the figure.

(iii) Now reconsider the operation $\{n \mid \tau\}$ at the point A. If we want this operation to be a symmetry operation of the crystal it must take the entire crystal into itself. This operation takes the circle labelled $\alpha$ with height denoted by the + sign into the one labelled $\beta$ at height $\tau+$. This operation makes the angle projected on the plane of the page $\alpha A\beta$ = 360/n. However, the symmetry operation of the lattice makes the projected angle $\alpha A\beta$ = 360/p. Thus, if we demand that the screw operation $\{n \mid \tau\}$ be a symmetry operation of the crystal, n must equal p. This means that what is true for proper rotations with respect to the conditions placed on the unit-cell axes and angles must also be true for screw rotations.

Another point to realize is that the choice of rotation does affect the value of $\tau$. We can demonstrate this in the following way. Consider an n-fold screw operation $\{R \mid \tau\}$ performed n times on a position vector $\mathbf{r}$. Just as with the proper rotations, this must rotate the object that is being operated on through a complete revolution of 360°. However, in contrast to proper rotations the object will also be moved along the rotation axis, in general, through an integral number N of unit lattice translations. Thus, we may write

$$\{R \mid \tau\}^n = \{1 \mid \mathbf{t}_N\} = \mathbf{t}_N \tag{5-5}$$

Now consider what $\{R \mid \tau\}^n$ is by writing it explicitly:

$$\begin{aligned} \{R \mid \tau\}^n \mathbf{r} &= \{R \mid \tau\}\{R \mid \tau\} \ldots \{R \mid \tau\}\{R \mid \tau\}\mathbf{r} \\ &= \{R \mid \tau\}\{R \mid \tau\} \ldots \{R \mid \tau\}(R\mathbf{r}+\tau) \\ &= \{R \mid \tau\}\{R \mid \tau\} \ldots (R^2\mathbf{r} + R\tau + \tau) \end{aligned} \tag{5-6a}$$

Since the translation $\tau$ is along the rotation axis, $R\tau$ is equal to $\tau$. Equation (5-6a) then, on continuing the process, reduces to

$$\{R \mid \tau\}^n\mathbf{r} = R^n\mathbf{r} + n\tau = \{R^n \mid n\tau\}\,\mathbf{r} \tag{5-6b}$$

Thus, from Eq. (5-5) and (5-6b) we see that

$$\{1 \mid \mathbf{t}_N\} = \{R^n \mid n\tau\} \tag{5-6c}$$

In other words, performing the rotation operation n times results in one or more unit cell translations given by $\mathbf{t}_N$. We see that the amount of translation is (1/n)th of one or more unit repeat distances. This point will become clearer in what follows.

In the example shown in Fig. 5-3 we have a 4-fold screw axis, with each rotation of $\mathbf{r}$ through 90° and translations $\tau$ of magnitude $\mathbf{c}/4$.

The diagram marked $4_1$ in Fig. 5-4 shows the same screw axis drawn in a more conventional manner looking down the $\mathbf{c}$-axis. The general point at (x,y,z) is taken by the first screw operation, which we denote $4_1$, to the point (−y, x, 1/4+z). The next screw operation $4_1{}^2$ takes this point to (−x, −y, 1/2+z). The third screw operation $4_1{}^3$ takes it to (y, −x, 3/4+z). Finally the fourth operation $4^4$ returns the general point to its initial position in projection, but translated along $\mathbf{c}$ through a unit repeat distance. Note that in designating the screw axes we use a subscript. In the International **notation** the screw axis symmetry operation is denoted $R_q$, where it is to be understood that the fractional unit of translation is q divided by the order n of the rotation R.

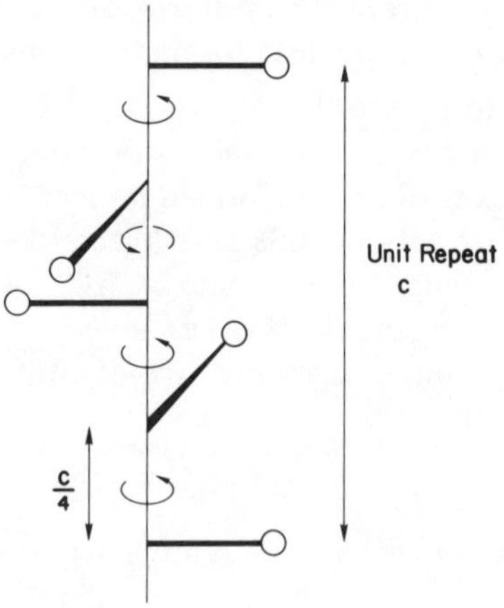


**Fig. 5-3** A $4_1$ screw operation.

Consider the case of the $4_2$ operation shown in Fig. 5-4. Here, for every rotation through $2\pi/4 = 90°$ the general point is displaced along **c** through a distance of (2/4)c. Thus the initial point at (x,y,z) is taken by $4_2$ to (−y, x, 1/2+z). The operation $(4_2)^2$ takes it to (−x, −y, 1+z) which by translational invariance is the same as (−x, −y, z). The third operation $(4_2)^3$ results in a point at (y, −x, 3/2+z) which is equivalent, by the same token, to (y, −x, 1/2+z). Finally, performing the operation four times, $(4_2)^4$, results in a point at (x, y, 2+z) which is equivalent, by translational symmetry, to the starting position. The important thing to note is that performing this operation four times corresponds to a total translation of two unit repeat distances. The basic translation as given by Eq. (5-6c), is equal to (1/4)th of the total translation of 2 unit repeats, i.e., it is 2/4 = 1/2 along **c**.

It should now be clear which screw axes are possible. There are 11 screw axes in all

$$2_1,\ 3_1,\ 3_2,\ 4_1,\ 4_2,\ 4_3,\ 6_1,\ 6_2,\ 6_3,\ 6_4,\ 6_5$$

and these are shown in Fig. 5-4.

It is an easy matter to work out the effect of applying a screw operation to the general point at (x,y,z) by applying the rotation matrix R from Appendix 1 and then adding the appropriate translation, $\tau$, as expressed by Eq. (5-4). Take for example the operation $3_2$ about [001]:

$$3_2[001] = \{3[001] \mid \tau(0, 0, 2/3)\} \tag{5-7a}$$

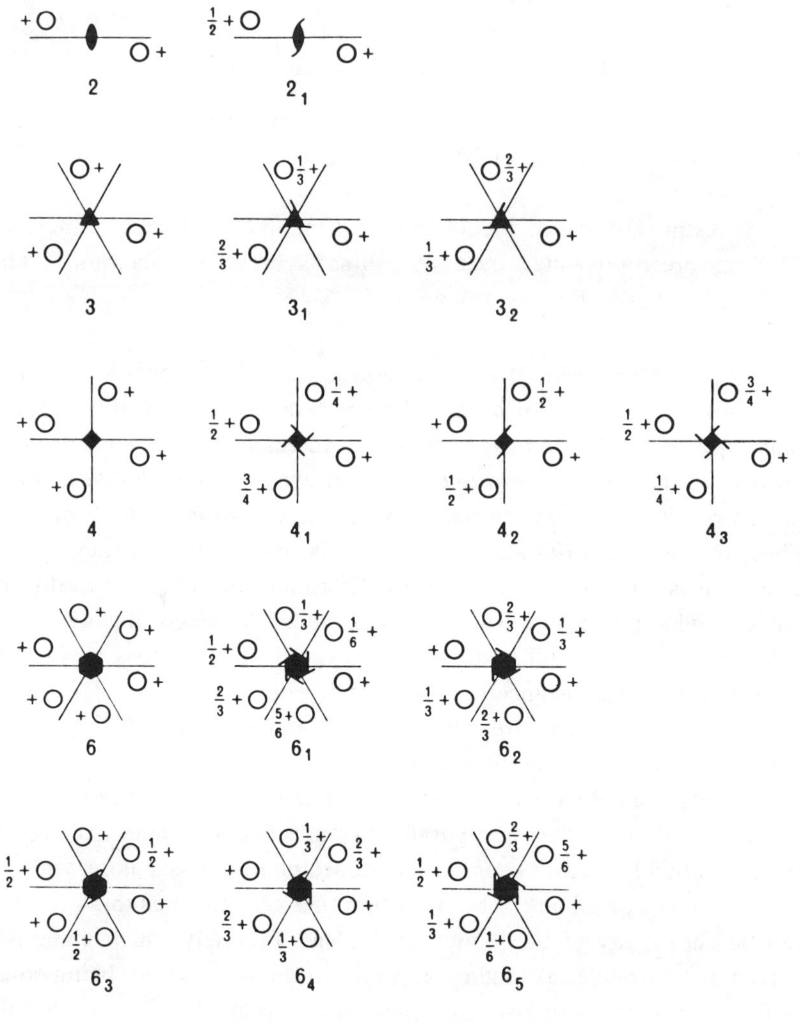

**Fig. 5-4** All the possible crystallographic screw operations (after McKie and McKie).

The vector $\boldsymbol{\tau}(0, 0, 2/3)$ means zero translations along **a** and **b** with a translation along **c** of (2/3)c. Now operate on a position vector **r**

$$\{3[001] \mid \boldsymbol{\tau}(0, 0, 2/3)\}\mathbf{r} = 3[001]\mathbf{r} + \boldsymbol{\tau}(0, 0, 2/3) \quad (5\text{-}7b)$$

which in matrix form is equal to

$$\begin{bmatrix} 0 & -1 & 0 \\ 1 & -1 & 0 \\ 0 & 0 & 1 \end{bmatrix} \begin{bmatrix} x \\ y \\ z \end{bmatrix} + \begin{bmatrix} 0 \\ 0 \\ 2/3 \end{bmatrix} = \begin{bmatrix} -y \\ x-y \\ 2/3+z \end{bmatrix} \tag{5-7c}$$

Thus the general point (x,y,z) is taken by the $3_2[001]$ operation to $(-y, x-y, 2/3+z)$.

As in the case of the symmetry elements in Chapter 1 these new elements are represented by conventional symbols on diagrams. These are listed in Appendix 6 as well as in Fig. 5-4.

**5-3b Glide plane** Just as we considered the combination of proper rotations with translation to get the screw axes, it is natural to try the same approach with improper rotations instead of proper rotations. It turns out that only one improper rotation can be combined with translation to result in a symmetry operation, namely, $\bar{2}$ or m. (See Problem 3.) Thus, the only appropriate combination is reflection plus translation to give what is known as a **glide plane**. There are, however, three different types of glide plane in crystals, the **axial glide**, the **diagonal glide**, and the "**diamond**" **glide**. In all of these glides one reflects across a plane and translates by some distance that is a **fraction** of the unit cell. The order in which these two steps are carried out is unimportant. We shall now discuss the three types of glide plane in turn.

In the **axial glide** the magnitude of the translation vector $\boldsymbol{\tau}$ is one half of a unit-cell translation parallel to the reflection plane. We refer to the axial glide as an a-, b-, or c-glide according to the axis along which the translation is carried out. The reflection that accompanies this translation can be across any of the planes **ab**, **bc**, **ca**. Precisely which plane is involved in a particular axial glide depends on the space group being considered; it is usually clear from the space group symbol. This point will be discussed in the next section.

As an example of an axial glide, Fig. 5-5 shows a b-glide with a reflection across a plane perpendicular to the **a**-axis. As in the case of reflection operations the glide operation produces the enantiomorph of the original object; thus the comma in the figure. In the same way as we did with the screw axis, we can use Eq. (5-4) to work out the fractional coordinates of a general point after the axial glide operation. For exam-

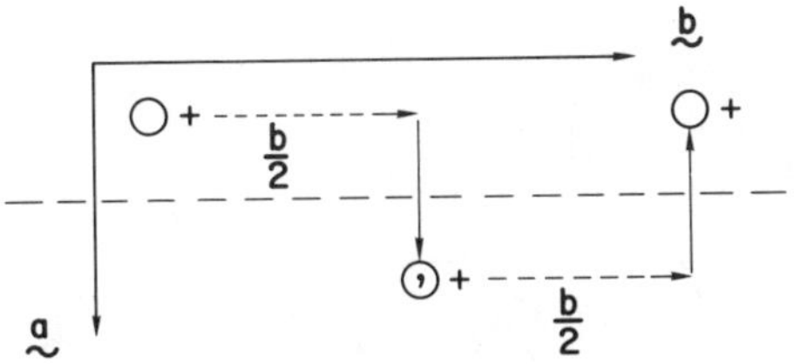


**Fig. 5-5** A b-glide operation.

ple, this b-glide, assuming that the mirror plane is at x=0, gives

$$\{m[100] \mid \tau(0, 1/2, 0)\}\mathbf{r} = m[100]\mathbf{r} + \tau(0, 1/2, 0) \tag{5-8a}$$

$$= \begin{bmatrix} -1 & 0 & 0 \\ 0 & 1 & 0 \\ 0 & 0 & 1 \end{bmatrix} \begin{bmatrix} x \\ y \\ z \end{bmatrix} + \begin{bmatrix} 0 \\ 1/2 \\ 0 \end{bmatrix} = \begin{bmatrix} -x \\ 1/2+y \\ z \end{bmatrix} \tag{5-8b}$$

so that the point at (x,y,z) is taken to (−x, 1/2+y, z). As noted above, the reflection plane accompanying the axial glide cannot be perpendicular to the glide direction. For example, if you try to draw a diagram of an a-glide with the reflection plane perpendicular to **a** you will find that the result will be an ordinary symmorphic mirror operation.

The next glide operation, the **diagonal glide**, usually called the **n-glide**, involves translations along two or three directions. In general, the translations are (**a**+**b**)/2, (**b**+**c**)/2 or (**c**+**a**)/2. However, in the case of tetragonal and cubic crystal systems the n-glide can also include a translation of (**a**+**b**+**c**)/2 (see Problem 9 at the end of the Chapter). Note that in the n-glide operation (and in the d-glide that follows) it is possible for the glide direction to have a component perpendicular to the reflection plane. This occurs only in tetragonal and cubic crystals.

Figure 5-6 illustrates an n-glide with a reflection across the plane perpendicular to **c**. The point at (x,y,z) is translated through (**a**/2)+(**b**/2) followed by reflection across the glide plane. Using Eq. (5-4) we can write this as (assuming that the mirror plane is at x=0)

$$\{m[001] \mid \tau(1/2, 1/2, 0)\}\mathbf{r} = m[001]\mathbf{r} + \tau(1/2, 1/2, 0) \tag{5-9a}$$

$$= \begin{bmatrix} 1 & 0 & 0 \\ 0 & 1 & 0 \\ 0 & 0 & -1 \end{bmatrix} \begin{bmatrix} x \\ y \\ z \end{bmatrix} + \begin{bmatrix} 1/2 \\ 1/2 \\ 0 \end{bmatrix} = \begin{bmatrix} 1/2+x \\ 1/2+y \\ -z \end{bmatrix} \tag{5-9b}$$

The point at (x,y,z) is taken by this operation to (1/2+x, 1/2+y, −z). As before, the column vector $\tau$ is obvious once one knows which n-glide is involved. The position of the symbol "n" in the space group symbol

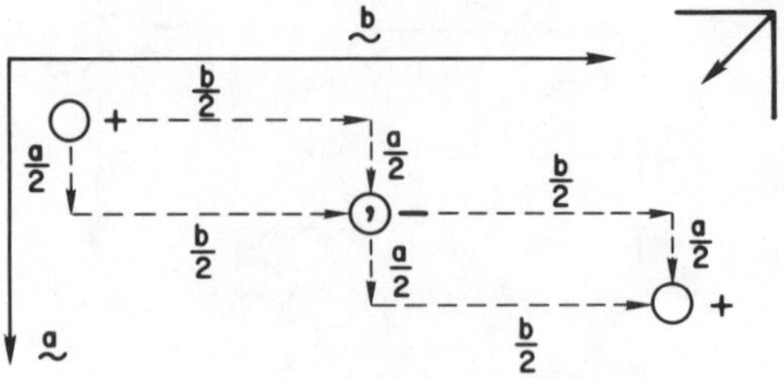


**Fig. 5-6** An n-glide operation.

determines the reflection plane and translation directions; as with the axial glide, we shall deal with this problem when we discuss the space groups in detail.

The last type of glide is the "**diamond**" or **d-glide**. Here the translations are $(\mathbf{a}\pm\mathbf{b})/4$ or $(\mathbf{b}\pm\mathbf{c})/4$ or $(\mathbf{a}\pm\mathbf{c})/4$ and $(\mathbf{a}\pm\mathbf{b}\pm\mathbf{c})/4$ in tetragonal and cubic crystals. The same general comments apply to the d-glide as to the others. For the moment we prefer not to go into any more detail, but instead we shall wait until we encounter it in one of the space group examples that follow. This is because there are some complexities with d-glides which are most easily understood with reference to a particular example.

The glide operations and their symbols are conveniently summarized in Appendix 6.

## 5-4 The Point Group of a Space Group and General Equivalent Positions

Before we go on to deal with some examples of space groups we shall settle the problem of the minimum number of operations that we need to specify the space group. In Section 5-1 we called these operations the essential space group operations. We shall see how the essential operations lead to a specific number of general equivalent positions. The group theoretical understanding of this, which is at the foundation of the theory of space groups is discussed and proved in Section 6-6. The more mathematically inclined may wish to glance at this section after reading the following discussion.

The **point group of a space group** $G_p$, often called simply the point group, is defined as the set of operations obtained when all translations, $\mathbf{t}_n$ as well as $\boldsymbol{\tau}$, of the space group are set equal to zero. Thus, $G_p$ has operations of the form $\{R\,|\,\mathbf{0}\}$. It is clear that, in general, the operations of $G_p$

are not symmetry operations of the space group G. For example, suppose $4_1$, $\{4 \mid \boldsymbol{\tau}(0,0,1/4)\}$, is a symmetry operation of G. The operation in $G_p$ obtained from this, $\{4 \mid \mathbf{0}\}$, cannot then be a symmetry operation of the space group. If this is the situation, we may ask what is the usefulness of the definition? Actually the concept is extremely useful, and in fact it is fundamental to the understanding of space groups.

Part of the set of symmetry operations that make up G consists of primitive lattice translations. The set of these translations, $\{1 \mid \mathbf{t}_n\}$, also forms a group which we call T. T is an infinite group because we have an infinite lattice of points. Since G contains T, the group G is also infinite. The other symmetry operations that make up G can be written in the form $\{R_i \mid \boldsymbol{\tau}_i\}$. The subscript i has been added here for clarity. We imagine dividing out of G all the primitive lattice translation operations, all of which are in T. This is what is normally called "forming the **factor group** of G with respect to the translation group T." This factor group is written G/T and is no longer of infinite order. However, G/T is indeed a group in the mathematical sense, but it has only a small number h of symmetry operations, where h is at most 48. These operations are of the form $\{R_i \mid \boldsymbol{\tau}_i\}$ where i equals 1 to h, representing each of the symmetry operations. The most important aspect of this is that there is an isomorphism, a one-to-one correspondence, between the symmetry operations of G/T and the operations of $G_p$. This means that the operations of $G_p$ also form a group and one may show that it is one of the 32 point groups given by $\{R_i \mid \mathbf{0}\}$, for i = 1 to h. Thus, to describe the **essential** symmetry operations of a space group we need the translation operations of T, which are trivial, and h other operations. The remaining symmetry operations in the space group can be obtained by the product of the h operations with those in T. By knowing the operations of the point group of the space group, we know what the operations $R_i$ are and only the corresponding translations that are fractions of the unit cell need to be supplied. Many examples of this will be described in the next section.

Another, very useful way of describing the space group is in terms of the **general equivalent positions**. These positions are obtained by starting with a general point at (x,y,z) and applying the h symmetry operations $\{R \mid \boldsymbol{\tau}\}$. (We drop the subscript in order to conform to normal practice.) Thus, the set of general equivalent positions consists of h positions and any essential or nonessential symmetry operation of the space group operating on this set of positions will not produce a new one. Naturally we may always apply the translational symmetry operations to gather these h positions about a convenient origin.

We should remark that in the International Tables one will find h, 2h, 3h, or 4h general equivalent positions given when the Bravais lattice is primitive, base- or body-centered, rhombohedral referred to hexagonal axes, or face-centered, respectively. This is because the conventional multiply-primitive unit cells are used in these tables. (Appendix 3 shows diagrams of these unit cells.) However, it is more fundamental to think in terms of the primitive cell of any lattice in which case there are only h general equivalent positions corresponding to the h symmetry operations $\{R \mid \tau\}$.

We should remark that the space group may be completely described by giving the lattice type (P, C, F, I) and a set of h general equivalent positions. The latter tells us all the symmetry operations of G/T and hence the crystal system, etc., while the lattice type tells us all the symmetry operations of T.

## 5-5 Space Groups

We are now in a position to describe the space groups using the symmetry operations that have been discussed. There are many ways of doing this, either by drawing appropriate space group diagrams or by using mathematical techniques. The method that we shall adopt involves both techniques. We shall see throughout that it is possible to explain the space group diagrams taken from the International Tables by using the matrix operators discussed in the preceding chapters. There are two main features that we have to explain: the coordinates of the general equivalent positions and the positions and occurrence of all the symmetry elements, both essential and nonessential, with respect to any particular choice of origin. As we shall see, all of this can be obtained from the International space group symbol alone. The procedure, then, will be to consider the point group of any space group, as discussed in the last section and to ascertain the number, h, of essential symmetry operations. This automatically tells us the number of general equivalent positions in the primitive unit cell. (We must be careful, however, since in the International Tables the conventional Bravais cells are used and this means that the number of general equivalent positions will be a multiple of that for the primitive cell.) Having done this, we shall then pick out certain features of the space group examples given and try to explain them by matrix operator methods. We shall see that, simply by using the Seitz operator together with the matrices in Appendix 1, we shall be able to determine the coordinates of all the general equivalent positions and, in so doing, the presence and positions of other symmetry elements not necessarily given in the space group symbol. While all this can be achieved purely by means of diagrams, and this is the way that most crystallographers construct a particular space group, we feel that it is useful to do this with some kind of mathematical formalism as well. This does have the benefit of making the process of constructing any space group more automatic and precise and also often gives more insight into the relationships between the various symmetry operations. No attempt will be made in this section to actually derive the space groups; we will indicate how this was done by Fedorov and Schoenflies in Section 5-6. Instead, we have chosen a few examples of space groups each of which display certain features which we consider worth discussing in detail. After reading this section the reader should be able to derive all of the general equivalent positions and symmetry elements of any space group, given only the International space group symbol. It is a remarkable fact that a single symbol can succinctly describe all of the features of a space group. The Schoenflies symbol for the space group, on the other hand, is made up from the Schoenflies point group symbol with a serial number as a superscript. The superscript serves only to differentiate between one space group and another; however it is arbitrary and does not allow one to generate all the symmetry elements or general equivalent positions. Nevertheless it is useful because it shows the point group of the space group at a glance and is independent of the choice of the axes of reference. In order to determine the point group from the International space group symbol, it is necessary to replace all nonsymmorphic elements, when they occur, by their symmorphic equivalents, i.e., replace all screw axes by proper rotation axes and all glides by mirrors.

Before going on to the examples, it is worth saying a little more about the International notation. We have already seen some of this in Section 5-1, but just to summarize: the space group symbol always takes the form of a letter, P, A, B, C, I, F, or R denoting the Bravais lattice, followed by one or more symmetry symbols. For example, Pnma and $P2_1/c$ are two space groups belonging to different crystal systems (their point groups are mmm($D_{2h}$) and 2/m($C_{2h}$), respectively) but both have primitive lattices. In the International Tables the standard space group symbols are listed. However, in the International notation, just as the point group symbols can be different according to our choice of axes of reference, so too can the space group symbols. The standard form adopted by the International Tables is for convenience only, and it is stated explicitly that "no official importance is attached to the particular setting of the space group adopted as standard." There are many reasons why a

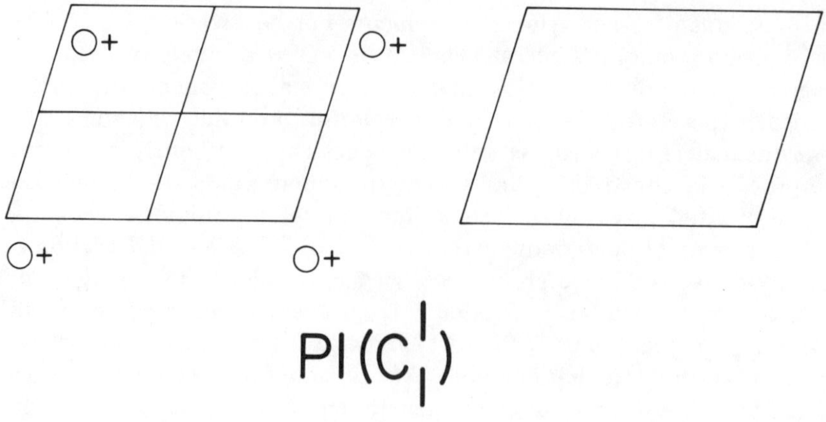


**Fig. 5-7**

particular crystal structure may be given a nonstandard space group symbol. For example, it may prove easier to visualize a particular structure in relation to some other form such as a high-temperature phase, by taking a nonstandard orientation for the axes of reference.

One final point of warning: by definition, a space group always includes the infinite number of translation operations $\{1 \mid \mathbf{t}_n\}$. This is so fundamental that it is sometimes ignored and attention is focused on the other h symmetry operations. Please remember that the translational symmetry is always understood to exist.

**5-5a Triclinic system** We have already seen that in the triclinic crystal system there is only one unique space lattice, the primitive lattice P. Furthermore, as discussed in Section 5-2, because there are only two triclinic point groups, $1(C_1)$ and $\overline{1}(C_i)$, there can only be two symmorphic triclinic space groups, $P1(C_1{}^1)$ and $P\overline{1}(C_i{}^1)$. Since reflection operations and rotations of order 2 or more are not compatible with triclinic symmetry, there cannot be any screw or glide operations. This implies that there are no nonsymmorphic triclinic space groups.

How do we represent these space groups diagrammatically? Figure 5-7 shows the way this is done in the International Tables for space group $P1(C_1{}^1)$. Two separate unit cells are shown side by side in precisely the same way as in the examples discussed briefly in Section 5-2. As before, the cell on the left illustrates the effect of the symmetry operations on a general point at (x,y,z), represented as usual by a circle, and the cell on the right shows the symmetry elements. Although this is a trivial example it does show certain features. Consider the right-hand cell. Since the

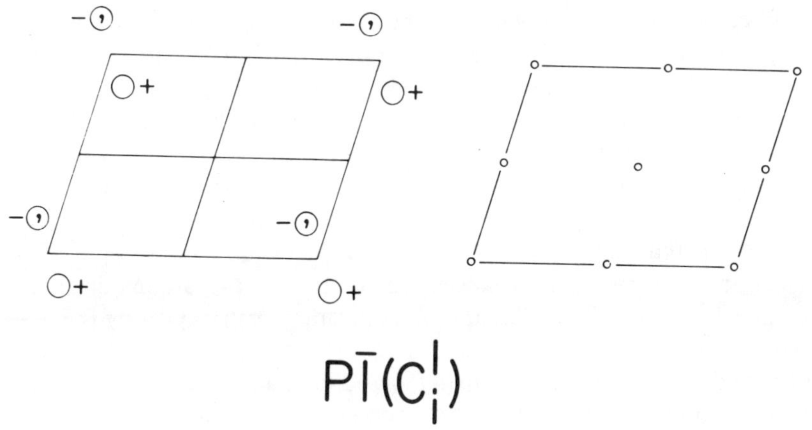

Fig. 5-8

point group of P1 is $1(C_1)$, the space group is completely specified by the identity operation 1(E) and the primitive lattice translations $\{1 \mid \mathbf{t}_n\}$. There is no special diagrammatic symbol for 1(E) and so only the basic outline of the unit cell is drawn. Notice that the unit cell has been deliberately drawn with nonorthogonal axes to exphasize that the space group is triclinic. In the left-hand cell, the general point at the top-left of the cell, which is deliberately shown to be above the plane of the paper, as indicated by the + sign, is operated on by the identity operation leaving it unchanged. This is further operated on by the primitive translations to produce other points related to it by unit translations along **a**, **b**, and **a+b**. Clearly, these belong in neighboring cells so that there is only one general equivalent position per unit cell, in agreement with the order of the point group. Going back to Eq. (5-4) we can write

$$\{1 \mid \mathbf{0}\}\mathbf{r} = \begin{bmatrix} 1 & 0 & 0 \\ 0 & 1 & 0 \\ 0 & 0 & 1 \end{bmatrix} \begin{bmatrix} x \\ y \\ z \end{bmatrix} = \begin{bmatrix} x \\ y \\ z \end{bmatrix} \tag{5-10}$$

Thus, operating on the general point at (x,y,z) by the identity operator gives us (x,y,z) again. This may seem a complicated way of looking at what is really a trivial problem but the approach will be appreciated when we come on to more complex space groups.

The second triclinic space group $P\bar{1}(C_i^1)$ is shown in Fig. 5-8. The point group of this space group, $\bar{1}(C_i)$, has two symmetry operations 1(E) and $\bar{1}$(i) so that we need two symmetry operations to completely specify the space group. The right-hand cell shows the $\bar{1}$ element, represented by a small circle. It is **conventional** to take an inversion element at the origin of the unit cell since such a placing halves the information needed to specify the electron density in the unit cell, each half being related by the $\bar{1}$(i) operation. This is particularly important in diffraction studies because it simplifies the phase relationships between scattered waves (for an elementary discussion of this, see the standard books on X-ray crystallography, such as those by Bragg, James, or Lipson and Cochran). You will have noticed that having placed a center of inversion at the origin of the unit cell, and hence, by translational invariance, at the origins of all unit cells, new centers of inversion appear at positions halfway along the axes, at the centers of the faces and in the center of the unit cell. This can be understood best by consulting the left-hand diagram. The point at (x,y,z) is operated on by $\{\bar{1} \mid \mathbf{0}\}$ to produce a new equivalent point thus:

$$\{\bar{1} \mid \mathbf{0}\}\mathbf{r} = \begin{bmatrix} -1 & 0 & 0 \\ 0 & -1 & 0 \\ 0 & 0 & -1 \end{bmatrix} \begin{bmatrix} x \\ y \\ z \end{bmatrix} = \begin{bmatrix} -x \\ -y \\ -z \end{bmatrix} \tag{5-11}$$

We see from this result that the general point at (x,y,z) has been taken to (−x, −y, −z) by the $\bar{1}$ operation at (0, 0, 0), forming an enantiomorph in the process. The same occurs at other places in the diagram separated by the unit translation distances. The result of this is that there are two general equivalent positions per unit cell (equal to the number of operations in the point group of the space group). We see now that the point at (x,y,z) is related to the point at (−x, 1−y, −z) by a new center of inversion at (0, 1/2, 0). These and other centers of inversion result from combining the point symmetry at the origin with the translation symmetry of the lattice. The point at (−x, 1−y, −z) is, of course, equivalent to the point at (−x, −y, −z) by the translational symmetry along **b**. We can write a similar expression to that used in Eq. (5-11) in order to relate the two general positions by the center of inversion at (0, 1/2, 0). This is done by including a translation vector which takes care of the shift of origin of this symmetry element. The expression is

$$\{\bar{1} \mid 2\tau(0, 1/2, 0)\}\mathbf{r} = \begin{bmatrix} -1 & 0 & 0 \\ 0 & -1 & 0 \\ 0 & 0 & -1 \end{bmatrix} \begin{bmatrix} x \\ y \\ z \end{bmatrix} + \begin{bmatrix} 0 \\ 1 \\ 0 \end{bmatrix} = \begin{bmatrix} -x \\ 1-y \\ -z \end{bmatrix} \tag{5-12}$$

We can see from this that in order to relate the two positions, we have to add a vector translation equal to twice the shift of origin of the symmetry element. This is simply a consequence of the fact that the inversion center must lie midway between points related by it. The same general rule applies to 2-fold rotations and mirror operations but more complicated rules are needed for other symmetry operations.

**5-5b Monoclinic system** In the monoclinic crystal system there are two unique space lattices, P and B (first setting) or C (2nd setting), and three point groups, 2, m, and 2/m ($C_2$, $C_s$ and $C_{2h}$). This means that we can have 2 × 3 = 6 space groups, P2, B2, Pm, Bm, P2/m, B2/m ($C_2^1$, $C_2^3$, $C_s^1$, $C_s^3$, $C_{2h}^1$, $C_{2h}^3$) as discussed in Section 5-2. The fact that the symmetry operations 2 and m are allowed in this system means that it is now possible to generate space groups containing $2_1$ screw axes and glide planes. (In the monoclinic system both axial and diagonal glides are permitted. However, it turns out that they become equivalent if one redefines the orientation of the unit cell.) We take, for this discussion the "1st setting" with the mirror planes perpendicular to the **c**-axis. Thus, the axial glide planes must also be perpendicular to the **c**-axis, leading only to a- and b-glides. However, since the assignment of **a**- and **b**-axes is arbitrary, there is only one unique glide direction. The a-glide can be called a b-glide simply by interchanging the labels of the **a**- and **b**-axes. In the International Tables the **convention** is to call it a b-glide (c-glide in the 2nd setting). Thus the possible space groups involving screw axes and glide planes are P$2_1$, B$2_1$, Pb, Bb, P$2_1$/m, B$2_1$/m, P2/b, B2/b, P$2_1$/b, B$2_1$/b. However, as we shall see, some of these are equivalent.

Before we look at some examples of monoclinic space groups in any detail it is worth saying something about the space group notation we are using. The symbols that we have used are known as the **standard short symbols**; this is because they contain sufficient information to determine the space group. There is a **full symbol** which is quoted sometimes. This takes the form Γ..., where Γ represents the symbol for the Bravais lattice, P, A, B, C, I, F, or R, and the dots denote the positions of the symbols for the symmetry operators, which in the monoclinic and orthorhombic systems are taken to be relative to the **a**-, **b**-, and **c**-axes, respectively. Thus a 2-fold axis parallel to **a** would be indicated by the figure "2" in the first place. An a-glide with the plane of reflection perpendicular to **c** would be denoted by "a" in the third place, and so on. In the monoclinic system, the "1st setting" convention is to place the 2 or $2_1$ axis parallel to **c** and the m or b-glide plane perpendicular to **c**. Thus the full symbol for P2, say, would be P112; this means that there is 1-fold symmetry along **a** and **b** and a 2-fold axis parallel to **c**. Similarly, the space group P$2_1$/b would be written as P11 $2_1$/b. It can be seen why the full symbol is not normally used in the monoclinic system; it gives no information that we do not know already. In the orthorhombic system, however, the full symbols are often necessary. In Appendix 7 all the short and full symbols are listed.

We shall consider three examples in all, one corresponding to each point group of the monoclinic system. Each example will illustrate certain points which can be easily applied to the other monoclinic space groups that we do not cover here. The space groups we have chosen are B2, Bb, and $P2_1/b$.

(1) Space group B2 ($C_2{}^3$), number 5 in the International Tables. Consider Fig. 5-9a where the unit cells are drawn in the usual orientation. The **c**-axis is out of the paper and perpendicular to **a** and **b**. The point group for B2 is obtained by removing all translations and so we have point group $2(C_2)$. In this point group there are two symmetry operations, 1 and 2 (E and $C_2$) so that these two operations together with the primitive lattice translation completely specify the space group. However, since in the International Tables the conventional Bravais cell is used, we take this into account in determining the general equivalent positions. Thus, in the B-centered cell every point specified with respect to an origin at (0, 0, 0) is repeated with respect to a lattice point at (1/2, 0, 1/2). This means that there will be twice as many general equivalent positions listed in these tables as symmetry operations in the point group, i.e., there are four in all. Returning to Eq. (5-4) we set the vector $\boldsymbol{\tau}$ equal to zero since we are considering only the 2-fold operation. The effect of this 2-fold axis on the general point is then given by

$$\{2[001] \mid \mathbf{0}\}\mathbf{r} = \begin{bmatrix} -1 & 0 & 0 \\ 0 & -1 & 0 \\ 0 & 0 & 1 \end{bmatrix} \begin{bmatrix} x \\ y \\ z \end{bmatrix} = \begin{bmatrix} -x \\ -y \\ z \end{bmatrix} \tag{5-13}$$

Thus the point at (x,y,z) is taken to (−x, −y, z), as shown on the left-hand diagram in Fig. 5-9a. We can now add the centering translation (1/2, 0, 1/2) to each of these equivalent points thus generating two new points at (1/2+x, y, 1/2+z) and (1/2−x, −y, 1/2+z). Again these are marked on the left-hand diagram of Fig. 5-9a. However, there are other symmetry operations that occur in this space group. Consider the two points at (x,y,z) and (1/2−x, −y, 1/2+z). In general, we may say that there is some symmetry operation $\{R \mid \boldsymbol{\tau}\}$ linking them. Therefore we can write

$$R \begin{bmatrix} x \\ y \\ z \end{bmatrix} + \boldsymbol{\tau} = \begin{bmatrix} 1/2-x \\ -y \\ 1/2+z \end{bmatrix} = \begin{bmatrix} -x \\ -y \\ z \end{bmatrix} + \begin{bmatrix} 0 \\ 0 \\ 1/2 \end{bmatrix} + \begin{bmatrix} 1/2 \\ 0 \\ 0 \end{bmatrix} \tag{5-14}$$

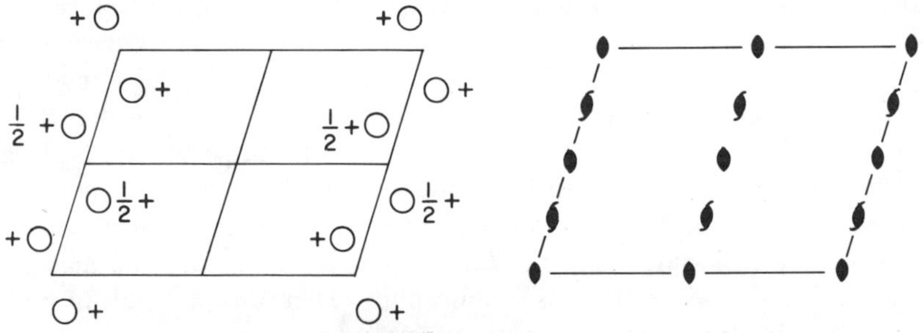

(a) B2($C_2^3$)

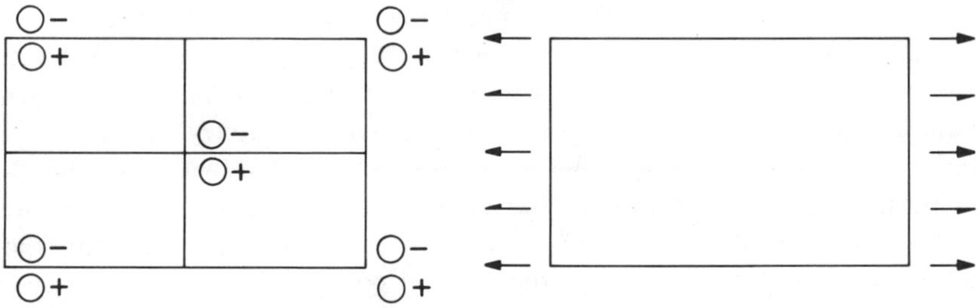

(b) C2($C_2^3$)

**Fig. 5-9**

The last two vectors are reminiscent of nonsymmorphic translations. The first vector on the right side corresponds to a 2-fold axis through the origin of the unit cell operating on the point at (x,y,z), so that we must consider the possibility of having a $2_1$ screw axis in this space group. In order to be consistent with monoclinic symmetry (and point group 2), this $2_1$ axis would have to lie along the **c** direction, and hence its translation vector would be consistent with the second vector on the right-hand side in Eq. (5-14). The third vector on the right-hand side of this equation is then seen to arise from a shift of origin for this screw axis. Since this must lie halfway between the points at (x,y,z) and (1/2−x, −y, 1/2+z), this additional translation vector (1/2, 0, 0) arises from the $2_1$ axis passing through 1/2(1/2, 0, 0) = (1/4, 0, 0). This and other screw axes that are present are marked on the right-hand diagram of Fig. 5-9a. Thus, we see that the space group B2 contains nonsymmorphic operations. Nevertheless, it is still a symmorphic space group, since we are able to specify the space group completely by symmorphic operations alone. The screw axes are nonessential symmetry elements and arise from combining the $2(C_2)$ point operation with translational symmetry. Of course we are quite at liberty to call this space group $B2_1$ should we wish to do so, rather than B2 in which case the 2-fold axes would be nonessential. Either would do; it is just conventional to use the latter symbol, which has the merit of revealing that the space group is symmorphic. Therefore, crystals of point group $2(C_2)$ belong to one of three possible space groups:

$$P2(C_2^{\ 1}), \qquad P2_1(C_2^{\ 2}) \quad \text{and} \quad B2 \text{ or } C2(C_2^{\ 3})$$

Figure 5-9b shows the space group diagrams for C2 (2nd setting).

(2) Space group $Bb(C_s^{\ 4})$, number 9 in the International Tables. Crystals having this space group belong to the point group $m(C_s$ or $C_{1h})$, because when the translational part of the b-glide is removed a mirror plane is obtained. Point group $m(C_{1h})$ has two symmetry operations, 1 and m (E and $\sigma_h$). When these operations are combined with the B-centering, we expect to obtain four general equivalent positions. Figure 5-10a shows the space group diagrams. Proceeding in the same manner as before, we apply the b-glide to the general point at (x,y,z) and obtain a new point at (x, 1/2+y, −z) and then apply the B-centering to get (1/2+x, y, 1/2+z) and (1/2+x, 1/2+y, 1/2−z). These are the four general equivalent positions in this space group. However, we can find other symmetry operations. Consider the relationship between the two points at (x,y,z) and (1/2+x, 1/2+y, 1/2−z). As before, we can subtract some translations from the latter:

$$R\begin{bmatrix} x \\ y \\ z \end{bmatrix} + \tau = \begin{bmatrix} 1/2+x \\ 1/2+y \\ 1/2-z \end{bmatrix} = \begin{bmatrix} x \\ y \\ -z \end{bmatrix} + \begin{bmatrix} 1/2 \\ 0 \\ 0 \end{bmatrix} + \begin{bmatrix} 0 \\ 1/2 \\ 0 \end{bmatrix} + \begin{bmatrix} 0 \\ 0 \\ 1/2 \end{bmatrix} \qquad (5\text{-}15)$$

The first vector suggests that R is a reflection operator acting on (x,y,z), and so we should suspect the presence of a glide element. The second and third vectors correspond to glides along both **a** and **b** simultaneously; this is equivalent to an n-glide perpendicular to **c**. We can locate the plane precisely by considering the fourth vector in Eq. (5-15). The magnitude of this vector represents the fractional distance along **c** that any general point is taken through on reflection across the mirror plane of the n-glide. Now this mirror plane must lie halfway between the two mirror-related points, so that the position of this plane is given by one-half of the fourth

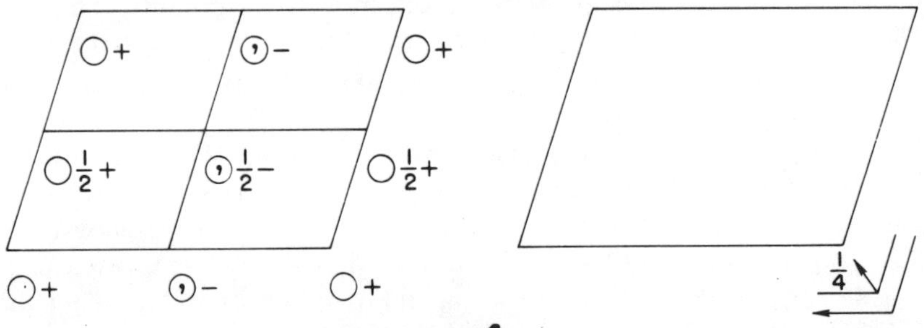

(a) $Bb(C_s^4)$

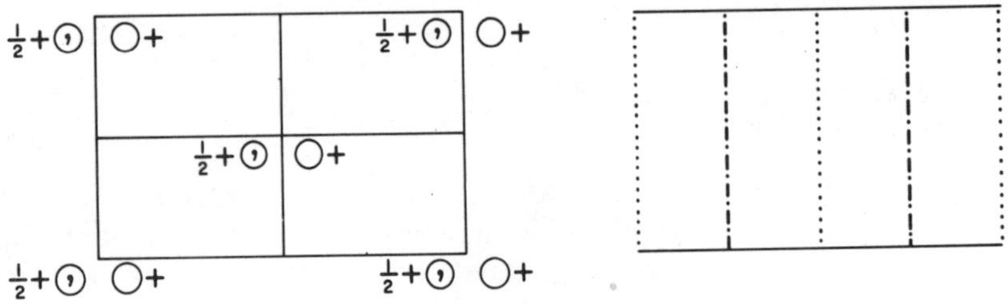

(b) $Cc\,(C_s^4)$

**Fig. 5-10**

vector (0, 0, 1/2). The n-glide plane, therefore, passes through (0, 0, 1/4) as shown on the right-hand diagram of Fig. 5-10a. Space group Bb can, of course, be labelled Bn. We could equally well have started with the n-glide plane passing through the origin and lying perpendicular to **c** and then have generated the b-glide, this time through (0, 0, 1/4). It is simply the normal custom to use the former symbol and origin. Figure 5-10b shows the 2nd setting, i.e., Cc. Proceeding in this way for all the possible space groups with point group $m(C_{1h}$ or $C_s)$, we find that the only uniquely different space groups are $Pm(C_s^1)$, $Pb(C_s^2)$, $Bm(C_s^3)$, and $Bb(C_s^4)$.

(3) Space group $P2_1/b$ $(C_{2h}^5)$, number 14 in the International Tables. This is a very important space group, particularly for organic crystal structures. A quick scan through the literature will show that this is by far the most common space group encountered in organic crystals. (It is not clear if this is a real effect or is simply due to a reluctance of

many people to study crystals with any different space group!) The point group of this space group is $2/m(C_{2h})$ which has four essential operations, 1, 2[001], m[001], and $\bar{1}$(E, $C_2$, $\sigma_h$ and i). We expect therefore, to generate four general equivalent positions.

Figure 5-11a shows the space group diagrams. We start with the $2_1$ axis and b-glide plane through the origin. The $2_1$ axis generates from the point (x,y,z) a new point at (−x, −y, 1/2+z) and the b-glide takes these two points to (x, 1/2+y, −z) and (−x, 1/2−y, 1/2−z), respectively. This can be verified by consulting the diagram or by applying the matrices of Chapter 1 in the way done previously for other space groups. Now consider the points at (x,y,z) and (−x, 1/2−y, 1/2−z) which are enantiomorphs of one another. The symmetry operation relating these points is given by

$$R\begin{bmatrix} x \\ y \\ z \end{bmatrix} + \tau = \begin{bmatrix} -x \\ 1/2-y \\ 1/2-z \end{bmatrix} = \begin{bmatrix} -x \\ -y \\ -z \end{bmatrix} + \begin{bmatrix} 0 \\ 1/2 \\ 1/2 \end{bmatrix} \tag{5-16}$$

We see then that R is the inversion operator. The center of inversion must lie midway between the two points related by it; in this case it is at 1/2(0, 1/2, 1/2) = (0, 1/4, 1/4). The existence of this center of inversion is a direct consequence of having the $2_1$ axis perpendicular to the b-glide plane. This is hardly surprising when we recall that the point group of this space group is $2/m(C_{2h})$, with the $2_1$ axis becoming $2(C_2)$ and b becoming m($\sigma$) after the nonsymmorphic translations are removed. We have already shown that 2/m is a centrosymmetric point group so that we expect that any space group with this point group will itself be centrosymmetric.

It is convenient to place the center of inversion at the origin of the unit cell (as explained in Section 5-5a). Figure 5-11b shows the conventional representation that is given in the International Tables, with the screw axes now displaced 1/4 along **b** and the b-glide plane passing through (0, 0, 1/4). The effect of this change of origin is to give four general equivalent positions with coordinates:

(x,y,z) (−x, 1/2−y, 1/2+z) (x, 1/2+y, 1/2−z) (−x, −y, −z)

Figure 5-11c shows the space group diagrams for the 2nd setting, $P2_1/c(C_{2h}{}^5)$, with $\bar{1}$ at the origin. Note that while the International symbol is different the Schoenflies symbol is the same. As we have already said, this space group seems to be popular for organic molecules, particularly for flat aromatic molecules. An example will be discussed in Chapter 7.

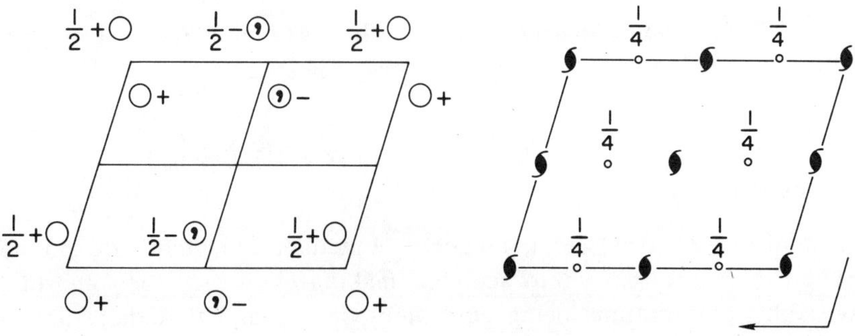

(a) $P2_1/b\,(C_{2h}^5)$

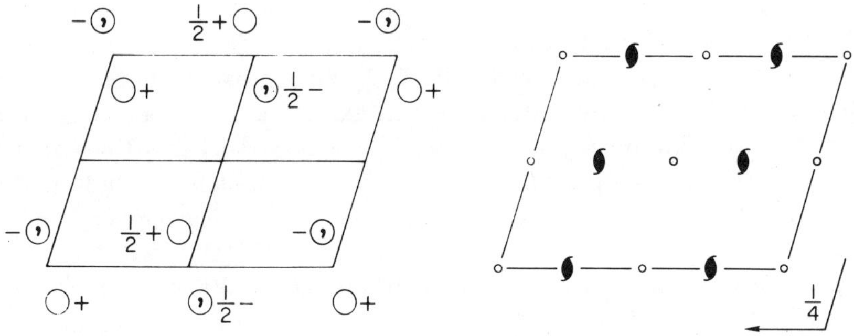

(b) $P2_1/b\,(C_{2h}^5)$

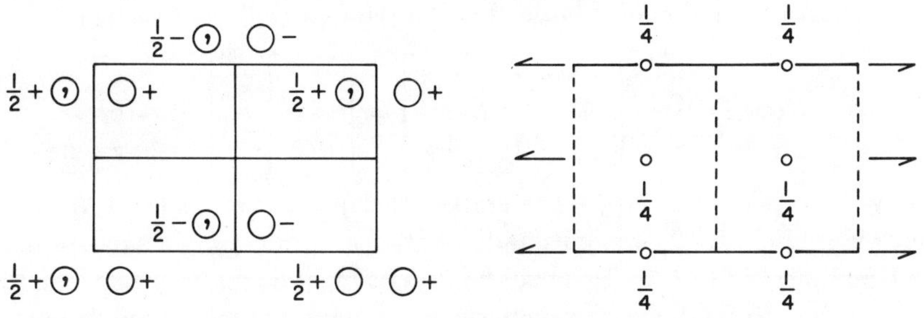

$P2_1/c\,(C_{2h}^5)$ (Center of Inversion at $0, \frac{1}{4}, \frac{1}{4}$)

**Fig. 5-11**

**5-5c Orthorhombic system** In this system there are three point groups and four different Bravais lattices. These are

$222(D_2)$
$mm2(C_{2v})$ with P, C (or A or B), F, and I
$mmm(D_{2h})$

In addition $2_1$ axes, axial, diagonal, and diamond glides are possible. When these are taken into account, making allowance for some of the possible combinations being equivalent, it is found that there are nine space groups with point group $222(D_2)$, 21 with point group $mm2(C_{2v})$ and 28 with point group $mmm(D_{2h})$. These are all listed in Appendix 7. We shall discuss three examples from the orthorhombic system, one corresponding to each point group.

(1) Space group $P2_12_12_1(D_2{}^4)$, number 19 in the International Tables. The space group symbol $P2_12_12_1$ means that the lattice is primitive, as indicated by the letter P; one $2_1$ axis is parallel to **a** (indicated by the $2_1$ in the first place after P), one $2_1$ axis is parallel to **b** (indicated by the $2_1$ in the second place), and one $2_1$ axis is parallel to **c** (indicated by the $2_1$ in the third place). Figure 5-12 shows the space group diagrams.

The point group of this space group is $222(D_2)$, which has four operations, 1, 2[001], 2[010], and 2[100] (E, $C_2[001]$, $C_2[010]$, and $C_2[100]$), so there are four general equivalent positions per unit cell. Notice also that the three screw axes have been deliberately drawn so that they do not intersect one another. Consider the effect of these operations on the general point (x,y,z). First, consider the $2_1$ axis along [001]. If it is taken, for the moment, to pass through the unit cell origin we get

$$\{2[001] \mid \tau(0,0,1/2\}\mathbf{r}= \begin{bmatrix} -1 & 0 & 0 \\ 0 & -1 & 0 \\ 0 & 0 & 1 \end{bmatrix} \begin{bmatrix} x \\ y \\ z \end{bmatrix} + \begin{bmatrix} 0 \\ 0 \\ 1/2 \end{bmatrix} = \begin{bmatrix} -x \\ -y \\ 1/2+z \end{bmatrix} \quad (5\text{-}17)$$

Now if we place the $2_1[001]$ operation through the point (1/4, 0, 0) as shown in Fig. 5-12, we must add to the coordinates a translation of 2(1/4, 0, 0) = (1/2, 0, 0), since the $2_1$ axis must lie midway between the points that it relates. The general equivalent position then becomes (1/2−x, −y, 1/2+z) as shown on the left-hand side of Fig. 5-12. We can apply the same procedure with the other screw axes to give the four general positions (x,y,z), (1/2−x, −y, 1/2+z), (1/2+x, 1/2−y, −z), (−x, 1/2+y, 1/2−z).

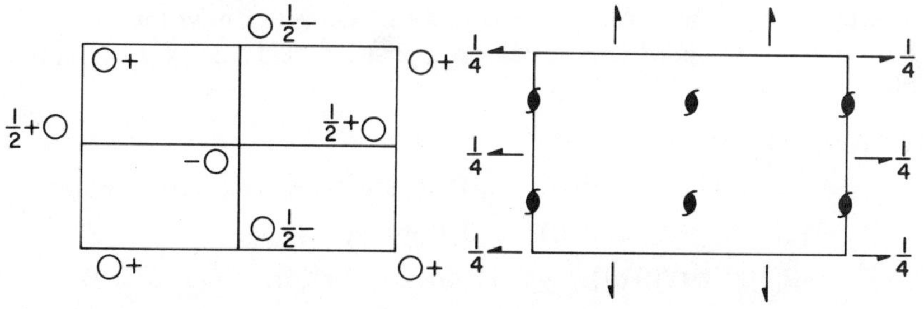

$P2_12_12_1(D_2^4)$

**Fig. 5-12**

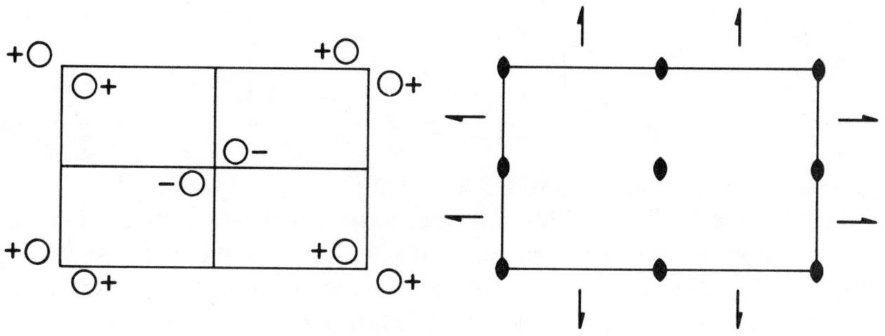

$P2_12_12(D_2^3)$

**Fig. 5-13**

You may be wondering why the three screw axes were made nonintersecting in the first place. In fact, why were they displaced from one another by a factor of 1/4 of a unit cell repeat? Why not 1/8 or 1/6 or any other value? Let us consider what happens if any two mutually perpendicular $2_1$ screw axes are displaced from each other through a coordinate distance n/2, where n has to be determined. For example, suppose we have a $2_1[100]$ axis passing through the origin of the unit cell and a $2_1[010]$ axis passing through the point (0, 0, n/2). The second operator is displaced through a distance n/2 along **c**, and will contain a translation vector $2\tau(0, 0, n/2) = \tau(0, 0, n)$ in addition to its normal nonsymmorphic translation of $\tau(0, 1/2, 0)$, since the $2_1[010]$ element lies midway between the points that it relates. Consider now the product of these two screw operations acting on a position vector **r**. We can express this as follows:

$$\begin{aligned}\{2_1[100]\}\,\{2_1[010]\}\mathbf{r} &= \{2[100]\,|\,\boldsymbol{\tau}(1/2, 0, 0)\}\,\{2[010]\,|\,\boldsymbol{\tau}(0, 1/2, 0) + \boldsymbol{\tau}(0, 0, n)\}\mathbf{r} \\ &= \{2[100]\,|\,\boldsymbol{\tau}(1/2, 0, 0)\}\,(2[010]\mathbf{r} + \boldsymbol{\tau}(0, 1/2, n)) \\ &= \{2[100]\}\,\{2[010]\}\mathbf{r} + \{2[100]\}\boldsymbol{\tau}(0, 1/2, n) + \boldsymbol{\tau}(1/2, 0, 0)\end{aligned} \tag{5-18a}$$

Writing this out in matrix form we get

$$\begin{bmatrix}1 & 0 & 0\\ 0 & -1 & 0\\ 0 & 0 & -1\end{bmatrix}\begin{bmatrix}-1 & 0 & 0\\ 0 & 1 & 0\\ 0 & 0 & -1\end{bmatrix}\begin{bmatrix}x\\ y\\ z\end{bmatrix} + \begin{bmatrix}1 & 0 & 0\\ 0 & -1 & 0\\ 0 & 0 & -1\end{bmatrix}\begin{bmatrix}0\\ 1/2\\ n\end{bmatrix} + \begin{bmatrix}1/2\\ 0\\ 0\end{bmatrix} \tag{5-18b}$$

which reduces to

$$\begin{bmatrix}-x\\ -y\\ z\end{bmatrix} + \begin{bmatrix}0\\ 0\\ -n\end{bmatrix} + \begin{bmatrix}1/2\\ -1/2\\ 0\end{bmatrix} \tag{5-18c}$$

We have deliberately written the result in three parts. The first term clearly corresponds to a 2-fold operation about the **c**-axis. The second term determines whether this operation is symmorphic or nonsymmorphic. Obviously there are only two possible values for n if we wish to have a symmetry operation at all. If $n = 1/2$, the generated operation is $2_1[001]$ consistent with space group $P2_12_12_1$. We see therefore that for this space group the first two screw axes had to be non-intersecting with a displacement between them of $(1/2)(0, 0, 1/2) = (0, 0, 1/4)$. The other case when $n = 0$ has two intersecting screw axes and gives space group $P2_12_12$. Note that in both space groups the third symmetry element does not intersect the first two. This is shown by the third column matrix in Eq. (5-18c) which represents the point through which the third element passes, i.e., $(1/2)(1/2, -1/2, 0) = (1/4, -1/4, 0)$. If in the case of $P2_12_12$, we do not take the point of intersection of the two screw axes to be at the origin but, instead, at $(-1/4, 1/4, 0)$, then the 2-fold axis along **c** passes through $(1/4, -1/4, 0) + (-1/4, 1/4, 0) = (0,0,0)$. This is the choice of origin used in the International Tables and is shown in Fig. 5-13.

Similar considerations apply when body-centering is added to $P2_12_12_1$ and $P2_12_12$. In the former case, additional 2-fold axes along **a**, **b**, and **c** are generated (see Fig. 5-14), which again do not intersect with one another. In the latter case, intersecting 2-fold axes are obtained

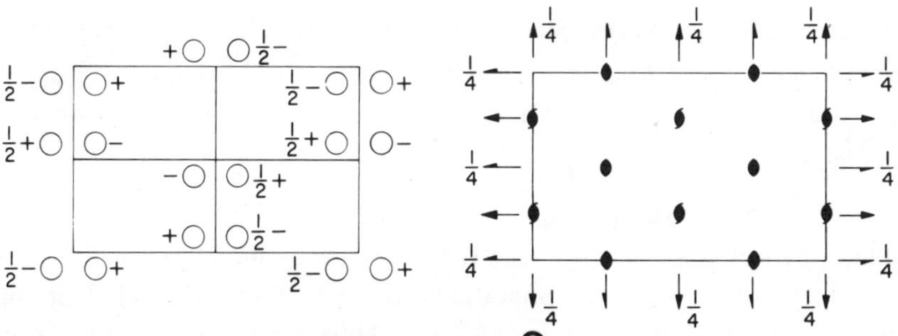

$I2_12_12_1(D_2^9)$

**Fig. 5-14**

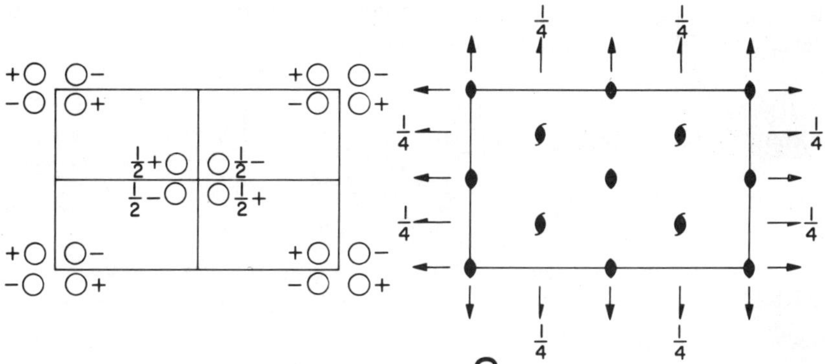

$I222\,(D_2^8)$

**Fig. 5-15**

along **a** and **b** together with a screw axis along **c** intersecting those already along **a** and **b** (see Fig. 5-15).

Strangely enough both space groups can equally well be called by the same name, I222 or $I2_12_12_1$, since both have three mutually perpendicular 2-fold and $2_1$-screw axes. The difference between them lies in whether or not the 2-fold axes intersect (this sort of ambiguity, fortunately, only occurs in two other space groups, namely, the cubic space groups I23 and $I2_13$). When they do the space group is symmorphic and when they do not it is nonsymmorphic.

The reader might be tempted to think that as the space group in Fig. 5-14 could be completely described by 2-fold axes rather than 2-fold screw axes it should be considered to symmorphic. However, it should be realized that these 2-fold axes are displaced from one another and therefore have $\tau \neq 0$ (they are not what are normally called screw axes since in this case $\tau$ is not a vector along the 2-fold axes).

(2) Space group $Pna2_1(C_{2v}^9)$, number 33 in the International Tables. Proceeding as before we note that the point group of $Pna2_1$ is $mm2(C_{2v})$, which has four operations, namely, 1, 2[001], m[010], and m[100] (E, $C_2$, $\sigma_v[010]$ and $\sigma_v[100]$). Thus we expect to have four general equivalent positions. Let us deal with each symmetry element separately. The n-glide symbol occurs in the first position of the space group symbol indicating that the reflection plane is perpendicular to **a**. The translations therefore must be along **b** and **c**. Thus, this n-glide operating on the general point (x,y,z) gives

$$\{m[100] \mid \tau(0,1/2,1/2)\}\mathbf{r} = \begin{bmatrix} -1 & 0 & 0 \\ 0 & 1 & 0 \\ 0 & 0 & 1 \end{bmatrix} \begin{bmatrix} x \\ y \\ z \end{bmatrix} + \begin{bmatrix} 0 \\ 1/2 \\ 1/2 \end{bmatrix} = \begin{bmatrix} -x \\ 1/2+y \\ 1/2+z \end{bmatrix} \tag{5-19}$$

The space groups diagrams are shown in Fig. 5-16. The n-glide plane is taken to be 1/4 along [100] in this diagram, so that in order to be consistent with this choice we must add 2(1/4, 0, 0) to the point that we have just generated. The general equivalent position will then become (1/2−x, 1/2+y, 1/2+z). The a-glide symbol is in the second place of the space group symbol; this means that its reflecting plane is perpendicular to **b**. Therefore, operating with the a-glide on the general point at (x,y,z) gives

$$\{m[010] \mid \tau(1/2,0,0)\}\mathbf{r} = \begin{bmatrix} 1 & 0 & 0 \\ 0 & -1 & 0 \\ 0 & 0 & 1 \end{bmatrix} \begin{bmatrix} x \\ y \\ z \end{bmatrix} + \begin{bmatrix} 1/2 \\ 0 \\ 0 \end{bmatrix} = \begin{bmatrix} 1/2+x \\ -y \\ z \end{bmatrix} \tag{5-20}$$

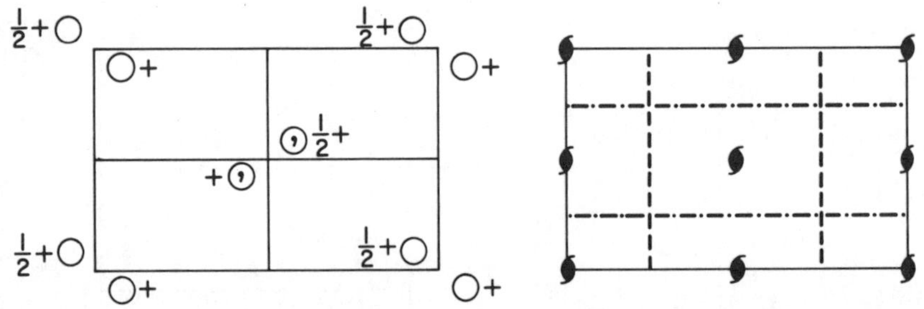

$Pna2_1\ (C_{2v}^9)$

Fig. 5-16

and operating on the point (1/2−x, 1/2+y, 1/2+z) gives

$$\{m[010]\,|\,\tau(1/2,0,0)\}\mathbf{r}$$

$$= \begin{bmatrix} 1 & 0 & 0 \\ 0 & -1 & 0 \\ 0 & 0 & 1 \end{bmatrix} \begin{bmatrix} 1/2-x \\ 1/2+y \\ 1/2+z \end{bmatrix} + \begin{bmatrix} 1/2 \\ 0 \\ 0 \end{bmatrix} \tag{5-21a}$$

$$= \begin{bmatrix} 1-x \\ 1/2-y \\ 1/2+z \end{bmatrix} = \begin{bmatrix} -x \\ 1/2-y \\ 1/2+z \end{bmatrix} \tag{5-21b}$$

In Fig. 5-16 we see that the a-glide plane is shifted from the origin by 1/4 along [010], so that we must add 2(0, 1/4, 0) to the coordinates we have just generated. This gives (1/2+x, 1/2−y, z) and (−x, −y, 1/2+z). Now consider the relationship between (x,y,z) and (−x, −y, 1/2+z).

$$R \begin{bmatrix} x \\ y \\ z \end{bmatrix} + \tau = \begin{bmatrix} -x \\ -y \\ z \end{bmatrix} + \begin{bmatrix} 0 \\ 0 \\ 1/2 \end{bmatrix} \tag{5-22}$$

which we see is a $2_1$ axis along [001] passing through the unit cell origin. This is the $2_1$ axis in the third place of the space group symbol.

(3) Space group Fddd ($D_{2h}^{24}$), number 70 in the International Tables. The point group of Fddd is mmm($D_{2h}$) which has eight operations, namely 1, 2[001], 2[010], 2[100], $\bar{1}$, m[001], m[010], and m[100]

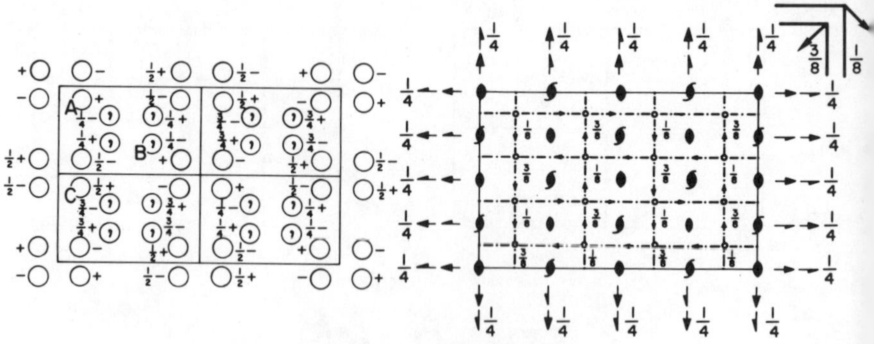

Fddd $(D_{2h}^{24})$

**Fig. 5-17**

(E, $C_2[001]$, $C_2[010]$, $C_2[100]$, i, $\sigma[001]$, $\sigma[010]$, $\sigma[100]$). Therefore there are eight general equivalent positions. The International Tables use the conventional multiply-primitive unit cell for this face-centered lattice. Thus, for every one of the eight general points generated for the primitive unit cell by the symmetry operations of the space group we must add (0, 1/2, 1/2), (1/2, 0, 1/2), and (1/2, 1/2, 0), giving $4 \times 8 = 32$ general equivalent positions for the all-face-centered unit cell. Figure 5-17 shows the space group diagrams for Fddd. Although they look complicated they are really simple if you consider each symmetry element in turn. We shall not deal with all these elements here; rather we concentrate on certain features. First, since the point group is mmm($D_{2h}$), it is centrosymmetric. We are therefore not surprised to find a center of inversion, which has been placed at (1/8, 1/8, 1/8). Second, consider the diamond glides. The space group symbol tells us that there are diamond glide planes perpendicular to **a**-, **b**-, and **c**-axes, since the symbol d appears in all three positions after the Bravais lattice symbol. We take the diamond glide plane perpendicular to **c** as an example. The effect of this on a general point at (x,y,z) is

$$\{m[001] \mid \boldsymbol{\tau}(1/4,1/4,0)\}\mathbf{r} = \begin{bmatrix} 1 & 0 & 0 \\ 0 & 1 & 0 \\ 0 & 0 & -1 \end{bmatrix} \begin{bmatrix} x \\ y \\ z \end{bmatrix} + \begin{bmatrix} 1/4 \\ 1/4 \\ 0 \end{bmatrix} = \begin{bmatrix} 1/4+x \\ 1/4+y \\ -z \end{bmatrix} \tag{5-23}$$

This means that the point at (x,y,z), which is marked A in Fig. 5-17, has been taken to (1/4+x, 1/4+y, −z), by this diamond glide at zero height. If we wish to be consistent with Fig. 5-17, however, we must place this glide plane at height 1/8 and therefore we add 2(0, 0, 1/8) to the coordinate (1/4+x, 1/4+y, −z) to obtain (1/4+x, 1/4+y, 1/4−z), marked B on the diagram. We see that this glide means a movement of the general point out of the plane of the paper and towards the lower right. This is indicated by the diagrammatic symbol at the top right, the arrow showing the general direction of movement. The figure 1/8 next to it gives the height of the glide plane. Notice that there is another "diamond" glide symbol with the arrow pointing to the lower left and with height marked 3/8. This second "diamond" glide plane may be thought of as a consequence of the face-centering. This can be seen in the following way. Consider the centering on the **ac**-face acting on the general point (x,y,z). This gives a new point at (x,y,z) + (1/2, 0, 1/2) = (1/2+x, y, 1/2+z), marked C. Now, what is the relationship between this point and the previous point B at (1/4+x, 1/4+y, 1/4−z) which we obtained after operating with the diamond glide at height 1/8? We can write

$$R\begin{bmatrix}1/4+x\\1/4+y\\1/4-z\end{bmatrix}+\tau=\begin{bmatrix}1/2+x\\y\\1/2+z\end{bmatrix} \tag{5-24a}$$

This can be rewritten as

$$R\begin{bmatrix}x\\y\\-z\end{bmatrix}+R\begin{bmatrix}1/4\\1/4\\1/4\end{bmatrix}+\tau=\begin{bmatrix}x\\y\\z\end{bmatrix}+\begin{bmatrix}1/2\\0\\1/2\end{bmatrix} \tag{5-24b}$$

which, comparing rotations gives

$$R=\begin{bmatrix}1&0&0\\0&1&0\\0&0&-1\end{bmatrix} \tag{5-24c}$$

$$\tau=\begin{bmatrix}1/2\\0\\1/2\end{bmatrix}-\begin{bmatrix}1&0&0\\0&1&0\\0&0&-1\end{bmatrix}\begin{bmatrix}1/4\\1/4\\1/4\end{bmatrix}=\begin{bmatrix}1/4\\-1/4\\3/4\end{bmatrix}=\begin{bmatrix}1/4\\-1/4\\0\end{bmatrix}+\begin{bmatrix}0\\0\\3/4\end{bmatrix} \tag{5-24d}$$

We can see immediately that R is a mirror operation, m[001]. The operation connecting these two points is therefore

$$\{m[001] \mid \tau(1/4,-1/4,0)\}\mathbf{r}+\tau(0,0,3/4) \tag{5-25}$$

The first term is a diamond glide towards the lower left of the space group diagram in Fig. 5-17. The vector $\tau(0, 0, 3/4)$ tells us that this diamond glide plane is at height 1/2(0, 0, 3/4) i.e. at 3/8 along **c**. This is then **c**/4 above the previous diamond glide plane. This alternation of glide directions with successive glide planes is characteristic of diamond glides. Although we have shown it to result from the all-face-centering combined with the diamond operation, we could equally well have shown that it resulted from having two diamond glides mutually perpendicular. These will give the face-centering; either approach is valid. It is difficult to give a ready explanation of where diamond glides are possible, although it is worth noting that they only occur in orthorhombic, tetragonal, and cubic space groups and are always found in conjunction with F- or I-centering.

Finally notice that the three diamond glides automatically produce three mutually perpendicular 2-fold axes. You can see that all the operations of the point group are found in the space group. The full International space group symbol for Fddd is F 2/d 2/d 2/d signifying that the 2-fold axes are perpendicular to the glide planes. This suggests another way of visualizing the Fddd space group. Consider the space group F222 with a center of inversion added. If we place the center at the origin of the unit cell coincident with the three intersecting 2-fold axes, then the space group F2/m 2/m 2/m = Fmmm is generated. If the center of inversion is placed at (1/8, 1/8, 1/8) with respect to the intersecting 2-fold axes, then Fddd is generated. The reader should verify this.

**5-5d Tetragonal system** In this system there are seven point groups and two Bravais lattices:

| | |
|---|---|
| $4\ (C_4)$ | |
| $\bar{4}\ (S_4)$ | |
| $4/m\ (C_{4h})$ | P and I (or C and F with **a** and **b** |
| $422\ (D_4)$ | axes rotated through 45° about **c**) |
| $4mm\ (C_{4v})$ | |
| $\bar{4}2m\ (D_{2d})$ | |
| $4/mmm\ (D_{4h})$ | |

Combining the seven point groups with the two Bravais lattices, and taking nonsymmorphic operations into account, one finds that there are 68 tetragonal space groups. We shall just take four space group examples, the first three belonging to point group $4(C_4)$.

(1) Space group $P4_1(C_4^2)$, number 75 in the International Tables. Figure 5-18 shows the space group diagrams. These diagrams are just the $4_1$ diagrams of Fig. 5-4 with translational symmetry added. The point

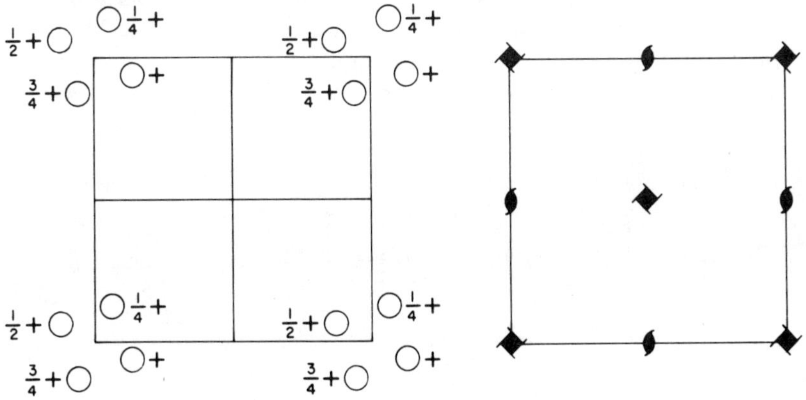

$P4_1\ (C_4^2)$

**Fig. 5-18**

group of this space group is $4(C_4)$ which has four operations 1, 4, 2 ($= 4^2$), and $4^3$ ($E$, $C_4$, $C_2$, and $C_4{}^3$), so that there are four general equivalent positions in the unit cell. You should be able to find for yourself the coordinates of these general equivalent positions by applying successive operations of $\{4[001] \mid \tau(0, 0, 1/4)\}$ to the point at (x,y,z). Notice that the general points form a spiral arrangement about the [001] direction through the unit cell origin (0, 0, 0) and face-center (1/2, 1/2, 0). Furthermore this spiral is anticlockwise out of the paper along the +**c** direction. A crystal having this space group would have a "handedness" and could show optical activity (i.e. it could rotate the plane of polarized light in a particular direction). The space group $P4_1$ is an example of an **enantiomorphic** or **chiral space group**.

One other feature that is worth mentioning here, is that we could have defined a different unit cell with new **a**-and **b**-axes set at 45° to the original **a**-and **b**-axes. These new axes would be longer and the resulting unit cell would be C-centered. The space group $P4_1$, then, could equally well be labelled $C4_1$ but with a larger unit cell. Often this latter cell is used in preference over the former. For example when tracing the relationship between different phases of a particular material it may be visually more convenient to have the larger unit cell.

(2) Space group $P4_2(C_4{}^3)$, number 77 in the International Tables. As in the previous space group the number of equivalent positions is 4. Figure 5-19 shows the space group diagrams which again are like the $4_2$ diagram of Fig. 5-4 with translational symmetry added.

We see that the point (x,y,z) operated on by the $4_2$ operation goes to the point

$$\{4[001] \mid \tau(0,0,1/2)\}\mathbf{r}$$

$$= \begin{bmatrix} 0 & -1 & 0 \\ 1 & 0 & 0 \\ 0 & 0 & 1 \end{bmatrix} \begin{bmatrix} x \\ y \\ z \end{bmatrix} + \begin{bmatrix} 0 \\ 0 \\ 1/2 \end{bmatrix} = \begin{bmatrix} -y \\ x \\ 1/2+z \end{bmatrix} \qquad (5\text{-}26)$$

Applying this operation again gives

$$\{4[001] \mid \tau(0,0,1/2)\}\mathbf{r}$$

$$= \begin{bmatrix} 0 & -1 & 0 \\ 1 & 0 & 0 \\ 0 & 0 & 1 \end{bmatrix} \begin{bmatrix} -y \\ x \\ 1/2+z \end{bmatrix} + \begin{bmatrix} 0 \\ 0 \\ 1/2 \end{bmatrix} = \begin{bmatrix} -x \\ -y \\ 1+z \end{bmatrix} \qquad (5\text{-}27)$$

The result (−x, −y, 1+z) is, by translational invariance, equivalent to (−x, −y, z). Proceeding thus we find that the four general equivalent positions are (x,y,z), (−y, x, 1/2+z), (−x, −y, z), and (y, −x, 1/2+z). Note that there is no sense of handedness about this space group so that crystals possessing it cannot be optically active.

(3) Space group $P4_3(C_4{}^4)$, number 78 in the International Tables. Figure 5-20 shows the space group diagram of $P4_3$. The important point is that it is very similar to $P4_1$, except that now the spiral arrangement of general positions is clockwise along the +**c** direction. Obviously, the "handedness" or chirality of this space group is opposite to that of $P4_1$, all other features being the same. This makes it possible for a particular substance to crystallize equally well in either space group, the differences between the crystals being revealed by their opposing optical activity.

(4) Space group $P\overline{4}2_1m(D_{2d}{}^3)$, number 113 in the International Tables. The point group of this space group $\overline{4}2m(D_{2d})$ has eight operations (see Appendix 8). Therefore, we expect to find eight general equivalent positions generated by the space group operations. Start by placing the axis of the $\overline{4}(S_4{}^3)$ symmetry operation parallel to **c** and at the unit cell origin as shown in Fig. 5-21. This results in points at (x,y,z), (−y, x, −z), (−x, −y, z), and (y, −x, −z). This combined with translational symmetry gives rise to another $\overline{4}(S_4{}^3)$ axis through the center of the unit cell and

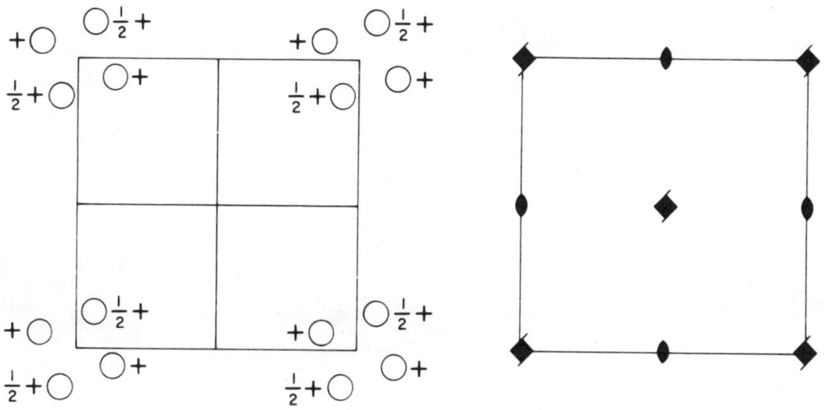

$P4_2\ (C_4^3)$

**Fig. 5-19**

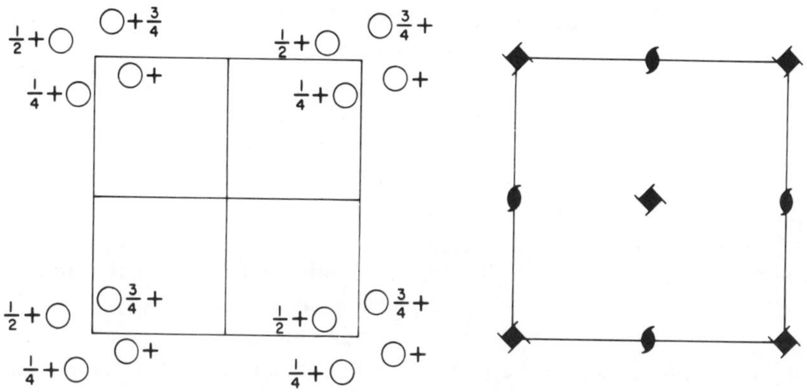

$P4_3\ (C_4^4)$

**Fig. 5-20**

parallel to **c**. Notice that in Fig. 5-21, screw axes have been placed perpendicular to the **c**-axis, just as with the 2-fold axes in point group $\bar{4}2m\ (D_{2d})$, and that they do not intersect the $\bar{4}$ axes, i.e., they are along

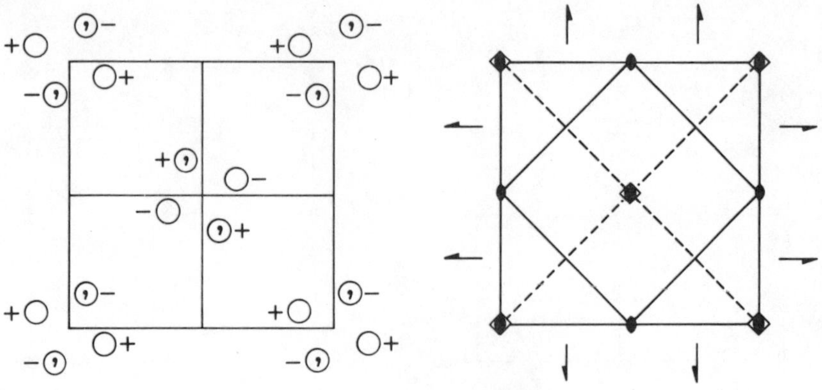

$P\bar{4}2_1m\ (D_{2d}^3)$

Fig. 5-21

lines such as x, 1/4, 0. The result of this is that four other general equivalent positions are generated, at (1/2+y, 1/2+x, z), (1/2−x, 1/2+y, −z), (1/2−y, 1/2−x, z) and (1/2+x, 1/2−y, −z). The last four points are related to the first four by mirror planes parallel to **c** and at 45° to the screw axes, (just like the mirror planes at 45° to the 2-fold axes in the point group $\bar{4}2m$). Note, from the diagram, that glide planes parallel to the diagonals of the unit cell along <110> directions are also generated. They are not axial glide planes, since the glide direction is not along an axis of the unit cell, nor are they diagonal glides, since there is no component along **c**. There is no notation for such glide planes. They are merely symmetry elements that follow as a consequence of the others (of course, if the unit cell is redefined by taking new unit cell axes **a** and **b**, at 45° to the old **a** and **b**-axes, a C-centered cell is obtained and the glide places can then be taken to be axial. Unfortunately, the screw axes then do not lie along axial directions).

Consider what happens if the screw axes are positioned to intersect the $\bar{4}(S_4^3)$ axes. In Fig. 5-22a we show this with the screw axes parallel to the **a** and **b**-axes as well, i.e., along lines [x,0,0] and [y,0,0]. Notice that there are now 16 general equivalent positions. By carefully studying this cell we see that it is C-centered. However, if the unit cell is now redefined by taking new **a**- and **b**-axes at 45° to the old axes, as outlined in the diagram, a primitive unit cell with eight general equivalent positions is obtained. The conventional space group diagrams for the new cell are

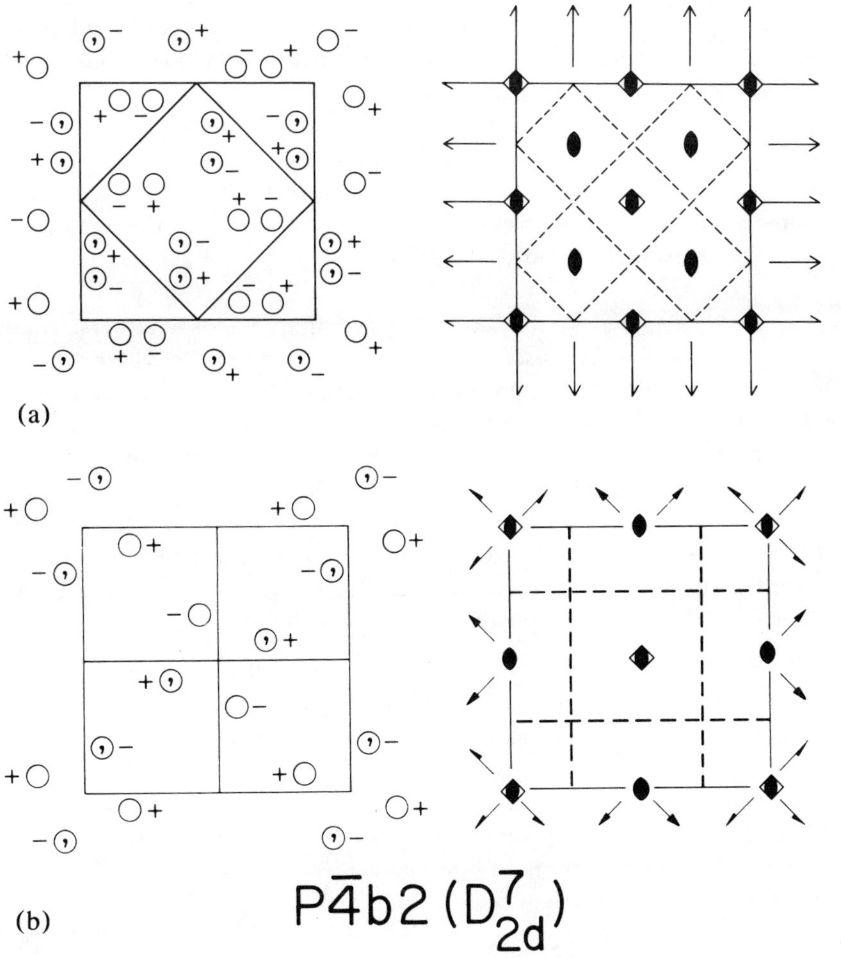


**Fig. 5-22**

shown in Fig. 5-22b, where it can be seen that axial glides are also present. This is space group P$\bar{4}$b$2_1$($D_{2d}{}^7$). Actually, there are also 2-fold axes present parallel to the screw axes but midway between them, so that the space group can also be called P$\bar{4}$b2. This is, in fact, the conventional name for this space group. Finally, note that in this space group, unlike in P$\bar{4}2_1$m, the mirror reflection symbol (b in this case) is placed second rather than third. This serves to indicate the difference in orientation of the reflecting planes in the two cases. In P$\bar{4}2_1$m they were at 45° to the **a** and **b**-axes, in P$\bar{4}$b2 they are perpendicular to them. It is interesting that simply by changing the positions of the screw axes such different space groups result. This is not the end of the matter. We could equally well have placed the screw axes along two other lines, [x,0,1/4] or [x,1/4,1/4]. The former case gives space group $P\bar{4}n2(D_{2d}{}^{8})$; the latter gives $P\bar{4}2_1c(D_{2d}{}^{4})$. Whereas $P\bar{4}n2$ is equivalent to $P\bar{4}n2_1$, $P\bar{4}2_1c$ is distinct from $P\bar{4}2c$ or $P\bar{4}c2$. You can see that the situation in these space groups is not trivial. However, one can go about deriving them in a logical way (see Section 5-6).

**5-5e Trigonal system** As discussed in previous chapters, some trigonal crystals may be described by a rhombohedral cell. There are two Bravais lattices which are appropriately labelled P and R, and five point groups, 3, $\bar{3}$, 32, 3m, and $\bar{3}$m ($C_3$, $S_6$, $D_3$, $C_{3v}$, $D_{3d}$). Combining the five point groups with the two Bravais lattices, and taking into account non-symmorphic operations, it turns out that there are 35 trigonal space groups. We have selected three examples of trigonal space groups. The first two illustrate the effect of taking a point group and allowing the symmetry elements to take up two possible orientations with respect to the lattice. The third example illustrates a rhombohedral unit cell.

(1) Space group P312 ($D_3{}^1$), number 149 in the International Tables. The point group of this symmorphic space group is 32($D_3$). We start by placing the 3-fold axis parallel to **c** and at the origin of the unit cell, and then find that translational symmetry gives rise to 3-fold axes through the points (2/3, 1/3, 0) and (1/3, 2/3, 0) as shown in Fig. 5-23. The 2-fold axes can be positioned in two ways. To obtain this space group the 2-fold axes are placed perpendicular to the **a**, **b** and [110] axes. This is why the figure 2 is placed in the third position of the symbol. In order to make it clear that this is the third position the identity 1 is written in the second position (see Appendix 6). The six general equivalent positions are (x,y,z), (−y, x−y, z), (y−x, −x, z), (−y, −x, −z), (x, x−y, −z), and (y−x, y, −z).

(2) Space group P321 ($D_3{}^2$), number 150 in the International Tables. Notice that in this space group we have placed the figure 1 in the third place. This is simply a convention to distinguish it from the previous one. Here the 2-fold axes are placed in the second possible orientation, they are rotated about **c** through 30° with respect to the previous case. Now they lie parallel to the **a**, **b** and [110] axes, as is seen in Fig. 5-24. Again there are six general equivalent positions:(x,y,z), (−y, x−y, z), (y−x, −x, z), (y, x, −z), (−x, y−x, −z), and (x−y, −y, −z).

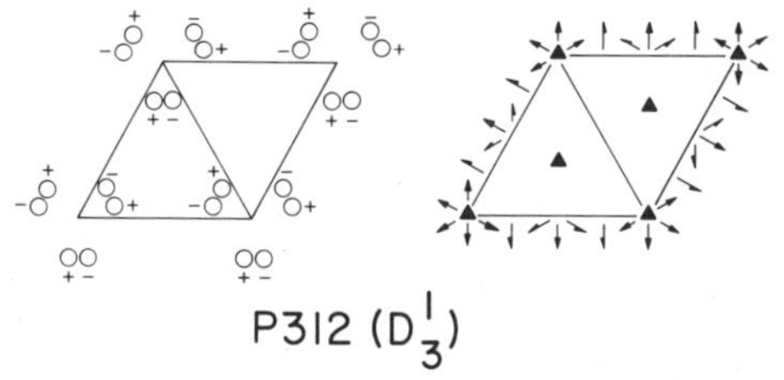


**Fig. 5-23**

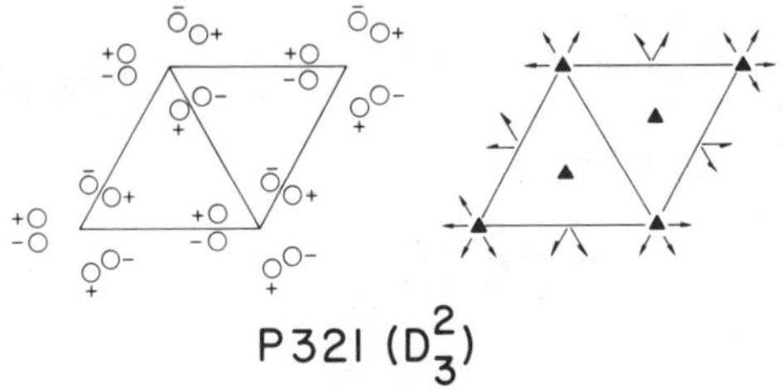


**Fig. 5-24**

(3) Space group R3c ($C_{3v}{}^{6}$), number 161 in the International Tables. Figure 5-25 shows the space groups diagrams for R3c. The R indicates a rhombohedral Bravais lattice. Two unit cells are outlined on the left-hand side; one is the trigonal cell and the other is the obverse rhombohedral cell viewed in projection down [111]. (If you do not understand which is which in this diagram we suggest you return to Fig. 2-8.) The c-glide planes pass through the 3-fold axes at the origin and centered positions. The reason for this goes back to the point we discussed in Chapters 2 and 3, namely, that the rhombohedral lattice is only obtained from a centered trigonal lattice. Therefore, as the c-glide plane passes through (0, 0, 0) it must, in order to keep the rhombohedral centering, pass through the centering positions ±(2/3, 1/3, 1/3). We leave it to the reader to show what the other, redundant, symmetry operations are and that the general equivalent positions are given by:

$$\left.\begin{matrix}(0,0,0)\\(1/3,\ 2/3,\ 2/3)\\(2/3,\ 1/3,\ 1/3)\end{matrix}\right\} + \left\{\begin{matrix}(x,y,z)\\(-y,\ x-y,\ z)\\(y-x,\ -x,\ z)\\(-y,\ -x,\ 1/2+z)\\(x,\ x-y,\ 1/2+z)\\(y-x,\ y,\ 1/2+z)\end{matrix}\right.$$

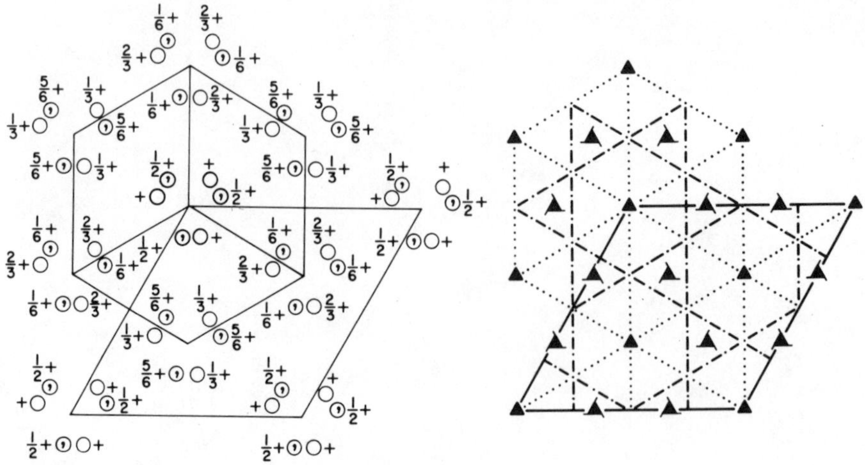

R3c ($C_{3v}^6$)

**Fig. 5-25**

with respect to hexagonal axes. There are thus 18 in all, corresponding to the six point group operators multiplied by three because of centering. We could alternatively have specified the coordinates with respect to the primitive rhombohedral cell. We can do this by applying the transformation matrix of Eq. (3-9a) which, for convenience, we repeat here:

$$\begin{bmatrix} x_r \\ y_r \\ z_r \end{bmatrix} = \begin{bmatrix} 1 & 0 & 1 \\ -1 & 1 & 1 \\ 0 & -1 & 1 \end{bmatrix} \begin{bmatrix} x_h \\ y_h \\ z_h \end{bmatrix} \tag{5-28}$$

where, as before, r and h refer to rhombohedral and hexagonal axes of reference, respectively. Equation (5-28) can be written in the form of simple equations, thus

$$\begin{aligned} x_r &= x_h + z_h \\ y_r &= -x_h + y_h + z_h \\ z_r &= -y_h + z_h \end{aligned} \tag{5-29}$$

Now apply the transformation matrix to the second general position, $(-y, x-y, z)$:

$$\begin{bmatrix} 1 & 0 & 1 \\ -1 & 1 & 1 \\ 0 & -1 & 1 \end{bmatrix} \begin{bmatrix} -y_h \\ x_h-y_h \\ z_h \end{bmatrix} = \begin{bmatrix} -y_h+z_h \\ x_h+z_h \\ -x_h+y_h+z_h \end{bmatrix} \tag{5-30}$$

The result can now be written in terms of the rhombohedral coordinates in Eq. (5-29), and we find that

$$\begin{aligned} -y_h + z_h &= z_r \\ x_h + z_h &= x_r \\ -x_h + y_h + z_h &= y_r \end{aligned} \tag{5-31}$$

Thus, the point (−y, x−y, z) is transformed to (z,x,y), with subscripts now dropped for convenience. Proceeding in this way we find that the 6 general equivalent positions grouped around the origin of the trigonal unit cell are transformed to (x,y,z), (z,x,y), (y,z,x), (1/2+x, 1/2+y, 1/2+z), (1/2+z, 1/2+x, 1/2+y) and (1/2+x, 1/2+z, 1/2+y). The other 12 general positions are related by the rhombohedral centering, but when we apply this transformation we now find that they lie outside the rhombohedral cell, i.e., in neighboring unit cells. For example, transform the point $(1/3+x_h, 2/3+y_h, 2/3+z_h)$. We get the following relations:

$$\begin{aligned} 1 + x_h + z_h &= 1 + x_r \\ 1 - x_h + y_h + z_h &= 1 + y_r \\ -y_h + z_h &= z_r \end{aligned} \tag{5-32}$$

which, by translational symmetry, is equivalent to the point (x,y,z). Clearly then, the rhombohedral unit cell has one third the volume of the trigonal cell. It is a primitive cell, and this is one reason why it is useful. Note that with the rhombohedral cell there are six general equivalent positions in agreement with the number of symmetry operations in the point group $3m(C_{3v})$.

**5-5f Hexagonal system** The hexagonal space groups are rather like the tetragonal ones, and so we shall not give any examples of them. There are seven point groups and one Bravais lattice (P). The point groups are 6, $\bar{6}$, 6/m, 622, 6mm, $\bar{6}$m2, and 6/mmm ($C_6$, $C_{3h}$, $C_{6h}$, $D_6$, $C_{6v}$, $D_{3h}$, and $D_{6h}$). From these it is possible to derive 27 hexagonal space groups, which are all listed in Appendix 7.

**5-5g Cubic system** In the cubic system there are three Bravais lattices, P, F, and I, and five point groups, 23, m3, 432, $\bar{4}$3m, and m3m (T, $T_h$, O, $T_d$, and $O_h$). When combined together with nonsymmorphic elements 36 cubic space groups result, and these are listed in Appendix 7.

In the International Tables (up to 1969, at least) diagrams are not given for the cubic space groups. This is because of the great complexity introduced by the high-symmetry of such space groups. It may seem surprising to the casual reader that the cubic space groups should be described as "complex"; after all, the symmetry being high should make things simpler. It is true that the symmetry is high, but it is also a fact that the number of general equivalent positions is large. This makes it difficult to keep track of all the symmetry-related points. If you examine the list of elements in Appendix 4, you will find that for the cubic point groups there are 12, 24, or 48 symmetry operations. That is, there are 12, 24, or 48 general equivalent positions in the primitive cell of the cubic space groups. Combine this with lattice centering, such as all-face-centering, and the total number of general positions can be as many as 196. Furthermore, bearing in mind that each general position may describe an assemblage of n atoms, there may be 196n atoms in the unit cell. Fortunately, things are rarely as bad as they seem at first sight. In many of the cubic crystals that are studied the atoms do not usually occupy general positions in the unit cell. Often they will lie at **special positions**. For example, certain atoms may lie exactly on mirror planes, and there will be half as many of such atoms in the unit cell as those in general positions. The placing of atoms in special positions means that there will be a reduction in the number of atoms in the unit cell. We shall deal more fully with special positions in the next chapter. Several examples of cubic crystal structures will be discussed in Section 6-4 and these will suffice to illustrate the important features.

## 5-6 Derivation of Space Groups

The derivation of the 230 space groups was due mainly to the efforts of three people: a Russian, E. S. Fedorov; a German, A. Schoenflies, and an Englishman, W. Barlow, all of them working roughly at the same time but independently from one another. Of these three, the derivation of Fedorov was completed first (1890) and followed soon after by that of Schoenflies (1891) and then Barlow (1894). However, because Fedorov's work was published in Russian while that of Schoenflies was in the more (at that time) acceptable scientific language of German, the Schoenflies approach made the most impression on the scientific community. Barlow's approach was not very clearly set out and, in any case, was incomplete.

Fedorov's method, which owed much to the earlier work of Sohnke, Moebius, and others, involved the division of space groups into three classes:

1) Symmorphic class, which Fedorov thought of in terms of symmorphic elements intersecting at a point.

2) Hemisymmorphic class, in which only proper symmetry elements intersect at a point.

3) Asymmorphic class, in which there are no such points of intersection.

As symmetry operations, Fedorov used rotations, reflections, and combined rotation-reflection operations. He disliked the use of inversion operations, preferring to accomplish the same effect by a 2-fold rotation-reflection. Fedorov's greatest accomplishment perhaps was the mathematical technique that he developed for expressing combinations of symmetry elements. With this, every space group was described by a set of three simple equations and it was the generalization of this that led to the discovery that there were 230 space groups in all. Fedorov subsequently took matters further and showed that similar results could be obtained by assuming that crystals could be described by convex polyhedra with pairs of equal opposite faces packed together through all space. However, curiously, this approach led Fedorov to reject some space groups as being impossible for real crystal structures. They were Fdd2($C_{2v}^{19}$), Fddd($D_{2h}^{24}$), $I\bar{4}3d$($T_d^6$), $P4_332$($O^6$), and $P4_132$($O^7$). In spite of this, we now know that there are several crystal structures with these space groups, and yet the fault in Fedorov's logic is not readily apparent. The reader is warmly recommended to read the series of Fedorov's papers translated into English by D. and K. Harker for a detailed understanding of these matters.

Let us turn to the Schoenflies approach which we should like to discuss in more detail since it is better known in the literature. The basic idea was simple and the systematic approach straightforward; and again, it owed much to the pioneering work of Sohnke and others. An appreciation of how this was done leads to a deeper understanding of the space groups themselves.

The Schoenflies approach to the determination of the 230 space groups started from that outlined in Section 5-2 for the symmorphic space groups. Schoenflies then allowed the possibility of glide planes and screw axes. Finally he coupled all these possibilities by realizing that to completely describe a space group all that is needed is the lattice (all the translation symmetry operations) and h space group operations, where h is the number of operations in the point group of the space group. These h operations of the space group are isomorphic to the h operations of the point group of the space group, a point that we discussed in Section 5-5 and we will prove in Section 6-6. This complicated idea actually is quite simple. For example, if for a given lattice and point group the symmorphic space group has a symmetry operation 4($C_4$), then the corresponding nonsymmorphic space groups may have a symmetry operation $4_1$ or $4_2$ or $4_3$ and none other. Similarly, a symmorphic operation m($\sigma$) may only be replaced, in nonsymmorphic space groups by one of the various types of glide planes. Thus, we see that although the task is very large, it is finite and has well-defined bounds. The examples that we show below are meant to give a flavor for the approach as well as make the remarks clearer.

The triclinic space groups are too trivial to clarify the above points and in any case, the techniques of Section 5-2 determine both of them perfectly well. This is because there is only the P-lattice to consider; the point group 1($C_1$) gives the space group that Schoenflies calls $C_1{}^1$ and the point group $\overline{1}$($C_i$) gives the space group $C_i{}^1$ (P1 and P$\overline{1}$, respectively).

For the monoclinic crystal system it is easier to see how the approach is used. There are only two space lattices, the P- and B-lattices, and the point groups that are consistent with monoclinic symmetry are 2($C_2$), m($C_s$ or $C_{1h}$), and 2/m($C_{2h}$). As discussed in Section 5-2 there are six symmorphic space groups that one can immediately obtain and they are listed in Table 5-1. Now, starting with the point group 2($C_2$) we may determine all of the space groups, including the nonsymmorphic ones, that have point group 2($C_2$). We start with the primitive lattice and the point group 2($C_2$) just as in Section 5-2 and find the first space group $C_2{}^1$ (P2 in the International notation). Then, we know that if the screw axis $2_1$ replaces the 2-fold axis as a symmetry operation, the point group of the resulting space group will still be 2($C_2$) and so we try it. If we do this, we obtain a new space group which is different from $C_2{}^1$ and which we can call $C_2{}^2$(P$2_1$). We now have exhausted all the possible nonsymmorphic operations that will yield space groups whose point groups are 2($C_2$). So we proceed to the base-centered lattice and immediately have the symmorphic space group which we call $C_2{}^3$(B2). The next possibility is a $2_1$ operation with a B-lattice. When we try this we obtain the same space group as $C_2{}^3$ but with the origin shifted. Thus, a new space group is not obtained in this case. The three unique space groups we have found in this way are $C_2{}^1$(P2), $C_2{}^2$(P$2_1$), and $C_2{}^3$(B2).

Now we proceed to monoclinic space groups whose point groups are m($C_s$). Here we know that the only possible nonsymmorphic operation is a b-glide. Thus we start with the P-lattice and the m($C_s$) operation and obtain $C_s{}^1$(Pm). Furthermore, we find that $C_s{}^2$(Pb) is different. For the base-centered lattice we obtain $C_s{}^3$(Bm) and $C_s{}^4$(Bb). Here a fourth unique space lattice is obtained.

For the monoclinic space groups whose point groups are 2/m($C_{2h}$), there are four possible combinations of symmetry operations:

$2/m$, $2_1/m$, $2/b$, and $2_1/b$. We may adjoin these to the two lattices P and B; six new space groups are then obtained. These can best be displayed as direct products of two groups; this brings out the simplicity of the approach.

$$
\begin{array}{lllll}
C_{2h}{}^1 = C_2{}^1 \times \{E,\sigma\} & \text{or} & P2/m & = & P2 \times \{1,m\} \\
C_{2h}{}^2 = C_2{}^2 \times \{E,\sigma\} & \text{or} & P2_1/m & = & P2_1 \times \{1,m\} \\
C_{2h}{}^3 = C_2{}^3 \times \{E,\sigma\} & \text{or} & B2/m & = & B2 \times \{1,m\} \\
C_{2h}{}^4 = C_2{}^1 \times \{E,b\} & \text{or} & P2/b & = & P2 \times \{1,b\} \\
C_{2h}{}^5 = C_2{}^2 \times \{E,b\} & \text{or} & P2_1/b & = & P2_1 \times \{1,b\} \\
C_{2h}{}^6 = C_2{}^3 \times \{E,b\} & \text{or} & B2/b & = & B2 \times \{1,b\}
\end{array}
$$

This also explains the order of space groups adopted by Schoenflies and the International Tables.

It is tempting to stop here because, in general, it gets more difficult for the other crystal systems. There is the occasional very simple situation, such as in the hexagonal crystal system, where with just a P-lattice, one may deduce the six space groups $C_6{}^1$ to $C_6{}^6$ ($P6$, $P6_1$, $P6_5$, $P6_2$, $P6_4$, $P6_3$) immediately. However, we discuss one more set of space groups simply to stress that it is nevertheless feasible.

Consider the orthorhombic system and, in particular, let us concentrate on the use of point group $mm2(C_{2v})$ in conjunction with a primitive lattice. There are ten space groups that can be generated with this. This large number is obtained because the various symmorphic or nonsymmorphic planes need not contain the 2 or $2_1$-axis (which we take here as the **c**-axis). These vertical planes may be displaced a distance $a/4$ or $b/4$. The displacement of 1/4 occurs for reasons similar to those found in Section 5-5c for the three screw axes in space group $P2_12_12_1$. For conciseness we can describe these space groups as a direct product of $C_2{}^1(P2)$ or $C_2{}^2(P2_1)$ with a group that involves a mirror plane $\sigma$ perpendicular to the **a**-axis at $x = 0$ or a similar plane $\sigma'$ displaced to $x = 1/4$.

The ten space groups obtained are

$$
\begin{aligned}
&\mathrm{Pm}{-}2 &&= \mathrm{Pmm2} &&= C_{2v}{}^{1} &&= C_2{}^{1} \times \{E,\sigma\}\\
&\mathrm{Pm}{-}2_1 &&= \mathrm{Pmc2_1} &&= C_{2v}{}^{2} &&= C_2{}^{2} \times \{E,\sigma\}\\
&\mathrm{Pc}{-}2 &&= \mathrm{Pcc2} &&= C_{2v}{}^{3} &&= C_2{}^{1} \times \{E,\{\sigma\,|\,\mathbf{c}/2\}\}\\
&\mathrm{Pm'}{-}2 &&= \mathrm{Pma2} &&= C_{2v}{}^{4} &&= C_2{}^{1} \times \{E,\sigma'\}\\
&\mathrm{Pc'}{-}2_1 &&= \mathrm{Pca2_1} &&= C_{2v}{}^{5} &&= C_2{}^{2} \times \{E,\{\sigma'\,|\,\mathbf{c}/2\}\}\\
&\mathrm{Pn}{-}2 &&= \mathrm{Pnc2} &&= C_{2v}{}^{6} &&= C_2{}^{1} \times \{E,\{\sigma\,|\,(\mathbf{b}+\mathbf{c})/2\}\}\\
&\mathrm{Pm'}{-}2_1 &&= \mathrm{Pmn2_1} &&= C_{2v}{}^{7} &&= C_2{}^{2} \times \{E,\sigma'\}\\
&\mathrm{Pb'}{-}2 &&= \mathrm{Pba2} &&= C_{2v}{}^{8} &&= C_2{}^{1} \times \{E,\{\sigma'\,|\,\mathbf{b}/2\}\}\\
&\mathrm{Pn'}{-}2_1 &&= \mathrm{Pna2_1} &&= C_{2v}{}^{9} &&= C_2{}^{2} \times \{E,\{\sigma'\,|\,(\mathbf{b}+\mathbf{c})/2\}\}\\
&\mathrm{Pn'}{-}2 &&= \mathrm{Pnn2} &&= C_{2v}{}^{10} &&= C_2{}^{1} \times \{E,\{\sigma'\,|\,(\mathbf{b}+\mathbf{c})/2\}\}
\end{aligned}
$$

The standard International and Schoenflies notations are used except for the symbol on the left. This symbol describes the operations that are absolutely necessary to obtain the space group and is just a short-hand notation for the direct product on the right. This symbol describes the P-lattice and 2 or $2_1$ along the **c**-axis corresponding to the Schoenflies space groups $C_2{}^1$ or $C_2{}^2$, respectively. The other symbol is a plane perpendicular to the **a**-axis (hence it is put in the first position of the symbol) which is at $x = 0$ or at $x = 1/4$; the latter is denoted by a prime. The symbol m, b, c, or n describes the direction of the glide in the usual way. The dash in the position of the plane perpendicular to the **b**-axis is a quantity derived from the rest of the information.

The complexity of the problem begins to become apparent, although the problem is clearly finite. It is instructive to read the original book by Schoenflies, since it gives one an appreciation of how ingenious the early determination of the 230 space groups was.

## 5-7 Two-Dimensional Space Groups

In Chapter 4 we discussed the ten 2-dimensional point groups. In order to obtain the **2-dimensional space groups** or **plane groups** we must combine these with the five 2-dimensional lattices. If we do this to generate the symmorphic plane groups, as we did in Section 5-2, then we obtain a total of 13 plane groups, two of which (p3m1 and p31m) differ only in the orientation of the symmetry elements with respect to the lattice (as in space groups P3m1 and P31m). The only nonsymmorphic operation permitted in two dimensions is the glide with reflection across a line in the **ab**-plane, given the symbol g. All the other nonsymmorphic

**Table 5-2** The 17 2-dimensional space groups.

| Lattice | Point group | Space group symbol Full | Short | Number |
|---|---|---|---|---|
| Oblique | 1 | p1 | p1 | 1 |
| p | 2 | p211 | p2 | 2 |
| Rectangular | m | p1m1 | pm | 3 |
| p or c | | p1g1 | pg | 4 |
| | | c1m1 | cm | 5 |
| | 2mm | p2mm | pmm | 6 |
| | | p2mg | pmg | 7 |
| | | p2gg | pgg | 8 |
| | | c2mm | cmm | 9 |
| Square | 4 | p4 | p4 | 10 |
| p | 4mm | p4mm | p4m | 11 |
| | | p4gm | p4g | 12 |
| Hexagonal | 3 | p3 | p3 | 13 |
| c | 3m | p3m1 | p3m1 | 14 |
| | | p31m | p31m | 15 |
| | 6 | p6 | p6 | 16 |
| | 6mm | p6mm | p6m | 17 |

operations we met in 3-dimensional space groups involve out-of-plane movements of the general point. Taking into account the glide line g, a further four nonsymmorphic plane groups are generated, making a total of 17 in all. They are listed in Table 5-2. It should be a simple matter for the reader to draw the space group diagrams for all these plane groups. The results can be checked by consulting the International Tables. Note that the order of symbols is not quite the same as in the three-dimensional space groups (see Table 3.2.1 of the International Tables).

## Problems

**1.** Within a given crystal system, show that the Bravais lattices always belong to the holosymmetric point group.

**2.** The diagram below shows the **hierarchy of the seven crystal systems** in which every crystal system can be produced by an infinitesimal distortion from one above, provided it is connected by a line. Show that this is indeed so. Consider placing an object at a lattice point in any crystal system. Show (a) that all the symmetry elements possessed by this object must be possessed by the lattice (the lattice can, of course, have more symmetry elements), and (b) the object must possess at least one symmetry element that is not found in the lattice that is next lower in the hierarchy of the crystal systems.

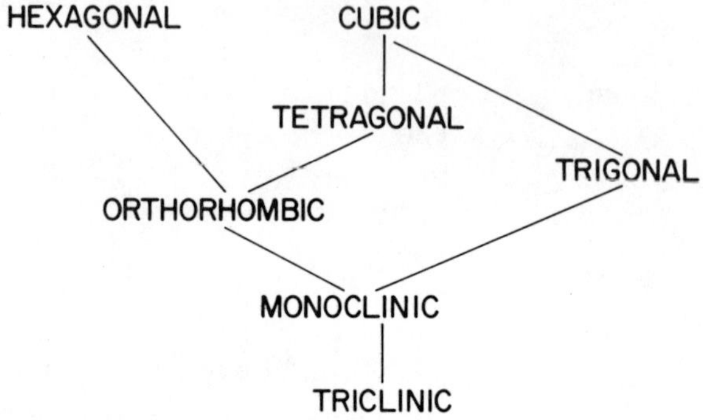


**3.** Show that the combination of an improper rotation, except $\overline{2}(S_2)$, with translation $\boldsymbol{\tau}$ does not result in a symmetry operation.

**4.** Draw the space group diagrams for space groups $C_4{}^1$, $C_{4v}{}^1$, and $C_{4h}{}^1$. Be sure to include the International symbol and all of the symmetry operations that are generated.

**5.** Draw a two-dimensional lattice and in a general position close to each lattice point place the symbol 6. Add further symbols to form a pattern in which the point symmetry at each lattice point is 2. Outline a unit cell of the pattern and indicate in red any symmetry elements which it displays. Repeat the above procedure to give patterns in which the point symmetry at each lattice point is m, mm2, 4 and 4mm, respectively. In each case base your pattern on a lattice having **a**, **b** and $\gamma$ appropriate to the point symmetry.

**6.** Using space group diagrams compare Cmm2 and Pmmm.

**7.** Find the coordinates of the point generated from the point (x,y,z) by the action of the following symmetry elements: (a) a c-glide plane at x,1/4,z followed by a $2_1$ axis along [0,y,1/4]. (b) an n-glide plane at x,0,z followed by a $4_2$ axis along [1/4,0,z]. What is the result when these operations are applied in reverse order?

**8.** Draw space group diagrams and give the general equivalent positions for $Cbc2_1$, Pmba, $Abc2_1$, and Pnma.

**9.** Consider the space group P4nc ($C_{4v}^6$) in the International Tables (No. 104). What is the resulting position produced by the n-glide plane perpendicular to **a** acting on the general position (x,y,z)? What is the result for the n-glide plane parallel to the diagonal $[1\bar{1}0]$? Notice that in the first case a translation of (**b**+**c**)/2 is involved, whereas in the second case it is (**a**+**b**+**c**)/2.

**10.** With reference to the space groups with a P-lattice and point group mm2($C_{2v}$), discussed in Section 5-6, show that the space groups Pb−2, Pb−$2_1$, and Pc−$2_1$ are the same as ones shown in the complete list in that section but with a redefinition of the **a**- and **b**-axes.

**11.** Find the type and position of the conventional symmetry element that is involved in the following mappings:

| | | |
|---|---|---|
| (x,y,z) | → | (1/2−x, 1/2−x, 1/2+z) |
| (x,y,z) | → | (1/2+z, 1/2−y, z) |
| (1/4+x, 1/4+y, 1/4−z) | → | (1/2+x, y, 1/2+z) |
| (y−x, y, 2/3−z) | → | (y−x, −x, 1/3+z) |

## Chapter 6

# PROPERTIES OF SPACE GROUPS

*And the Circumference still expands going forward to Eternity,*
*And the center has Eternal States; these States we now explore.*

*Blake, "Jerusalem"*

## 6-1 Introduction

In this chapter we show how a very large amount of information, of direct interest to the solid state scientist, can be obtained from a knowledge of the space group of a crystal. Normally, a solid state scientist works with a crystal whose space group and structure are known. There are a number of questions that could or should arise:

(a) What are the positions of the various atoms in the crystal?
(b) What symmetry do these various atoms see?
(c) How are they related to other similar atoms?
(d) What is the maximum number of similar atoms allowed by the space group?
(e) What are the restrictions on the macroscopic properties imposed by the space group?
(f) What is the crystal class and Bravais lattice?
(g) What is the point group of the space group and what is its significance?
(h) What are the implications of having glide planes and screw axes as symmetry operations instead of point operations?
(i) What is the relationship (the isomorphism or the one-to-one correspondence) between these glide planes and screw axes,

which are symmetry operations, and the simple point operations, which are not necessarily symmetry operations?

(j) How can we find the smallest number of symmetry operations needed to specify the space group fully?

These are the kinds of questions that one would normally ask, or be aware of, whether the interest is in the atomic positions per se, the lattice vibrations, electronic band theory, or practically any other solid-state questions. We shall try to answer such questions in this chapter.

One should remember that from a quantum mechanical point of view, the space group describes all of the spatial symmetry of the crystal, and so from it one should be able to determine all of the exact solutions of the Hamiltonian that result from the spatial symmetry. This means that we want to describe how all the different eigenfunctions transform under the symmetry operations, and this is the same thing as labeling the eigenfunctions with the irreducible representations of the point group of the space group and **k** (wave vector) values. We shall not deal here with the specialized problems of the irreducible representations of the space groups. However, we shall show how the symmetry operations of the space groups are related to the operations that appear in the character tables (Appendix 8) for the 32 point groups.

Clearly the answers to many of these questions involve simple geometry while others require involved Group Theory. In this chapter we shall start with the simple aspects of what one can learn when the space group and crystal structure are known, and then cover some of the more involved matters towards the end of the chapter. Some of what we say here will of necessity be repetition of the important points made in the preceding chapters. Thus, to some extent this chapter can be read on its own and serves as a summary of the important features of space groups.

## 6-2 Crystal Structure and Space Group

A **crystal structure** is described by a lattice plus a basis (sometimes called **lattice complex**). The **basis** is a collection of atoms (or any object) associated with a lattice point, which by translational symmetry is repeated throughout. This concept may be expressed as

$$\text{crystal structure} = \text{lattice} + \text{basis}$$

Any object that has such a structure is, by definition, **a crystal**.

The structural crystallographer can determine relatively easily the crystal system and unit cell geometry for a particular crystal, usually by employing X-ray diffraction techniques. The determination of the point and space groups is often more difficult. It is normally accomplished by looking for the systematic presence or absence of certain X-ray diffraction spots. It is known that lattice centering and nonsymmorphic elements cause certain classes of X-ray spots to have zero intensity. Hence it is, in principle, possible to work back and determine what the centering and nonsymmorphic elements are. However, it is often found that there are still several possible space groups which satisfy these X-ray diffraction conditions, and it can be very difficult to make the correct choice. For example, as we discussed briefly when we dealt with the 11 Laue Groups in Section 4-6, X-rays usually add a center of inversion to the diffraction pattern, so that distinction between centrosymmetric and noncentrosymmetric space groups may have to be made by resorting to examining the crystal properties. That is, it may be necessary to see if the crystal shows polar properties such as pyroelectricity or piezoelectricity. Alternatively it may be necessary to try all the possibilities and see which one fits the best (trial-and-error method).

Once the space group and the number of formula units (or molecules) per unit cell are known, the relative positions of the atoms in the unit cell can often be guessed. The number of formula units per cell, n, is often determined from the measured crystal density $\rho$ and its unit cell volume V. It is given by $n = \rho NV/M$, where M is the formula weight and N is Avogadro's constant. However, with the exception of simple compounds, a complete crystal structure analysis is required to determine with any degree of certainty the exact positions of the atoms, that is, whether the atoms are at certain special positions or at general positions, and what the values of their fractional coordinates (x, y, z) are. This is what is called the **crystal structure determination**, i.e., the determination of the space group and the positions of the atoms in the unit cell. This is commonly carried out by careful measurement of the diffracted X-ray intensities, which are proportional to the square of the scattered X-ray amplitudes. From this, provided all the phase relationships between the scattered waves are known, the complete crystal structure can be worked out. In general, however, these phase relationships cannot be measured directly and their determination constitutes one of the greatest problems in crystal structure analysis. Several sophisticated techniques have been devised over the years for solving this so-called "phase problem," including the least squares refinement of trial structures and statistical inference (direct methods). The derivation of most crystal structures, at least those with relatively few atoms (say, less than 100) in the unit cell, is no longer the difficult and time-consuming operation that it used to be, and, to some extent, has become largely automatic. For a full explanation of crystal structure determination, any standard book on X-ray crystallography can be consulted. A particularly good and readable book is "The Determination of Crystal Structures" by Lipson and Cochran.

Given a particular chemical compound, there are several source books and journals that can be consulted to find out if the crystal structure has been determined. The reader will, undoubtedly, be already familiar with Chemical or Physics Abstracts, which often form a useful starting point. It is also worth looking through the indices of the crystallographic journals such as Acta Crystallographica and Zeitschrift für Kristallografie. Another useful place to look is in the series of books by Wyckoff entitled "Crystal Structures," or else in Structure Reports. Full details of these volumes are given in the Bibliography. A typical illustration of how crystal structure information is often given is shown here for the mineral calcite ($CaCO_3$):

$R\bar{3}c$ ($D_{3d}^{6}$)

Ca in 6(b) : 0,0,0
C in 6(a) : 0, 0, 1/4
O in 18(e) : x, 0, 1/4 with x = 0.257

This contains sufficient information to enable one to draw a diagram of the crystal structure. In the unit cell of calcite there are 30 atoms, and yet, as can be seen, it is not necessary to give the positions of all of them separately; only the three basic positions are given and the space group symmetry determines where the other 27 are, showing just how neatly the use of symmetry simplifies the description of something that may be inherently quite complicated. The positions of the atoms are denoted by fractional coordinates and by various labels, e.g., Ca in 6(b). The meaning of these will become clearer in the next section.

## 6-3 "Typical" Page of the International Tables

There are 230 space groups, and we may pick any one as "typical." We shall show examples of various pages of the International Tables for several space groups and discuss the meaning of the information given.

First of all, let us summarize some important ideas from the previous chapter. We have already defined the term space group in Section 5-1. As explained, the symmetry operations of a space group include all the primitive lattice translations $\{1 \mid \mathbf{t}_n\}$. The lattice may either be taken as infinite or as finite with periodic boundary conditions, in which case we let m equal the number of symmetry operations for the finite lattice. Besides these operations we need h symmetry operations, i.e., the point, glide, or screw-symmetry operations. The space group, therefore, has hm symmetry operations in all. We call these h operations "essential" operations and refer to any other point, glide, or screw-symmetry operations that are generated by the product of these h operations with the primitive lattice translations as "nonessential." (However, we stress once again that they are symmetry operations of the space group.) It is often a matter of taste as to exactly which symmetry operations we want to use as essential. The value of h is equal to the order of the point group of the space group. This and related matters have been discussed earlier in Chapter 5 and we shall return to this important concept later.

In order to describe the symmetry operations in a convenient manner, we use the usual Seitz operator. $\{R \mid \mathbf{t}\}$ is an operation acting on a point in space, where R refers to rotations or reflections, followed by a translation through an amount $\mathbf{t}$. Thus, the pure primitive lattice translations are given by $\{1 \mid \mathbf{t}_n\}$ in the International notation or $\{E \mid \mathbf{t}_n\}$ in the Schoenflies notation, where $\mathbf{t}_n = n_1\mathbf{a}+n_2\mathbf{b}+n_3\mathbf{c}$. The other symmetry operations necessary to describe the space group are given by the h operators $\{R \mid \boldsymbol{\tau}\}$, where $\boldsymbol{\tau}$ is a fraction of a primitive lattice vector and may be zero. The nonessential symmetry operations whose elements are in the unit cell under consideration can be written in the same manner. Crystallographers tend to take different origins within the unit cell for different symmetry operations. However, it is possible to take them with respect to one origin and we shall show how this is done later.

**6-3a A page from the International Tables** Figure 6-1a shows the page from the International Tables for space group $P4/m(C_{4h}{}^1)$ and Fig. 6-1b shows that for $P4/n(C_{4h}{}^3)$. We shall first discuss the symbols at the top of the page starting at the right and going to the left. First the symbol for the space group is given in the International notation and, immediately below it, in the Schoenflies notation. This is followed by the serial number of the space group. The space groups are numbered sequentially from 1 to 230 starting with the triclinic space group P1, number 1, and ending with the cubic space group Ia3d, number 230; this can be used as a rapid means of finding a particular space group provided it is supplied along with the crystal data. Next, the "full" International symbol for the space group appears. As can be seen for the two examples given here it is the same as the symbol on the right, sometimes referred to as the "short" symbol. After this we find the symbol for the point group written in the International notation (4/m here) followed by the crystal system (tetragonal). Before dealing with the rest of the information given, we should now like to go back to these various symbols and discuss, in more detail, what we can learn from them.

**6-3b Space group symbols** In the International notation the first letter of the space group symbol describes the type of lattice with P = primitive, I = body-centered, F = face-centered, C (or A or B) = base (or one face)-centered, and R = rhombohedral, as discussed fully in Chapter 3. Thus, from this symbol together with a knowledge of the crystal system, we know which of the 14 Bravais lattices we are dealing with. It is to the conventional unit cell (shown in Appendix 3) that the rest of the data on the page refer to. After the capital letter, in both full and short symbol, the remaining numbers and letters refer to the symmetry operations of the space group as we discussed in Chapters 4 and 5. You will recall that the symbol 4/m means that there is a mirror plane perpendicular to a 4-fold symmetry axis. Similarly, the 4/n means that there is an n-glide plane perpendicular to the 4-fold axis. (A full summary of the notation is given in Appendix 6.) The short International symbol is the one that is used most frequently since it succinctly describes the space group and enables one to determine all of the symmetry operations; many examples of how this is done are given in Chapter 5. The full International symbol shows more specific information; however, the extra symmetry operations shown can always be obtained from those in the short symbol, and this is why it is not quoted very often. Nevertheless, the full symbol can be particularly useful since it tells very quickly where some of the other symmetry elements are.

The Schoenflies symbol for the space group, $C_{4h}^1$ or $C_{4h}^3$ in Figs. 6-1a and 6-1b, contains less space group information. Since the various space groups with a common point group are denoted solely by a serial number, it is not possible to derive the space group operations. The superscript 1 always denotes a symmorphic space group (no glide planes or screw axes), but other than this small piece of information the numbering is essentially arbitrary. On the other hand, it does have the advantage that it is independent of the choice of unit cell axes, while the International symbol is not. For example, for the space group P4/m($C_{4h}^1$) one might choose a unit cell, with twice the volume, whose **a**- and **b**- axes are at 45° to those of the smaller unit cell. The symbol in this case would be

Tetragonal $4/m$ $P\,4/m$ No. 83 $P\,4/m$ $C_{4h}^{1}$

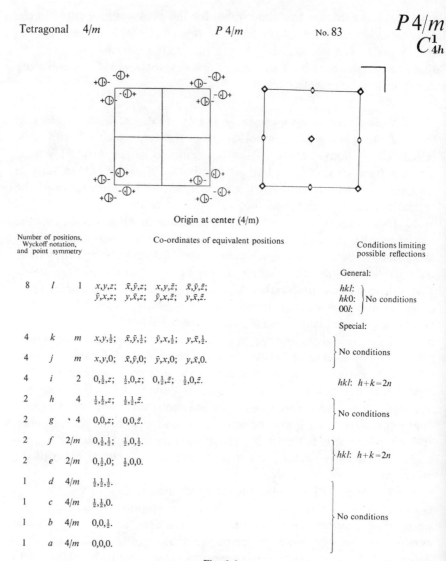

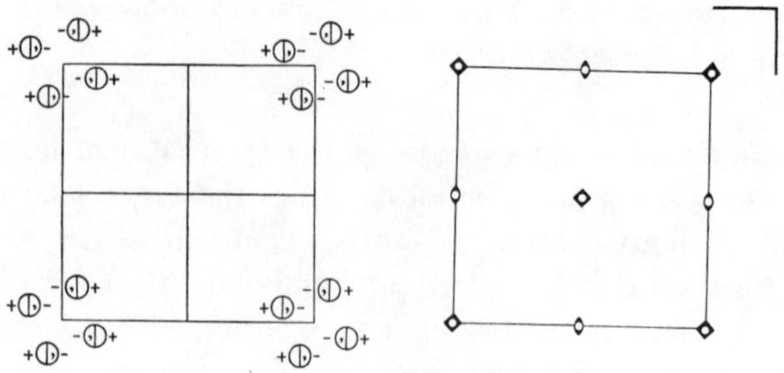

Origin at center (4/m)

| Number of positions, Wyckoff notation, and point symmetry | | | Co-ordinates of equivalent positions | Conditions limiting possible reflections |
|---|---|---|---|---|
| | | | | General: |
| 8 | *l* | 1 | $x,y,z;\ \bar{x},\bar{y},z;\ x,y,\bar{z};\ \bar{x},\bar{y},\bar{z};$ $\bar{y},x,z;\ y,\bar{x},z;\ \bar{y},x,\bar{z};\ y,\bar{x},\bar{z}.$ | *hkl*: *hk*0: 00*l*: No conditions |
| | | | | Special: |
| 4 | *k* | *m* | $x,y,\frac{1}{2};\ \bar{x},\bar{y},\frac{1}{2};\ \bar{y},x,\frac{1}{2};\ y,\bar{x},\frac{1}{2}.$ | No conditions |
| 4 | *j* | *m* | $x,y,0;\ \bar{x},\bar{y},0;\ \bar{y},x,0;\ y,\bar{x},0.$ | |
| 4 | *i* | 2 | $0,\frac{1}{2},z;\ \frac{1}{2},0,z;\ 0,\frac{1}{2},\bar{z};\ \frac{1}{2},0,\bar{z}.$ | *hkl*: $h+k=2n$ |
| 2 | *h* | 4 | $\frac{1}{2},\frac{1}{2},z;\ \frac{1}{2},\frac{1}{2},\bar{z}.$ | No conditions |
| 2 | *g* | 4 | $0,0,z;\ 0,0,\bar{z}.$ | |
| 2 | *f* | $2/m$ | $0,\frac{1}{2},\frac{1}{2};\ \frac{1}{2},0,\frac{1}{2}.$ | *hkl*: $h+k=2n$ |
| 2 | *e* | $2/m$ | $0,\frac{1}{2},0;\ \frac{1}{2},0,0.$ | |
| 1 | *d* | $4/m$ | $\frac{1}{2},\frac{1}{2},\frac{1}{2}.$ | No conditions |
| 1 | *c* | $4/m$ | $\frac{1}{2},\frac{1}{2},0.$ | |
| 1 | *b* | $4/m$ | $0,0,\frac{1}{2}.$ | |
| 1 | *a* | $4/m$ | $0,0,0.$ | |

**Fig. 6-1a**

$C4/m(C_{4h}^{1})$ since the new unit cell is base-centered. In the examples shown in Fig. 6-1, the symbol $C_{4h}$ shows that there is a plane of reflection perpendicular to the 4-fold axis just as with the International symbol $4/m$.

**6-3c Point group** We see that from the Schoenflies space-group symbol, the point group of the space group is instantly apparent. If the

# $P\,4/n$ $C_{4h}^3$

Tetragonal $4/m$ — $P\,4/n$ — No. 85

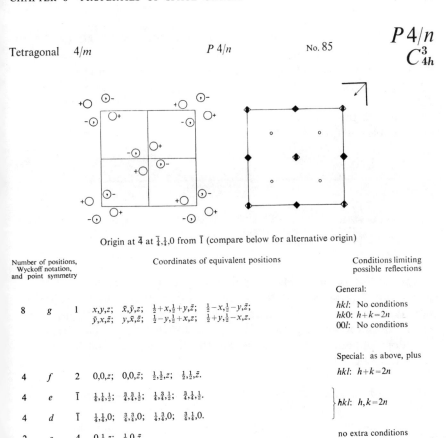

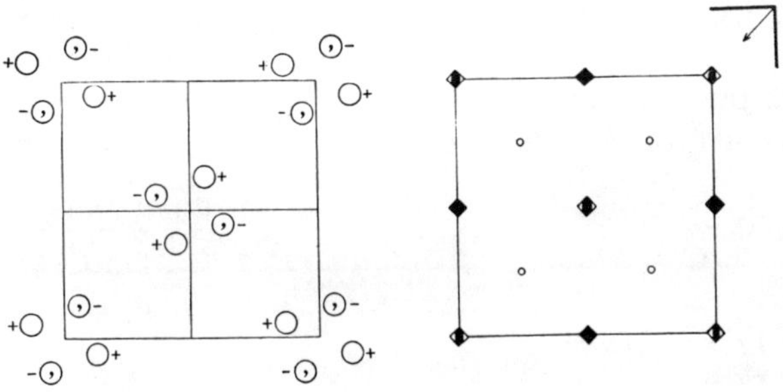

Origin at $\bar{4}$ at $\bar{\frac{1}{4}},\frac{1}{4},0$ from $\bar{1}$ (compare below for alternative origin)

| Number of positions, Wyckoff notation, and point symmetry | | | Coordinates of equivalent positions | Conditions limiting possible reflections |
|---|---|---|---|---|
| | | | | General: |
| 8 | $g$ | 1 | $x,y,z$; $\bar{x},\bar{y},z$; $\frac{1}{2}+x,\frac{1}{2}+y,\bar{z}$; $\frac{1}{2}-x,\frac{1}{2}-y,\bar{z}$; $\bar{y},x,\bar{z}$; $y,\bar{x},\bar{z}$; $\frac{1}{2}-y,\frac{1}{2}+x,z$; $\frac{1}{2}+y,\frac{1}{2}-x,z$. | $hkl$: No conditions; $hk0$: $h+k=2n$; $00l$: No conditions |
| | | | | Special: as above, plus |
| 4 | $f$ | 2 | $0,0,z$; $0,0,\bar{z}$; $\frac{1}{2},\frac{1}{2},z$; $\frac{1}{2},\frac{1}{2},\bar{z}$. | $hkl$: $h+k=2n$ |
| 4 | $e$ | $\bar{1}$ | $\frac{1}{4},\frac{1}{4},\frac{1}{2}$; $\frac{3}{4},\frac{3}{4},\frac{1}{2}$; $\frac{1}{4},\frac{3}{4},\frac{1}{2}$; $\frac{3}{4},\frac{1}{4},\frac{1}{2}$. | $hkl$: $h,k=2n$ (e and d) |
| 4 | $d$ | $\bar{1}$ | $\frac{1}{4},\frac{1}{4},0$; $\frac{3}{4},\frac{3}{4},0$; $\frac{1}{4},\frac{3}{4},0$; $\frac{3}{4},\frac{1}{4},0$. | |
| 2 | $c$ | 4 | $0,\frac{1}{2},z$; $\frac{1}{2},0,\bar{z}$. | no extra conditions |
| 2 | $b$ | $\bar{4}$ | $0,0,\frac{1}{2}$; $\frac{1}{2},\frac{1}{2},\frac{1}{2}$. | $hkl$: $h+k=2n$ ($a$ and $b$) |
| 2 | $a$ | $\bar{4}$ | $0,0,0$; $\frac{1}{2},\frac{1}{2},0$. | |

Origin at $\bar{1}$ at $\frac{1}{4},\bar{\frac{1}{4}},0$ from $\bar{4}$ (compare above for alternative origin)

| | | | | |
|---|---|---|---|---|
| 8 | $g$ | 1 | $x,y,z$; $\frac{1}{2}-x,\frac{1}{2}-y,z$; $\frac{1}{2}-y,x,z$; $y,\frac{1}{2}-x,z$; $\bar{x},\bar{y},\bar{z}$; $\frac{1}{2}+x,\frac{1}{2}+y,\bar{z}$; $\frac{1}{2}+y,\bar{x},\bar{z}$; $\bar{y},\frac{1}{2}+x,\bar{z}$. | General and special conditions as above |
| 4 | $f$ | 2 | $\frac{1}{4},\frac{3}{4},z$; $\frac{3}{4},\frac{1}{4},\bar{z}$; $\frac{1}{4},\frac{3}{4},\bar{z}$; $\frac{3}{4},\frac{1}{4},z$. | |
| 4 | $e$ | $\bar{1}$ | $0,0,\frac{1}{2}$; $\frac{1}{2},\frac{1}{2},\frac{1}{2}$; $0,\frac{1}{2},\frac{1}{2}$; $\frac{1}{2},0,\frac{1}{2}$. | |
| 4 | $d$ | $\bar{1}$ | $0,0,0$; $\frac{1}{2},\frac{1}{2},0$; $0,\frac{1}{2},0$; $\frac{1}{2},0,0$. | |
| 2 | $c$ | 4 | $\frac{1}{4},\frac{1}{4},z$; $\frac{3}{4},\frac{3}{4},\bar{z}$. | |
| 2 | $b$ | $\bar{4}$ | $\frac{1}{4},\frac{3}{4},\frac{1}{2}$; $\frac{3}{4},\frac{1}{4},\frac{1}{2}$. | |
| 2 | $a$ | $\bar{4}$ | $\frac{1}{4},\frac{3}{4},0$; $\frac{3}{4},\frac{1}{4},0$. | |

**Fig. 6-1b**

chief interest is in point groups, then the Schoenflies space group symbol is convenient. The point group of the space group is also obtained without difficulty from the International space group symbol. If all screw axes are replaced by their equivalent symmorphic rotation axes, all of the glides a, (or b or c), n, and d are replaced by m, and the lattice symbol omitted, then the International point group symbol is obtained. We list a few examples just to emphasize how easy this is:

| Space group | Point group |
|---|---|
| $Cc(C_s^4)$ | $m(C_s)$ |
| $P2_1/c(C_{2h}^5)$ | $2/m(C_{2h})$ |
| $I2_12_12_1(D_2^9)$ | $222(D_2)$ |
| $Pna2_1(C_{2v}^9)$ | $mm2(C_{2v})$ |
| $I4_1/acd(D_{4h}^{20})$ | $4/mmm(D_{4h})$ |
| $Fd3c(O_h^8)$ | $m3m(O_h)$ |

This procedure of obtaining the point group of the space group from the space group symbol is just the same as in our mathematical definition. Namely, if all the translations are set equal to zero the set of operations remaining is the point group. In Section 6-6 we prove that the set of operations obtained in this way is indeed a group and, in particular, it is one of the 32 crystallographic point groups.

**6-3d Diagram** Working downwards in Figs. 6-1a and 6-1b, we come to the space group diagrams. These are given for all space groups, except for the cubic ones. You will recall from the preceding chapter that the **convention** for these diagrams is to take the origin at the top-left corner, the **a**-axis towards the bottom of the page, the **b**-axis towards the right, and the **c**-axis out of the plane of the page. As can be seen, the left-hand diagram shows the effect of the symmetry operations on a general point represented by a circle. As explained in Section 1-2, circles above the **ab**-plane are marked with a plus sign and those below with a minus sign. The comma stands for the enantiomorph (mirror image) of a general point, represented by a circle without a comma. In the case where one circle lies directly above another, both are shown by dividing the circle in half by a vertical line as in Fig. 6-1a. Also note that the diagrams are always of the conventional Bravais unit cell.

The diagram on the right locates the symmetry elements in the unit cell. Notice the symbol at the top right which denotes the m-plane or the n-plane (see Appendix 6). By comparing the diagrams in Figs. 6-1a and 6-1b, we see that very closely related space groups can have symmetry operations acting at quite different positions in the unit cell.

**6-3e Number of general equivalent positions** Notice that within the unit cell outlined in Figs. 6-1a and 6-1b there are eight circles. This number is equal to the order (the number of symmetry operations) of the point group. Thus, for the space groups that have $4/m(C_{4h})$ as their point group we may have R = 1, 4, 2, $4^3$, $\bar{1}$, $\bar{4}$, m, $\bar{4}^3$ (E, $C_4$, $C_2$, $C_4{}^3$, i, $S_4{}^3$, $\sigma_h$, $S_4$), and the values of $\tau$ that correspond to each R will depend on the particular space group. However, the conventional unit cells of the body-centered, face-centered, and base-centered Bravais lattices contain a factor 2, 4, or 2 times the number of lattice points of their primitive cells. Thus, the diagram in the International Tables for these lattices will always have a factor of 2, 4, or 2 times the number of general equivalent positions found in the primitive unit cell. For an R-lattice referred to the hexagonal cell, there are 3 times as many general equivalent positions as are found in the rhombohedral cell. Remember this important point.

It should be noted that in any counting problem associated with the space group, such as the enumeration of the proper number of normal modes of vibration or electronic energy levels, it is usual to work with the h operations of the appropriate primitive unit cell. One can work with the multiply-primitive, conventional Bravais-lattice unit cells in counting problems as long as great care is taken to put in the centering conditions.

**6-3f Multiply-primitive cells** Figure 6-2 shows pages taken from the International Tables for two space groups that are closely related to those in Fig. 6-1, namely, space groups I4/m ($C_{4h}{}^5$) and $I4_1/a$ ($C_{4h}{}^6$). We see immediately that the point group of these space groups is 4/m ($C_{4h}$), just as in Fig. 6-l. However, the "I" in the International symbol shows that the Bravais lattice is body-centered. Correspondingly, there are 2h = 16 circles (general equivalent positions) in the conventional Bravais unit cell shown in the diagram for each of these space groups.

**6-3g Nonessential symmetry operations** From the symbol I4/m in Fig. 6-2a, we can say that the space group is symmorphic. (We shall shortly discuss another method of ascertaining this from the information given in the International Tables.) However, the diagram shows an n-glide at a height of c/4, as well as $2_1$ and $4_2$ screw axes. One might think that the presence of these operations would make the space group nonsymmorphic, but this would be incorrect. The important point to realize is that, apart from the translation operations $\{1 \mid t_n\}$ which are always understood to occur even though we do not explicitly keep mentioning them, we can completely describe the space group symmetry operations by the h essential symmetry operations of the form $\{R \mid \tau\}$. These h

Tetragonal $4/m$ $I\,4/m$ No. 87 $I4/m$ $C_{4h}^{5}$

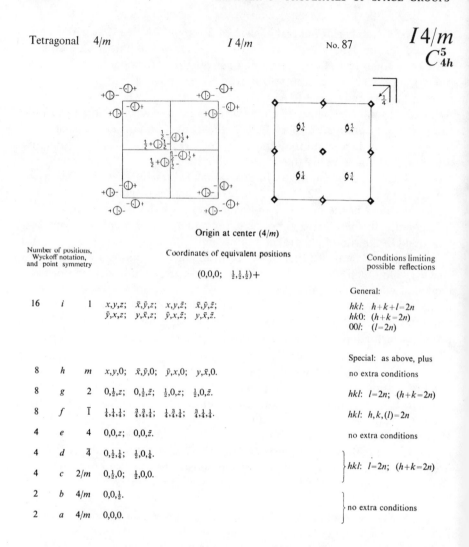

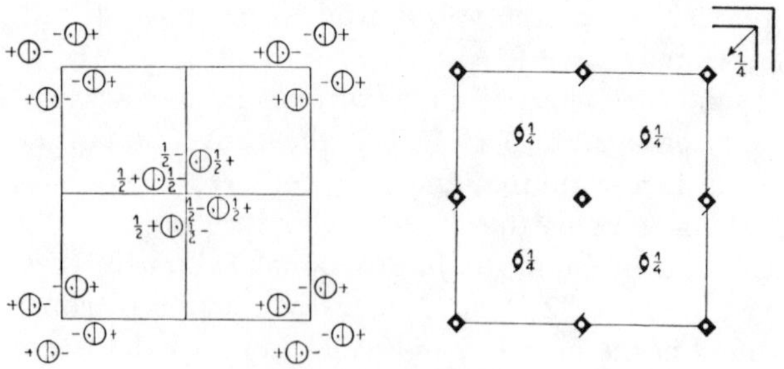

Origin at center ($4/m$)

| Number of positions, Wyckoff notation, and point symmetry | | | Coordinates of equivalent positions $(0,0,0;\ \frac{1}{2},\frac{1}{2},\frac{1}{2})+$ | Conditions limiting possible reflections |
|---|---|---|---|---|
| | | | | General: |
| 16 | *i* | 1 | $x,y,z;\ \bar{x},\bar{y},z;\ x,y,\bar{z};\ \bar{x},\bar{y},\bar{z};$ $\bar{y},x,z;\ y,\bar{x},z;\ \bar{y},x,\bar{z};\ y,\bar{x},\bar{z}.$ | $hkl$: $h+k+l=2n$; $hk0$: $(h+k=2n)$; $00l$: $(l=2n)$ |
| | | | | Special: as above, plus |
| 8 | *h* | $m$ | $x,y,0;\ \bar{x},\bar{y},0;\ \bar{y},x,0;\ y,\bar{x},0.$ | no extra conditions |
| 8 | *g* | 2 | $0,\frac{1}{2},z;\ 0,\frac{1}{2},\bar{z};\ \frac{1}{2},0,z;\ \frac{1}{2},0,\bar{z}.$ | $hkl$: $l=2n$; $(h+k=2n)$ |
| 8 | *f* | $\bar{1}$ | $\frac{1}{4},\frac{1}{4},\frac{1}{4};\ \frac{3}{4},\frac{3}{4},\frac{1}{4};\ \frac{1}{4},\frac{3}{4},\frac{1}{4};\ \frac{3}{4},\frac{1}{4},\frac{1}{4}.$ | $hkl$: $h,k,(l)=2n$ |
| 4 | *e* | 4 | $0,0,z;\ 0,0,\bar{z}.$ | no extra conditions |
| 4 | *d* | $\bar{4}$ | $0,\frac{1}{2},\frac{1}{4};\ \frac{1}{2},0,\frac{1}{4}.$ | $hkl$: $l=2n$; $(h+k=2n)$ (for *d* and *c*) |
| 4 | *c* | $2/m$ | $0,\frac{1}{2},0;\ \frac{1}{2},0,0.$ | |
| 2 | *b* | $4/m$ | $0,0,\frac{1}{2}.$ | no extra conditions (for *b* and *a*) |
| 2 | *a* | $4/m$ | $0,0,0.$ | |

**Fig. 6-2a**

operations, along with the primitive cell of the appropriate Bravais lattice, determine everything that is required about the space group. However, the h symmetry operations for a given unit cell will often imply other symmetry operations produced by the product $\{R\,|\,\boldsymbol{\tau}\}\{1\,|\,\mathbf{t}_n\}$. We do not need the example in Fig. 6-2a of I4/m ($C_{4h}{}^{5}$) to see this. The less complex space group P4/m ($C_{4h}{}^{1}$) in Fig. 6-1a shows this same effect. The

# $I4_1/a$ $C_{4h}^6$

No. 88 $I\,4_1/a$ $4/m$ Tetragonal

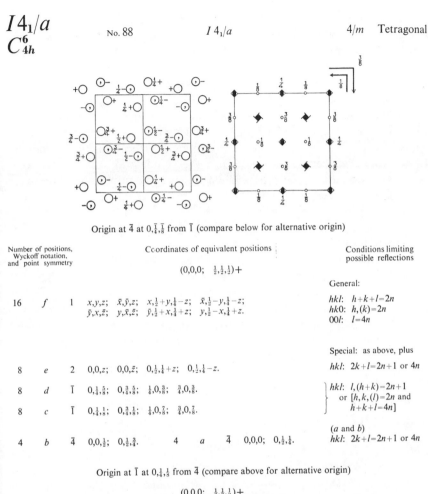

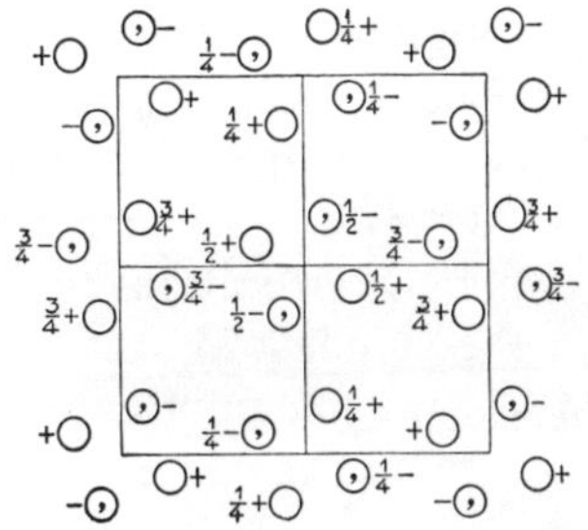

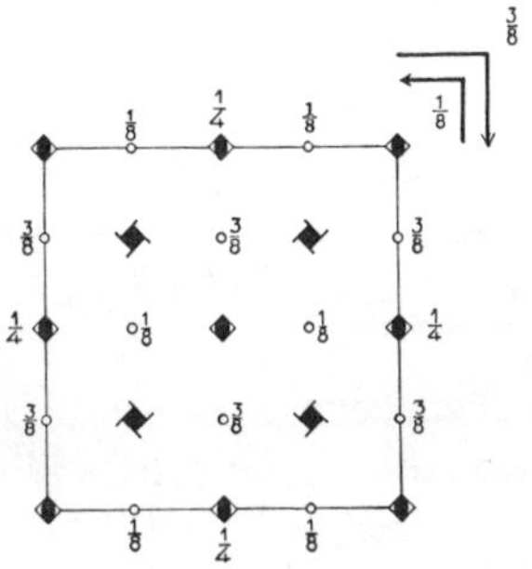


Origin at $\bar{4}$ at $0,\bar{\frac{1}{4}},\bar{\frac{1}{8}}$ from $\bar{1}$ (compare below for alternative origin)

| Number of positions, Wyckoff notation, and point symmetry | | | Coordinates of equivalent positions | Conditions limiting possible reflections |
|---|---|---|---|---|
| | | | $(0,0,0;\ \frac{1}{2},\frac{1}{2},\frac{1}{2})+$ | General: |
| 16 | $f$ | 1 | $x,y,z;\ \bar{x},\bar{y},z;\ x,\frac{1}{2}+y,\frac{1}{4}-z;\ \bar{x},\frac{1}{2}-y,\frac{1}{4}-z;$ <br> $\bar{y},x,\bar{z};\ y,\bar{x},\bar{z};\ \bar{y},\frac{1}{2}+x,\frac{1}{4}+z;\ y,\frac{1}{2}-x,\frac{1}{4}+z.$ | $hkl$: $h+k+l=2n$ <br> $hk0$: $h,(k)=2n$ <br> $00l$: $l=4n$ |
| | | | | Special: as above, plus |
| 8 | $e$ | 2 | $0,0,z;\ 0,0,\bar{z};\ 0,\frac{1}{2},\frac{1}{4}+z;\ 0,\frac{1}{2},\frac{1}{4}-z.$ | $hkl$: $2k+l=2n+1$ or $4n$ |
| 8 | $d$ | $\bar{1}$ | $0,\frac{1}{4},\frac{5}{8};\ 0,\frac{3}{4},\frac{5}{8};\ \frac{1}{4},0,\frac{3}{8};\ \frac{3}{4},0,\frac{3}{8}.$ | $hkl$: $l,(h+k)=2n+1$ or $[h,k,(l)=2n$ and $h+k+l=4n]$ |
| 8 | $c$ | $\bar{1}$ | $0,\frac{1}{4},\frac{1}{8};\ 0,\frac{3}{4},\frac{1}{8};\ \frac{1}{4},0,\frac{7}{8};\ \frac{3}{4},0,\frac{7}{8}.$ | |
| 4 | $b$ | $\bar{4}$ | $0,0,\frac{1}{2};\ 0,\frac{1}{2},\frac{3}{4}.$ 4 $a$ $\bar{4}$ $0,0,0;\ 0,\frac{1}{2},\frac{1}{4}.$ | ($a$ and $b$) <br> $hkl$: $2k+l=2n+1$ or $4n$ |

Origin at $\bar{1}$ at $0,\frac{1}{4},\frac{1}{8}$ from $\bar{4}$ (compare above for alternative origin)

| | | | | |
|---|---|---|---|---|
| | | | $(0,0,0;\ \frac{1}{2},\frac{1}{2},\frac{1}{2})+$ | |
| 16 | $f$ | 1 | $x,y,z;\ \bar{x},\frac{1}{2}-y,z;\ \frac{3}{4}-y,\frac{1}{4}+x,\frac{1}{4}+z;\ \frac{1}{4}+y,\frac{1}{4}-x,\frac{1}{4}+z;$ <br> $\bar{x},\bar{y},\bar{z};\ x,\frac{1}{2}+y,\bar{z};\ \frac{1}{4}+y,\frac{3}{4}-x,\frac{3}{4}-z;\ \frac{3}{4}-y,\frac{3}{4}+x,\frac{3}{4}-z.$ | General and special conditions as above |
| 8 | $e$ | 2 | $0,\frac{1}{4},z;\ 0,\frac{3}{4},\bar{z};\ 0,\frac{1}{4},\frac{1}{4}-z;\ 0,\frac{3}{4},\frac{3}{4}+z.$ | |
| 8 | $d$ | $\bar{1}$ | $0,0,\frac{1}{2};\ 0,\frac{1}{2},\frac{1}{2};\ \frac{1}{4},\frac{1}{4},\frac{3}{4};\ \frac{3}{4},\frac{1}{4},\frac{3}{4}.$ | |
| 8 | $c$ | $\bar{1}$ | $0,0,0;\ 0,\frac{1}{2},0;\ \frac{1}{4},\frac{1}{4},\frac{1}{4};\ \frac{3}{4},\frac{1}{4},\frac{1}{4}.$ | |
| 4 | $b$ | $\bar{4}$ | $0,\frac{1}{4},\frac{5}{8};\ 0,\frac{3}{4},\frac{3}{8}.$ 4 $a$ $\bar{4}$ $0,\frac{1}{4},\frac{1}{8};\ 0,\frac{3}{4},\frac{7}{8}.$ | |

**Fig. 6-2b**

eight symmetry operations of the form $\{R\,|\,\mathbf{0}\}$, where R = the eight point operations of the point group $4/m(C_{4h})$, completely describe the space group. However, these operations also imply 2-fold axes through (1/2, 0, 0) and (0, 1/2, 0). There is a difference of interest, with respect to symmetry operations, between crystallographers and other workers in the solid state field. Crystallographers usually want to know every symmetry operation of the space group since this helps them to understand the relationship among the atoms. Other solid state scientists usually want to know the smallest number of symmetry operations that completely describe the space group, and also the simplest kinds of operations. Actually, since the lattice type and list of general equivalent positions are all that are required to specify the space group exactly, everything else is redundant information, although nevertheless very useful.

**6–3h Origin** In Figs. 6-1 and 6-2 one can see that just below the diagrams there is a statement that describes the position of the origin used to describe the coordinates of the various equivalent positions. The site symmetry of the origin which we shall discuss below is also given in parentheses. In symmorphic space groups, the origin is usually taken at a point having site symmetry equal to that of the point group of the space group. This can readily be seen for the space groups P4/m and I4/m. For nonsymmorphic space groups, however, the origin is often picked at the site that has the highest site symmetry. If there is a site that has a center of inversion, then the origin is often placed there. For the space groups P4/n and $I4_1/a$ we can see that the coordinates are given with respect to two different origins. It is important to realize that the choice of origin is merely a matter of convenience and can be chosen anywhere within the unit cell.

**6–3i Conditions limiting possible reflections** On the right-hand side of each page in the International Tables a list of conditions that limit the possible X-ray reflections are given. These conditions are of great interest to crystallographers, since they help in the determination of the space group from the X-ray diffraction pattern. They are also relevant in lattice-potential calculations of electronic band structures. However, we shall not discuss this information further.

**6–3j Number of positions, Wyckoff notation, point symmetry and coordinates of equivalent positions** We now discuss the rest of the data for each space group. The information given under these four headings is very closely related so we include it in one subsection. Each type of possible site is given a letter, starting with "a" for a site of the highest site symmetry (note, several sites can have equally high site symmetry), and sequentially going through the alphabet until the lowest site symmetry $1(C_1)$ is reached (that of a general position). The letters associated with the sites are called the **Wyckoff notation** and are normally listed down the page in reverse order. The earlier example of calcite given in Section 6-2 shows how crystallographers usually make use of the Wyckoff notation in displaying the site information for a structure.

Along with the Wyckoff symbol is a number which describes the **number of symmetry-related positions** that the particular site has in each space group. In the space group P4/m ($C_{4h}^1$), shown in Fig. 6-1a, there is only one possible position for each of the sites that are labelled a, b, c, and d; there are two possible positions for sites labelled e, f, g, and h; four for i, j, and k; and eight possible positions for sites that are labelled *l*.

For each type of site, the symmetry operations of the space group $\{R \mid \tau\}$ will transform the various coordinates among themselves. As can be seen, all of these coordinates are explicitly written out for each type of site. Thus, for P4/m, for example, the site 8*l*, has eight coordinates that describe the eight general equivalent positions in the unit cell of this space group. These eight positions are, of course, related to one another by the symmetry operations $\{R \mid \tau\}$ of the space group, as you should check for yourself. Under all these symmetry operations, the positions described as 1a, 1b, 1c, and 1d each transform into themselves. For the 2e site there are two points that transform between each other, and so on with the other sites.

Therefore, the **site symmetry** for each position is the point symmetry of the crystal when viewed from that particular position; in other words, with the particular position taken as an origin. It tells us under which operations the crystal will transform into an equivalent position while still keeping this origin fixed. This set of point symmetry operations always forms one of the 32 crystallographic point groups. These are listed, using the International notation, in the column labelled point symmetry.

Consider again the symmorphic space group P4/m($C_{4h}^1$) in Fig. 6-1a. There are four different positions, 1a, 1b, 1c, and 1d, having site symmetry 4/m($C_{4h}$). By looking at the coordinates and the diagram, it can be seen that these positions are on 4-fold axes at height 0 or c/2, coincident with the mirror planes. Any other site that is at a height of 0 or c/2 will at least have the mirror symmetry and sites 2e, 2f, 4j, and 4k show this. Similarly, we can see that the site symmetry of positions 2g and 2h is 4($C_4$) because the equivalent positions are on the various 4-fold axes, but above or below the mirror planes. The site symmetry of a general position is, of necessity, $1(C_1)$, since by definition it does not lie on any symmetry element. Atoms that are situated at points other than those that have $1(C_1)$ symmetry are said to be at **special positions**.

Remember that the site symmetry is a point group with respect to the particular site that is held fixed. In nonsymmorphic space groups, operations with nonzero $\tau$ are omitted when determining site symmetry. For instance, while the position (0,0,0) or (0,0,1/2) in the space group P4/m has site symmetry 4/m ($C_{4h}$), in the nonsymmorphic space group P4/n this same position only has site symmetry $\bar{4}(S_4)$.

For the multiply-primitive unit cells used for the centered I, F, C (A or B) Bravais lattices, there are, respectively, 2, 4, and 2 times as many positions listed as there are in the primitive unit cell of each of these lattices. In I4/m, for example, the "coordinates of equivalent points" are obtained by taking the coordinates as listed, as well as by adding to each (1/2, 1/2, 1/2). This operation is indicated on the page in a shorthand fashion by "(0, 0, 0; 1/2, 1/2, 1/2) +," which is precisely the centering condition for a body-centered lattice. For a space group with an F-Bravais space lattice, the expression is "(0, 0, 0; 0, 1/2, 1/2; 1/2, 0, 1/2; 1/2, 1/2, 0) +," with a similar meaning. For a C-centered lattice, "(0, 0, 0; 1/2, 1/2, 0) +," appears. This enables fewer coordinates to be written out explicitly on the page.

Note that for a crystal to belong to a specific space group it is not necessary for the atoms to be at all the different positions, a, b, .... For example, a crystal may belong to space group P4/m ($C_{4h}^1$) and yet have atoms only on the 1a and 8*l* positions. A different crystal can have the same space group and yet have atoms on all 1a, 1b, ..., 8*l* positions or just on the 8*l* positions. Another point to note is that having placed an atom at a certain site, symmetry demands symmetry-related atoms of an identical type. Thus if an oxygen atom, say, is placed at a 4k site in P4/m, then there will be necessarily 4 oxygen atoms, one at each of the coordinate positions related by the mirror symmetry. Perhaps we should stress this by saying that under all the symmetry operations of the space group, the eight positions, labelled 8*l*, transform among themselves and therefore all the eight positions must be occupied by by the same kind of atom. However, it is possible that there could be eight atoms of one kind in the 8*l* positions and eight atoms of another kind also in the 8*l* positions. The values of (x,y,z) will differ for the two sets of atoms since they cannot physically overlap one another. There may, in fact, be many sets of atoms with this same type of position. It is only possible to have more than one kind of atom in the same type of position when there is at least one freely adjustable parameter in the coordinates, i.e., a parameter not fixed by symmetry. For example, in $P4/m(C_{4h}{}^1)$ positions a–f are completely fixed by the symmetry, whereas positions g–*l* have adjustable parameters.

**6-3k How to detect a symmorphic space group** The International standard short symbol, the symbol that appears on the top right or left of the page in the International Tables, has the information necessary to determine if the space group is symmorphic or nonsymmorphic. In this symbol, if there are no screw axes or glide planes marked, then the space group is symmorphic. If any of these symbols appear, then the space group is nonsymmorphic. However, care must be taken in using this criterion since the International notation changes according to the setting chosen for the unit cell axes (see the next section). There is another simple method to detect if the space group is symmorphic. A symmorphic space group must have at least one point in the unit cell that has a site symmetry which is the same as the point group of the space group. By looking at the positions in the four space groups in Figs. 6-1 and 6-2, we immediately see that for space groups $P4/m$ ($C_{4h}{}^1$) and $I4/m$ ($C_{4h}{}^5$) there are several positions that have site symmetry 4/m. However, for space groups $P4/n$ ($C_{4h}{}^3$) and $I4_1/a$ ($C_{4h}{}^6$) there are no positions with site symmetry 4/m. Thus these latter space groups must be nonsymmorphic.

Consider primitive unit cells for the moment. In a symmorphic space group, the "number of positions" for positions that have site symmetry equal to the point group of the space group must always be one. For example, 1a, 1b, 1c, or 1d for P4/m. Clearly this is because this position must always transform into itself under all the point group and space group operations. (Remember we can always move points by a primitive lattice translation $\{1\,|\,\mathbf{t}_n\}$ and all points related by this translation we call the same or equivalent points.) For a nonsymmorphic space group, all positions must have at least two for the "number of positions" because there is no position in the unit cell that remains stationary under all the symmetry operations of the space group. Thus in P4/n we see that for the site with highest symmetry ($\bar{4}$) there are two equivalent positions. Generally, for a given set of equivalent positions, the number of equivalent positions times the order of the site-symmetry point group is equal to the order of the point group of the space group. All the statements in this paragraph clearly apply to any Bravais lattice provided you work with a primitive cell instead of the conventional multiply primitive cell. Alternatively, the above statements apply if for an I, F, or C (or A or B) Bravais lattice, the "number of positions" listed in the International tables is divided by 2, 4, or 2. This can be seen in Fig. 6-2 for space groups I4/m and $I4_1/a$.

**6-3l Various settings** This subsection is in a sense a cautionary note. The International Tables give, for each of the 230 space groups, the "standard short symbol" and "standard full symbol." However, there are other choices of axes that are occasionally used, which make the International symbol for a given space group look quite different. Fortunately, the much more arbitrary Schoenflies symbol is independent of such details. If it is also used in specifying the space group of a particular crystal, the confusion is reduced. Table 6.2.1 in the International Tables gives a list of the space group symbols when various settings of the unit cells are taken.

The possibility of different settings in monoclinic space groups has already been discussed in earlier chapters. As a reminder, the "1st setting" takes the 2-fold axis along **c**, while the "2nd setting" takes it along **b**. For example,, space group $C_{2h}{}^5$ is called, in the International notation, $P2_1/b$ in the 1st setting and $P2_1/c$ in the second setting. Crystallographers usually, but not always, use the 2nd setting.

For orthorhombic space groups the situation is a little more complicated since the **a**-, **b**-, and **c**-axes are often interchanged. For example, space group No. 41, $C_{2v}{}^{17}$ can be written, depending on the choice of axes, as: Aba2; B2cb; Cc2a; Ac2a; Bba2; C2cb. To the untrained eye these look very different. However, the reader of this book would immediately realize that with any one of these symbols we are dealing with a base-centered Bravais lattice with point group mm2. Hence all symbols refer to the orthorhombic crystal system, with axial glides in the two directions perpendicular to the 2-fold direction. This information separates this space group from most other space groups.

For tetragonal space groups, instead of using the **a**-, **b**-, and **c**-axes of a primitive cell, new axes **a+b**, **b−a**, **c** are sometimes used which effectively convert the P-unit cell to a larger C-centered cell. For example, in No. 92, $D_4{}^4$, the symbol $P4_12_12$ becomes $C4_122_1$ with this new choice of axes. Similarly, tetragonal body-centered, I-space groups become F-space groups; e.g., $D_{2d}{}^{12}$, $I\bar{4}2d$ becomes $F\bar{4}d2$. Notice the change in the order of the symbols.

This ability of the International space group symbols to change for different settings of the same unit cell is logical although at times may seem slightly confusing to a solid state scientist. At any rate, it can be seen that there is an advantage in using the Schoenflies symbol as well as the serial number of the space group along with the International space group symbol in order to make it quite clear which space group is being referred to.

**6-3m Other examples of space groups** In this section we should like to go through a few more examples of space groups and very briefly indicate the kind of information that can be gleaned from the International Tables, simply in order to emphasize the points that we have learned in this chapter. The reader should turn to the appropriate page in the International Tables as we come to each example.

Starting with the triclinic space group No. 1, $P1(C_1{}^1)$, we find that there is only one symmetry operation $\{1 \mid \mathbf{0}\}$, and so only one type of position, 1a. Therefore, all atoms in a crystal structure having this space group are at this type of position with different x,y,z. In the other triclinic space group No. 2, $P\bar{1}(C_i{}^1)$, there are two symmetry operations $\{1 \mid \mathbf{0}\}$ and $\{\bar{1} \mid \mathbf{0}\}$. This gives rise to eight special positions 1a - 1h at centers of inversion, i.e., site symmetry $\bar{1}$ ($S_2$ or $C_i$ in the Schoenflies notation). Clearly, since the special positions with the highest symmetry have the symmetry of the point group, both of these space groups are symmorphic.

For the monoclinic space groups, as in the triclinic space groups, there are so few symmetry operations, and therefore so few general positions, that writing out the symmetry operations of the space group is not difficult. It is also easy to see the relationships between the special positions and the space group symmetry operations. We shall use the 2nd setting in this discussion. Consider No.4, $P2_1(C_2{}^2)$. This space group is nonsymmorphic with point group $2(C_2)$, and since the point group has only two symmetry operations, 1 and 2[010], every position must be a general position. The two general positions are related by the $2_1$-screw operation. From the diagram we easily determine that the essential space group symmetry operations are $\{1 \mid \mathbf{0}\}$ and $\{2[010] \mid \tau(0, 1/2, 0)\}$ (or $\{E \mid \mathbf{0}\}$ and $\{C_2[010] \mid \tau(0, 1/2, 0)\}$). For the symmorphic space group No.5, $C2(C_2{}^3)$, which is base-centered, there are two essential symmetry operations. However the diagram shows the multiply-primitive conventional Bravais unit cell which contains two lattice points related by the normal centering condition (0, 0, 0; 1/2, 1/2, 0). Notice how the 2-fold symmetry operation along with the centering leads to $2_1$-screw symmetry operations. The special positions 2a and 2b have site symmetry $2(C_2)$ which is the point group of the space group, as expected for a symmorphic space group. Now consider the primitive nonsymmorphic space group No.14, $P2_1/c(C_{2h}{}^5)$. The point group of this space group is $2/m(C_{2h})$

which has four symmetry operations. From the diagram, with respect to a fixed origin taken arbitrarily at the center of the cell shown, we can determine that the space group symmetry operations are

$$\{1 \mid \mathbf{0}\},\ \{2[010] \mid \tau(0, 1/2, 1/2)\},\ \{m[010] \mid \tau(0, 1/2, 1/2)\},\ \{\bar{1} \mid \mathbf{0}\}$$

The special positions are all on the centers of inversion. It is interesting to note that the two symmetry operations involving nonsymmorphic translations written here, are not the pure glide planes or screw axes that we have defined before. They arise simply because we are insisting on specifying a fixed origin for all the symmetry operations; this amounts to an alternate way of describing the space-group symmetry. In order to have a pure screw axis or glide plane the origins must be taken at different places as shown in the space group diagram. This concept of specifying the symmetry operations, with respect to a fixed origin, is discussed at length in Section 6-5.

In the case of the orthorhombic crystal system, consider the two space groups No.16, $P222(D_2{}^1)$ and No.17, $P222_1(D_2{}^2)$. The symmorphic space group shows exactly what one would expect. The special positions are either at the intersection of the three 2-fold axes, and thus have site symmetry $222(D_2)$ or are on one of the three 2-fold axes with site symmetry $2(C_2)$. For the nonsymmorphic space group the presence of a screw axis requires that the other two 2-fold axes do not intersect. Thus, the 2a – 2d sites have site symmetry $2(C_2)$, each with two positions related to each other by the screw axis. The four symmetry operations for space group $P222_1$ can easily be determined from the diagram. Taking the origin at the top left corner of the unit cell, we can write the symmetry operations as:

$$\{1 \mid \mathbf{0}\},\ \{2[100] \mid \mathbf{0}\},\ \{2[010] \mid \tau(0, 0, 1/2)\},\ \{2[001] \mid \tau(0, 0, 1/2)\}.$$

The third symmetry operation is not a screw axis while the fourth one is.

Other examples are given in the next section where we discuss some simple crystal structures.

## 6-4 **Some Simple Crystal Structures**

In order to make more concrete the points discussed in the preceding sections, we shall now consider some examples of rather elementary crystal structures. We deliberately choose them to be cubic since this illustrates rather well the effect of having atoms on special positions. Moreover, in the International Tables no diagrams are given for the cubic space groups and yet, as we shall see, this does not make it particularly difficult to see where the symmetry elements are nor how the various space groups are interrelated. We shall deal with these crystal structures according to their space groups.

**6-4a Fm3m($O_h^5$)** Figure 6-3a shows the crystal structure of copper (Cu). The structure is very elementary with one copper atom located at each lattice point of a face-centered cubic lattice. Examination of the diagram shows that, in addition to the 3-fold axes along <111> there are mirror planes perpendicular to <100> and <110>. Thus, the space group is Fm3m($O_h^5$). The other diagrams in this figure show different ways of looking at the same crystal structure. As can be seen, even in this very simple crystal structure, different views can be used to emphasize quite different aspects of the structure, but in all of them you should be able to discern the symmetry elements of space group Fm3m($O_h^5$). Figure 6-4 shows this crystal structure again, along with other structures that have the same space group. Figure 6-5 shows the relevant page from the International Tables. For this extremely simple crystal structure the Cu atoms are located at the 4a positions. The coordinates of this position are given in Fig. 6-5 and are quite trivial since these are just the lattice points. As always, there is one lattice point, and therefore in this structure one atom, in the primitive unit cell, as has been discussed in Chapter 3 and four lattice points with four atoms in the F-unit cell as shown in Figure 6-3.

We should like to emphasize an important point about the occupation of the positions of a space group. In the case of the copper crystal structure only one type of position, 4a, is occupied by atoms. We could have another crystal structure where only the 192*l* positions are occupied. Both of these crystal structures would have the same space group Fm3m($O_h^5$) but they would look completely different. After all, the lattice is a cubic F-lattice and about each lattice point all the 48 point symmetry operations of the point group m3m($O_h$) are symmetry operations of the space group. In the case of atoms at the 192*l* positions, the atoms would be located at the 48 positions surrounding each lattice point with coordinates given by the list in Fig. 6-5. The fact that there are four lattice points in the conventional cell means that there would be $4 \times 48 = 192$ atoms. Naturally the coordinates of atoms about a lattice point transform among themselves under all the symmetry operations of the point group m3m($O_h$). Similarly, each of the various positions shown in Fig. 6-5 for this space group may or may not be occupied with different types or the same types of atoms. Complicated chemical compounds may

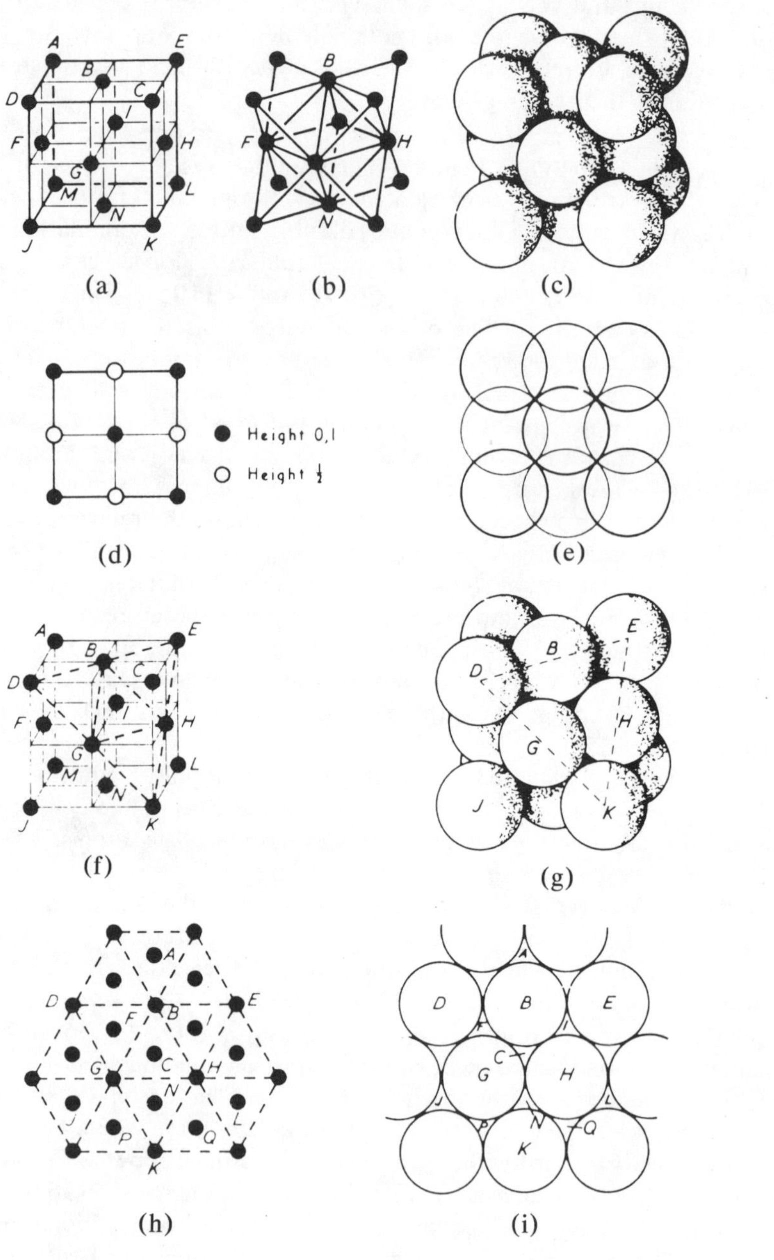


**Fig. 6-3** The crystal structure of copper viewed in different ways (after Megaw).

crystallize into a crystal structure with this space group, in which case quite a number of different types of position may be occupied.

Figure 6-4b shows the crystal structure of sodium chloride (NaCl), sometimes called the rock-salt structure. The space group is again Fm3m($O_h^5$). For this crystal structure Na atoms are located at the 4a positions and Cl atoms at the 4b positions. As can be seen in the diagram, the site symmetry of both of these positions is the full point symmetry m3m($O_h$) and therefore one may equally well take the Cl atoms at 4a positions and the Na atoms at 4b positions. In order to describe this crystal structure, one may also say that the space group is Fm3m($O_h^5$) and the basis (or lattice complex) is Na at (0,0,0) and Cl at (1/2, 1/2, 1/2). Yet another way of describing this crystal structure is in terms of a Na atom at a lattice point surrounded by six Cl atoms at the corners of an octahedron. This is consistent with the fact that an octahedron has m3m($O_h$) symmetry itself.

In Fig. 6-4c we show the crystal structure of calcium fluoride ($CaF_2$), sometimes called the fluorite structure. The space group again is Fm3m($O_h^5$) but this time it has Ca atoms at 4a positions and F atoms at the 8c positions. (Clearly, from the chemical formula, there must be twice as many positions for the F atoms as for the Ca atoms.) We may also describe this structure by saying that the space group is Fm3m($O_h^5$) with Ca at (0,0,0) and F at (1/4, 1/4, 1/4). Note that in this case the basis consists of the Ca atom at (0,0,0) and F atoms at ±(1/4, 1/4, 1/4). Here again, we may describe this structure in terms of a Ca atom at a lattice point surrounded by eight F atoms at the corners of a cube, so that around each lattice point the point symmetry is m3m($O_h$) (the symmetry of a cube).

We can find more complicated examples of structures with this space group, for example, $Na_3FeF_6$. Fe atoms are on the 4a positions, Na(1) on the 4b positions, Na(2) on the 8c positions, and Fe atoms on the 24e positions with $x \approx 0.23$. With this small amount of information you should be able to draw a diagram of the crystal structure for yourself. Note how the same types of atoms may be on different positions in the unit cell.

**6-4b Pm3m($O_h^1$)** Figure 6-4d shows the crystal structure of cesium chloride (CsCl). The space group is Pm3m($O_h^1$) which is a simple cubic symmorphic space group. The relevant page of the International Tables is shown in Fig. 6-6. The Cs atom is at position 1a and the Cl atom is at 1b. Clearly from the equality of site symmetry these two

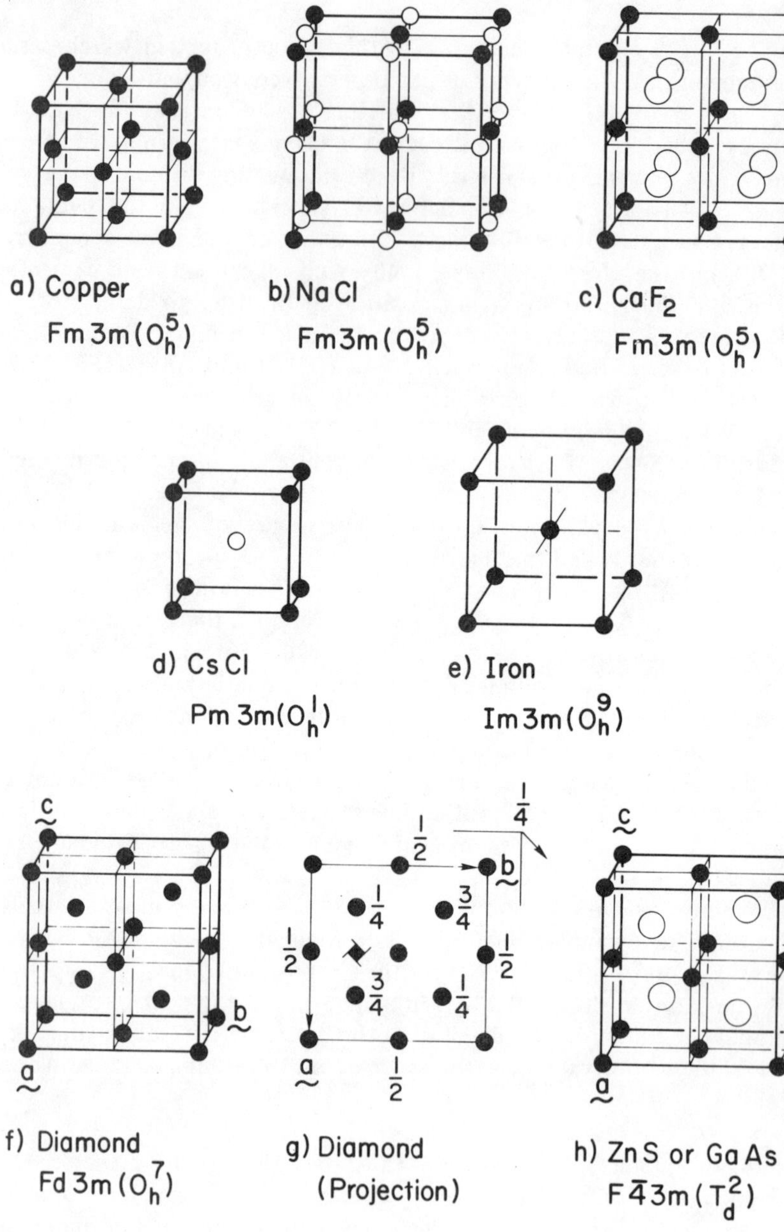


**Fig. 6-4** Various cubic crystal structures.

positions can be interchanged. Another way of describing this crystal structure is to say that the space group is $Pm3m(O_h{}^1)$ and the basis is Ca at (0,0,0) and Cl at (1/2, 1/2, 1/2). Otherwise, we may describe this structure by saying that at each lattice point of a cubic P-lattice there is a Cs atom surrounded by eight Cl atoms at the corners of a cube. Thus, surrounding each lattice point, one has an object with point symmetry $m3m(O_h)$, immediately leading to space group $Pm3m(O_h{}^1)$. It is a very common mistake to refer to this structure as body-centered. Remember that a body-centered structure means that if an atom is placed at (0,0,0), the same type of atom is at (1/2, 1/2, 1/2). In CsCl we have different atoms at each site and hence the unit cell is primitive.

In the next chapter we shall consider the perovskite crystal structure . A number of compounds with the formula $ABO_3$ have this crystal structure which in its ideal form belongs to space group $Pm3m(O_h{}^1)$. The A atom is at the 1a position, the B atom at the 1b position, and the O atoms at the 3c positions. Thus, one may see with the aid of a diagram, that surrounding each B atom are six O atoms at the corners of an octahedron and surrounding each A atom are twelve O atoms, each at the mid-point of a cube edge. The compound $WO_3$ also has the perovskite structure and space group $Pm3m(O_h{}^1)$, with the W atom at the 1b position and with the O atoms again at 3c positions.

**6-4c $Im3m(O_h{}^9)$** Figure 6-4e shows the structure of iron (Fe). As can be seen, the Fe atoms are located at the lattice points of a cubic I-lattice and because the symmetry at a lattice point of the cubic crystal system is $m3m(O_h)$, the space group must be $Im3m(O_h{}^9)$. Without even looking at the International Tables we know that the Fe atoms are located at 2a positions with site symmetry $m3m(O_h)$.

**6-4d $Fd3m(O_h{}^7)$** Figure 6-4f shows the diamond structure, which serves also for silicon (Si) and germanium (Ge), and Fig. 6-4g gives a projection with some space group elements indicated. The space group is $Fd3m(O_h{}^7)$, which means that the lattice is all-face-centered, and is nonsymmorphic and has point group $m3m(O_h)$. Figure 6-7 shows the relevant page of the International Tables. The atoms are at the 8a positions, with point symmetry $\bar{4}3m(T_d)$, which, you will note, is of lower symmetry than the point group of the space group, as indeed it must always be for nonsymmorphic space groups. From the full space group symbol, we see that there is a $4_1$ symmetry element parallel to the z-axis at $x = 1/2$ and $y = 1/4$ and this is shown in Fig. 6-4g. This symmetry

# $Fm3m$ $O_h^5$

No. 225 $F\,4/m\,\bar{3}\,2/m$ $m\,3\,m$ Cubic

Origin at center ($m3m$)

| Number of positions, Wyckoff notation, and point symmetry | | | Co-ordinates of equivalent positions<br>$(0,0,0;\ 0,\frac{1}{2},\frac{1}{2};\ \frac{1}{2},0,\frac{1}{2};\ \frac{1}{2},\frac{1}{2},0)+$ | Conditions limiting possible reflections |
|---|---|---|---|---|
| | | | | General: |
| 192 | $l$ | 1 | $x,y,z;\ z,x,y;\ y,z,x;\ x,z,y;\ y,x,z;\ z,y,x;$<br>$x,\bar{y},\bar{z};\ z,\bar{x},\bar{y};\ y,\bar{z},\bar{x};\ x,\bar{z},\bar{y};\ y,\bar{x},\bar{z};\ z,\bar{y},\bar{x};$<br>$\bar{x},y,\bar{z};\ \bar{z},x,\bar{y};\ \bar{y},z,\bar{x};\ \bar{x},z,\bar{y};\ \bar{y},x,\bar{z};\ \bar{z},y,\bar{x};$<br>$\bar{x},\bar{y},z;\ \bar{z},\bar{x},y;\ \bar{y},\bar{z},x;\ \bar{x},\bar{z},y;\ \bar{y},\bar{x},z;\ \bar{z},\bar{y},x;$<br>$\bar{x},\bar{y},\bar{z};\ \bar{z},\bar{x},\bar{y};\ \bar{y},\bar{z},\bar{x};\ \bar{x},\bar{z},\bar{y};\ \bar{y},\bar{x},\bar{z};\ \bar{z},\bar{y},\bar{x};$<br>$\bar{x},y,z;\ \bar{z},x,y;\ \bar{y},z,x;\ \bar{x},z,y;\ \bar{y},x,z;\ \bar{z},y,x;$<br>$x,\bar{y},z;\ z,\bar{x},y;\ y,\bar{z},x;\ x,\bar{z},y;\ y,\bar{x},z;\ z,\bar{y},x;$<br>$x,y,\bar{z};\ z,x,\bar{y};\ y,z,\bar{x};\ x,z,\bar{y};\ y,x,\bar{z};\ z,y,\bar{x}.$ | $hkl$: $h+k,k+l,(l+h)=2n$<br>$hhl$: $(l+h=2n)$; ↻<br>$0kl$: $(k,l=2n)$; ↻ |
| | | | | Special: as above, plus |
| 96 | $k$ | $m$ | $x,x,z;\ z,x,x;\ x,z,x;\ \bar{x},\bar{x},\bar{z};\ \bar{z},\bar{x},\bar{x};\ \bar{x},\bar{z},\bar{x};$<br>$x,\bar{x},\bar{z};\ z,\bar{x},\bar{x};\ x,\bar{z},\bar{x};\ \bar{x},x,z;\ \bar{z},x,x;\ \bar{x},z,x;$<br>$\bar{x},x,\bar{z};\ \bar{z},x,\bar{x};\ \bar{x},z,\bar{x};\ x,\bar{x},z;\ z,\bar{x},x;\ x,\bar{z},x;$<br>$\bar{x},\bar{x},z;\ \bar{z},\bar{x},x;\ \bar{x},\bar{z},x;\ x,x,\bar{z};\ z,x,\bar{x};\ x,z,\bar{x}.$ | no extra conditions (96$k$ to 48$h$) |
| 96 | $j$ | $m$ | $0,y,z;\ z,0,y;\ y,z,0;\ 0,z,y;\ y,0,z;\ z,y,0;$<br>$0,\bar{y},\bar{z};\ \bar{z},0,\bar{y};\ \bar{y},\bar{z},0;\ 0,\bar{z},\bar{y};\ \bar{y},0,\bar{z};\ \bar{z},\bar{y},0;$<br>$0,y,\bar{z};\ \bar{z},0,y;\ y,\bar{z},0;\ 0,\bar{z},y;\ y,0,\bar{z};\ \bar{z},y,0;$<br>$0,\bar{y},z;\ z,0,\bar{y};\ \bar{y},z,0;\ 0,z,\bar{y};\ \bar{y},0,z;\ z,\bar{y},0.$ | |
| 48 | $i$ | $mm$ | $\frac{1}{2},x,x;\ x,\frac{1}{2},x;\ x,x,\frac{1}{2};\ \frac{1}{2},x,\bar{x};\ \bar{x},\frac{1}{2},x;\ x,\bar{x},\frac{1}{2};$<br>$\frac{1}{2},\bar{x},\bar{x};\ \bar{x},\frac{1}{2},\bar{x};\ \bar{x},\bar{x},\frac{1}{2};\ \frac{1}{2},\bar{x},x;\ x,\frac{1}{2},\bar{x};\ \bar{x},x,\frac{1}{2}.$ | |
| 48 | $h$ | $mm$ | $0,x,x;\ x,0,x;\ x,x,0;\ 0,x,\bar{x};\ \bar{x},0,x;\ x,\bar{x},0;$<br>$0,\bar{x},\bar{x};\ \bar{x},0,\bar{x};\ \bar{x},\bar{x},0;\ 0,\bar{x},x;\ x,0,\bar{x};\ \bar{x},x,0.$ | |
| 48 | $g$ | $mm$ | $x,\frac{1}{4},\frac{1}{4};\ \frac{1}{4},x,\frac{1}{4};\ \frac{1}{4},\frac{1}{4},x;\ x,\frac{1}{4},\frac{3}{4};\ \frac{3}{4},x,\frac{1}{4};\ \frac{1}{4},\frac{3}{4},x;$<br>$\bar{x},\frac{1}{4},\frac{1}{4};\ \frac{1}{4},\bar{x},\frac{1}{4};\ \frac{1}{4},\frac{1}{4},\bar{x};\ \bar{x},\frac{1}{4},\frac{3}{4};\ \frac{3}{4},\bar{x},\frac{1}{4};\ \frac{1}{4},\frac{3}{4},\bar{x}.$ | $hkl$: $h,(k,l)=2n$ |
| 32 | $f$ | $3m$ | $x,x,x;\ x,\bar{x},\bar{x};\ \bar{x},x,\bar{x};\ \bar{x},\bar{x},x;$<br>$\bar{x},\bar{x},\bar{x};\ \bar{x},x,x;\ x,\bar{x},x;\ x,x,\bar{x}.$ | no extra conditions (32$f$, 24$e$) |
| 24 | $e$ | $4mm$ | $x,0,0;\ 0,x,0;\ 0,0,x;\ \bar{x},0,0;\ 0,\bar{x},0;\ 0,0,\bar{x}.$ | |
| 24 | $d$ | $mmm$ | $0,\frac{1}{4},\frac{1}{4};\ \frac{1}{4},0,\frac{1}{4};\ \frac{1}{4},\frac{1}{4},0;\ 0,\frac{1}{4},\frac{3}{4};\ \frac{3}{4},0,\frac{1}{4};\ \frac{1}{4},\frac{3}{4},0.$ | $hkl$: $h,(k,l)=2n$ (24$d$, 8$c$) |
| 8 | $c$ | $\bar{4}3m$ | $\frac{1}{4},\frac{1}{4},\frac{1}{4};\ \frac{3}{4},\frac{3}{4},\frac{3}{4}.$ | |
| 4 | $b$ | $m3m$ | $\frac{1}{2},\frac{1}{2},\frac{1}{2}.$ | no extra conditions (4$b$, 4$a$) |
| 4 | $a$ | $m3m$ | $0,0,0.$ | |

**Fig. 6-5**

operation takes the atom at (1/4, 1/4, 1/4) to the atom at the face-center (1/2, 0, 1/2). Similarly, the diamond glide plane perpendicular to this $4_1$-axis is located at z = 1/4. The atom at (1/4, 1/4, 1/4) lies on this glide plane and it is reflected into itself and subsequently translated

# $Pm3m$ No. 221 $P\,4/m\,\bar{3}\,2/m$ $m\,3\,m$ Cubic

## $O_h^1$

Origin at center ($m3m$)

| Number of positions, Wyckoff notation, and point symmetry | | | Coordinates of equivalent positions | | | | | |
|---|---|---|---|---|---|---|---|---|
| 48 | $n$ | 1 | $x,y,z$; | $z,x,y$; | $y,z,x$; | $x,z,y$; | $y,x,z$; | $z,y,x$; |
| | | | $x,\bar{y},\bar{z}$; | $z,\bar{x},\bar{y}$; | $y,\bar{z},\bar{x}$; | $x,\bar{z},\bar{y}$; | $y,\bar{x},\bar{z}$; | $z,\bar{y},\bar{x}$; |
| | | | $\bar{x},y,\bar{z}$; | $\bar{z},x,\bar{y}$; | $\bar{y},z,\bar{x}$; | $\bar{x},z,\bar{y}$; | $\bar{y},x,\bar{z}$; | $\bar{z},y,\bar{x}$; |
| | | | $\bar{x},\bar{y},z$; | $\bar{z},\bar{x},y$; | $\bar{y},\bar{z},x$; | $\bar{x},\bar{z},y$; | $\bar{y},\bar{x},z$; | $\bar{z},\bar{y},x$; |
| | | | $\bar{x},\bar{y},\bar{z}$; | $\bar{z},\bar{x},\bar{y}$; | $\bar{y},\bar{z},\bar{x}$; | $\bar{x},\bar{z},\bar{y}$; | $\bar{y},\bar{x},\bar{z}$; | $\bar{z},\bar{y},\bar{x}$; |
| | | | $\bar{x},y,z$; | $\bar{z},x,y$; | $\bar{y},z,x$; | $\bar{x},z,y$; | $\bar{y},x,z$; | $\bar{z},y,x$; |
| | | | $x,\bar{y},z$; | $z,\bar{x},y$; | $y,\bar{z},x$; | $x,\bar{z},y$; | $y,\bar{x},z$; | $z,\bar{y},x$; |
| | | | $x,y,\bar{z}$; | $z,x,\bar{y}$; | $y,z,\bar{x}$; | $x,z,\bar{y}$; | $y,x,\bar{z}$; | $z,y,\bar{x}$. |
| 24 | $m$ | $m$ | $x,x,z$; | $z,x,x$; | $x,z,x$; | $\bar{x},\bar{x},\bar{z}$; | $\bar{z},\bar{x},\bar{x}$; | $\bar{x},\bar{z},\bar{x}$; |
| | | | $x,\bar{x},\bar{z}$; | $z,\bar{x},\bar{x}$; | $x,\bar{z},\bar{x}$; | $\bar{x},x,z$; | $\bar{z},x,x$; | $\bar{x},z,x$; |
| | | | $\bar{x},x,\bar{z}$; | $\bar{z},x,\bar{x}$; | $\bar{x},z,\bar{x}$; | $x,\bar{x},z$; | $z,\bar{x},x$; | $x,\bar{z},x$; |
| | | | $\bar{x},\bar{x},z$; | $\bar{z},\bar{x},x$; | $\bar{x},\bar{z},x$; | $x,x,\bar{z}$; | $z,x,\bar{x}$; | $x,z,\bar{x}$. |
| 24 | $l$ | $m$ | $\frac{1}{2},y,z$; | $z,\frac{1}{2},y$; | $y,z,\frac{1}{2}$; | $\frac{1}{2},z,y$; | $y,\frac{1}{2},z$; | $z,y,\frac{1}{2}$; |
| | | | $\frac{1}{2},\bar{y},\bar{z}$; | $\bar{z},\frac{1}{2},\bar{y}$; | $\bar{y},\bar{z},\frac{1}{2}$; | $\frac{1}{2},\bar{z},\bar{y}$; | $\bar{y},\frac{1}{2},\bar{z}$; | $\bar{z},\bar{y},\frac{1}{2}$; |
| | | | $\frac{1}{2},y,\bar{z}$; | $\bar{z},\frac{1}{2},y$; | $y,\bar{z},\frac{1}{2}$; | $\frac{1}{2},\bar{z},y$; | $y,\frac{1}{2},\bar{z}$; | $\bar{z},y,\frac{1}{2}$; |
| | | | $\frac{1}{2},\bar{y},z$; | $z,\frac{1}{2},\bar{y}$; | $\bar{y},z,\frac{1}{2}$; | $\frac{1}{2},z,\bar{y}$; | $\bar{y},\frac{1}{2},z$; | $z,\bar{y},\frac{1}{2}$. |
| 24 | $k$ | $m$ | $0,y,z$; | $z,0,y$; | $y,z,0$; | $0,z,y$; | $y,0,z$; | $z,y,0$; |
| | | | $0,\bar{y},\bar{z}$; | $\bar{z},0,\bar{y}$; | $\bar{y},\bar{z},0$; | $0,\bar{z},\bar{y}$; | $\bar{y},0,\bar{z}$; | $\bar{z},\bar{y},0$; |
| | | | $0,y,\bar{z}$; | $\bar{z},0,y$; | $y,\bar{z},0$; | $0,\bar{z},y$; | $y,0,\bar{z}$; | $\bar{z},y,0$; |
| | | | $0,\bar{y},z$; | $z,0,\bar{y}$; | $\bar{y},z,0$; | $0,z,\bar{y}$; | $\bar{y},0,z$; | $z,\bar{y},0$. |
| 12 | $j$ | $mm$ | $\frac{1}{2},x,x$; | $x,\frac{1}{2},x$; | $x,x,\frac{1}{2}$; | $\frac{1}{2},x,\bar{x}$; | $\bar{x},\frac{1}{2},x$; | $x,\bar{x},\frac{1}{2}$; |
| | | | $\frac{1}{2},\bar{x},\bar{x}$; | $\bar{x},\frac{1}{2},\bar{x}$; | $\bar{x},\bar{x},\frac{1}{2}$; | $\frac{1}{2},\bar{x},x$; | $x,\frac{1}{2},\bar{x}$; | $\bar{x},x,\frac{1}{2}$. |
| 12 | $i$ | $mm$ | $0,x,x$; | $x,0,x$; | $x,x,0$; | $0,x,\bar{x}$; | $\bar{x},0,x$; | $x,\bar{x},0$; |
| | | | $0,\bar{x},\bar{x}$; | $\bar{x},0,\bar{x}$; | $\bar{x},\bar{x},0$; | $0,\bar{x},x$; | $x,0,\bar{x}$; | $\bar{x},x,0$. |
| 12 | $h$ | $mm$ | $x,\frac{1}{2},0$; | $0,x,\frac{1}{2}$; | $\frac{1}{2},0,x$; | $x,0,\frac{1}{2}$; | $\frac{1}{2},x,0$; | $0,\frac{1}{2},x$; |
| | | | $\bar{x},\frac{1}{2},0$; | $0,\bar{x},\frac{1}{2}$; | $\frac{1}{2},0,\bar{x}$; | $\bar{x},0,\frac{1}{2}$; | $\frac{1}{2},\bar{x},0$; | $0,\frac{1}{2},\bar{x}$. |
| 8 | $g$ | $3m$ | $x,x,x$; | $x,\bar{x},\bar{x}$; | $\bar{x},x,\bar{x}$; | $\bar{x},\bar{x},x$; | | |
| | | | $\bar{x},\bar{x},\bar{x}$; | $\bar{x},x,x$; | $x,\bar{x},x$; | $x,x,\bar{x}$. | | |
| 6 | $f$ | $4mm$ | $x,\frac{1}{2},\frac{1}{2}$; | $\frac{1}{2},x,\frac{1}{2}$; | $\frac{1}{2},\frac{1}{2},x$; | $\bar{x},\frac{1}{2},\frac{1}{2}$; | $\frac{1}{2},\bar{x},\frac{1}{2}$; | $\frac{1}{2},\frac{1}{2},\bar{x}$. |
| 6 | $e$ | $4mm$ | $x,0,0$; | $0,x,0$; | $0,0,x$; | $\bar{x},0,0$; | $0,\bar{x},0$; | $0,0,\bar{x}$. |
| 3 | $d$ | $4/mmm$ | $\frac{1}{2},0,0$; | $0,\frac{1}{2},0$; | $0,0,\frac{1}{2}$. | | | |
| 3 | $c$ | $4/mmm$ | $0,\frac{1}{2},\frac{1}{2}$; | $\frac{1}{2},0,\frac{1}{2}$; | $\frac{1}{2},\frac{1}{2},0$. | | | |
| 1 | $b$ | $m3m$ | $\frac{1}{2},\frac{1}{2},\frac{1}{2}$. | | | | | |
| 1 | $a$ | $m3m$ | 0.0,0. | | | | | |

Conditions limiting possible reflections

General:

$hkl$:, $hhl$:, $0kl$: No conditions

Special:

No conditions

**Fig. 6-6**

through $\tau(1/4,\ 1/4,\ -1/4)$ to the atom at $(1/2,\ 1/2,\ 0)$. The atoms do not lie on a center of inversion, i.e., a center of inversion is not a symme-

# *Fd*3*m* No. 227 $F\,4_1/d\,\bar{3}\,2/m$ $m\,3\,m$ Cubic

## $O_h^7$

Origin at $\bar{4}3m$, at $\bar{\frac18},\bar{\frac18},\bar{\frac18}$ from centre ($\bar{3}m$) (compare next page for alternative origin)

| Number of positions, Wyckoff notation, and point symmetry | | | Co-ordinates of equivalent positions | Conditions limiting possible reflections |
|---|---|---|---|---|
| | | | $(0,0,0;\ 0,\frac12,\frac12;\ \frac12,0,\frac12;\ \frac12,\frac12,0)+$ | |
| | | | | General: |
| 192 | *i* | 1 | $x,y,z;\ z,x,y;\ y,z,x;\ x,z,y;\ y,x,z;\ z,y,x;$ | *hkl*: $h+k,k+l,(l+h)=2n$ |
| | | | $x,\bar{y},\bar{z};\ z,\bar{x},\bar{y};\ y,\bar{z},\bar{x};\ x,\bar{z},\bar{y};\ y,\bar{x},\bar{z};\ z,\bar{y},\bar{x};$ | *hhl*: $(l+h=2n)$; ↻ |
| | | | $\bar{x},y,\bar{z};\ \bar{z},x,\bar{y};\ \bar{y},z,\bar{x};\ \bar{x},z,\bar{y};\ \bar{y},x,\bar{z};\ \bar{z},y,\bar{x};$ | $0kl$: $(k,l=2n)$; $k+l=4n$ |
| | | | $\bar{x},\bar{y},z;\ \bar{z},\bar{x},y;\ \bar{y},\bar{z},x;\ \bar{x},\bar{z},y;\ \bar{y},\bar{x},z;\ \bar{z},\bar{y},x;$ | ↻ |
| | | | $\frac14-x,\frac14-y,\frac14-z;\ \frac14-z,\frac14-x,\frac14-y;\ \frac14-y,\frac14-z,\frac14-x;$ | |
| | | | $\frac14-x,\frac14+y,\frac14+z;\ \frac14-z,\frac14+x,\frac14+y;\ \frac14-y,\frac14+z,\frac14+x;$ | |
| | | | $\frac14+x,\frac14-y,\frac14+z;\ \frac14+z,\frac14-x,\frac14+y;\ \frac14+y,\frac14-z,\frac14+x;$ | |
| | | | $\frac14+x,\frac14+y,\frac14-z;\ \frac14+z,\frac14+x,\frac14-y;\ \frac14+y,\frac14+z,\frac14-x;$ | |
| | | | $\frac14-x,\frac14-z,\frac14-y;\ \frac14-y,\frac14-x,\frac14-z;\ \frac14-z,\frac14-y,\frac14-x;$ | |
| | | | $\frac14-x,\frac14+z,\frac14+y;\ \frac14-y,\frac14+x,\frac14+z;\ \frac14-z,\frac14+y,\frac14+x;$ | |
| | | | $\frac14+x,\frac14-z,\frac14+y;\ \frac14+y,\frac14-x,\frac14+z;\ \frac14+z,\frac14-y,\frac14+x;$ | |
| | | | $\frac14+x,\frac14+z,\frac14-y;\ \frac14+y,\frac14+x,\frac14-z;\ \frac14+z,\frac14+y,\frac14-x.$ | |
| | | | | Special: as above, plus |
| 96 | *h* | 2 | $\frac18,x,\frac14-x;\ \frac18,\frac14-x,x;\ \frac38,x,\frac14+x;\ \frac38,\frac14+x,x;$ | |
| | | | $\frac14-x,\frac18,x;\ x,\frac18,\frac14-x;\ \frac14+x,\frac38,x;\ x,\frac38,\frac14+x;$ | |
| | | | $x,\frac14-x,\frac18;\ \frac14-x,x,\frac18;\ x,\frac14+x,\frac38;\ \frac14+x,x,\frac38;$ | |
| | | | $\frac18,\bar{x},\frac34+x;\ \frac18,\frac34+x,\bar{x};\ \frac38,\bar{x},\frac34-x;\ \frac38,\frac34-x,\bar{x};$ | |
| | | | $\frac34+x,\frac18,\bar{x};\ \bar{x},\frac18,\frac34+x;\ \frac34-x,\frac38,\bar{x};\ \bar{x},\frac38,\frac34-x;$ | |
| | | | $\bar{x},\frac34+x,\frac18;\ \frac34+x,\bar{x},\frac18;\ \bar{x},\frac34-x,\frac38;\ \frac34-x,\bar{x},\frac38.$ | |
| | | | | no extra conditions (96 *h* and 96 *g*) |
| 96 | *g* | *m* | $x,x,z;\ z,x,x;\ x,z,x;\ \bar{x},x,\bar{z};\ \bar{z},x,\bar{x};\ \bar{x},z,\bar{x};$ | |
| | | | $x,\bar{x},\bar{z};\ z,\bar{x},\bar{x};\ x,\bar{z},\bar{x};\ \bar{x},\bar{x},z;\ \bar{z},\bar{x},x;\ \bar{x},\bar{z},x;$ | |
| | | | $\frac14-x,\frac14-x,\frac14-z;\ \frac14-z,\frac14-x,\frac14-x;\ \frac14-x,\frac14-z,\frac14-x;$ | |
| | | | $\frac14-x,\frac14+x,\frac14+z;\ \frac14-z,\frac14+x,\frac14+x;\ \frac14-x,\frac14+z,\frac14+x;$ | |
| | | | $\frac14+x,\frac14-x,\frac14+z;\ \frac14+z,\frac14-x,\frac14+x;\ \frac14+x,\frac14-z,\frac14+x;$ | |
| | | | $\frac14+x,\frac14+x,\frac14-z;\ \frac14+z,\frac14+x,\frac14-x;\ \frac14+x,\frac14+z,\frac14-x.$ | |
| 48 | *f* | *mm* | $x,0,0;\ \bar{x},0,0;\ \frac14+x,\frac14,\frac14;\ \frac14-x,\frac14,\frac14;$ | *hkl*: $h+k+l=2n+1$ or $4n$ |
| | | | $0,x,0;\ 0,\bar{x},0;\ \frac14,\frac14+x,\frac14;\ \frac14,\frac14-x,\frac14;$ | |
| | | | $0,0,x;\ 0,0,\bar{x};\ \frac14,\frac14,\frac14+x;\ \frac14,\frac14,\frac14-x.$ | |
| 32 | *e* | 3*m* | $x,x,x;\ \frac14-x,\frac14-x,\frac14-x;$ | no extra conditions |
| | | | $x,\bar{x},\bar{x};\ \frac14-x,\frac14+x,\frac14+x;$ | |
| | | | $\bar{x},x,\bar{x};\ \frac14+x,\frac14-x,\frac14+x;$ | |
| | | | $\bar{x},\bar{x},x;\ \frac14+x,\frac14+x,\frac14-x.$ | |
| 16 | *d* | $\bar{3}m$ | $\frac58,\frac58,\frac58;\ \frac58,\frac78,\frac78;\ \frac78,\frac58,\frac78;\ \frac78,\frac78,\frac58.$ | *hkl*: $h=2n+1$, $k=2n+1$, $l=2n+1$ (16 *d* and 16 *c*) |
| | | | | or $4n+2$, $4n+2$, $4n+2$ or $4n$, $4n$, $4n$ |
| 16 | *c* | $\bar{3}m$ | $\frac18,\frac18,\frac18;\ \frac18,\frac38,\frac38;\ \frac38,\frac18,\frac38;\ \frac38,\frac38,\frac18.$ | |
| 8 | *b* | $\bar{4}3m$ | $\frac12,\frac12,\frac12;\ \frac34,\frac34,\frac34.$ | *hkl*: $h+k+l=2n+1$ or $4n$ (8 *b* and 8 *a*) |
| 8 | *a* | $\bar{4}3m$ | $0,0,0;\ \frac14,\frac14,\frac14.$ | |

**Fig. 6-7**

try operation of the point group $43m(T_d)$. However, the space group does have $\bar{1}(i)$ as a symmetry operation. Normally this would be shown in the space group diagram, but we can also determine this fact by noting that the site symmetry of the 16c position is $\bar{3}m(D_{3d})$, which does have a center of symmetry. From the Tables we see that there are centers at (1/8, 1/8, 1/8) and (1/8, 3/8, 3/8). Clearly the center of inversion at (1/8, 1/8, 1/8) takes the atom at (1/4, 1/4, 1/4) to the atom at (0, 0, 0), while the center at (1/8, 3/8, 3/8) takes it into the one at (0, 1/2, 1/2). Another way of describing this crystal structure is to say that the space group is Fd3m and the basis consists of atoms at (0, 0, 0) and (1/4, 1/4, 1/4). Note that, at times, one may want to take the origin at the center of inversion instead of at the position with site symmetry $\bar{4}3m(T_d)$. The next page in the International Tables, which is not shown here, does exactly that. Thus, the 8a position with $\bar{4}3m$ site symmetry has coordinates (1/8, 1/8, 1/8); (7/8, 7/8, 7/8) and the 16c position with site symmetry $\bar{3}m$ has coordinates (0, 0, 0), etc.

The mineral spinel also has this space group. (Actually, there is some recent evidence that because of possible cation displacements it may really be $F\bar{4}3m$. However, if true the displacements are certainly small and to a first approximation, Fd3m is sufficiently close). The chemical formula is $MgAl_2O_4$. The Mg atoms are located at the 8a positions, the Al atoms at the 16c positions, and the O atoms at the 32e positions. We can see from this that there are eight formula units per face-centered unit cell or two formula units per primitive unit cell. For most materials with this crystal structure the parameter for the 32e position is close to 3/8.

**6-4e $F\bar{4}3m(T_d^2)$** Figure 6-4h shows the zinc-blende (ZnS) or gallium arsenide (GaAs) structure. It can be seen that there is a close relationship between this structure, the diamond structure, and the fluorite structure. Figure 6-8 shows the relevant page of the International Tables for this space group. The Zn or Ga atoms are located at 4a positions and the S or As atoms at 4c positions (or vice versa). The relationship between this structure and the diamond structure is particularly interesting. For Fd3m the diamond glide and the screw axes would take the atoms at positions totally within the unit cell, such as (1/4, 1/4, 1/4) to positions at the face-centers of the cell as drawn. Such operations cannot be symmetry operations for $F\bar{4}3m$ because these two positions are not occupied by the same types of atoms. In fact we see from the symbol that $F\bar{4}3m$ is a symmorphic space group. The point group is $\bar{4}3m(T_d)$, which has half as many symmetry operations as for the point group of the Fd3m space group. In fact one may show that the space group

Cubic $\bar{4}\,3\,m$ $F\bar{4}\,3\,m$ No. 216 $F\bar{4}3m$ $T_d^2$

Origin at $\bar{4}3m$

Co-ordinates of equivalent positions

$(0,0,0;\ 0,\tfrac{1}{2},\tfrac{1}{2};\ \tfrac{1}{2},0,\tfrac{1}{2};\ \tfrac{1}{2},\tfrac{1}{2},0)+$

| Number of positions, Wyckoff notation, and point symmetry | | | Co-ordinates of equivalent positions | Conditions limiting possible reflections |
|---|---|---|---|---|
| | | | | General: |
| 96 | *i* | 1 | $x,y,z;\ z,x,y;\ y,z,x;\ x,z,y;\ y,x,z;\ z,y,x;$ | *hkl*: $h+k, k+l, (l+h)=2n$ |
| | | | $x,\bar{y},\bar{z};\ z,\bar{x},\bar{y};\ y,\bar{z},\bar{x};\ x,\bar{z},\bar{y};\ y,\bar{x},\bar{z};\ z,\bar{y},\bar{x};$ | *hhl*: $(h+l=2n)$ |
| | | | $\bar{x},y,\bar{z};\ \bar{z},x,\bar{y};\ \bar{y},z,\bar{x};\ \bar{x},z,\bar{y};\ \bar{y},x,\bar{z};\ \bar{z},y,\bar{x};$ | C |
| | | | $\bar{x},\bar{y},z;\ \bar{z},\bar{x},y;\ \bar{y},\bar{z},x;\ \bar{x},\bar{z},y;\ \bar{y},\bar{x},z;\ \bar{z},\bar{y},x.$ | |
| | | | | Special: as above only |
| 48 | *h* | *m* | $x,x,z;\ z,x,x;\ x,z,x;\ \bar{x},x,\bar{z};\ \bar{z},x,\bar{x};\ \bar{x},z,\bar{x};$ | |
| | | | $x,\bar{x},\bar{z};\ z,\bar{x},\bar{x};\ x,\bar{z},\bar{x};\ \bar{x},\bar{x},z;\ \bar{z},\bar{x},x;\ \bar{x},\bar{z},x.$ | |
| 24 | *g* | *mm* | $x,\tfrac{1}{4},\tfrac{1}{4};\ \tfrac{1}{4},x,\tfrac{1}{4};\ \tfrac{1}{4},\tfrac{1}{4},x;\ \bar{x},\tfrac{1}{4},\tfrac{3}{4};\ \tfrac{3}{4},\bar{x},\tfrac{1}{4};\ \tfrac{1}{4},\tfrac{3}{4},\bar{x}.$ | |
| 24 | *f* | *mm* | $x,0,0;\ 0,x,0;\ 0,0,x;\ \bar{x},0,0;\ 0,\bar{x},0;\ 0,0,\bar{x}.$ | |
| 16 | *e* | $3m$ | $x,x,x;\ x,\bar{x},\bar{x};\ \bar{x},x,\bar{x};\ \bar{x},\bar{x},x.$ | |
| 4 | *d* | $\bar{4}3m$ | $\tfrac{3}{4},\tfrac{3}{4},\tfrac{3}{4}.$ | |
| 4 | *c* | $\bar{4}3m$ | $\tfrac{1}{4},\tfrac{1}{4},\tfrac{1}{4}.$ | |
| 4 | *b* | $\bar{4}3m$ | $\tfrac{1}{2},\tfrac{1}{2},\tfrac{1}{2}.$ | |
| 4 | *a* | $\bar{4}3m$ | $0,0,0.$ | |

**Fig. 6-8**

$F\bar{4}3m(T_d^2)$ is a subgroup of $Fd3m(O_h^7)$. We also see in Fig. 6-8 that for space group $F\bar{4}3m(T_d^2)$, there is no position that has a center of inversion since this would result in taking a Zn or Ga atom at (0, 0, 0) into a S or As atom at (1/4, 1/4, 1/4).

As an example of a more complicated material that has this space group we note that the mineral zunyite $Al_{13}Si_5O_{20}(OH,F)Cl$ has: Cl – 4b; Si(1) – 4c; Si(2) – 16e; Al(1) – 4d; Al(2) – 48h; O(1) – 16e; O(2) – 16e; O(3) – 48h; (OH,F)(1) – 24f; (OH,F)(2) – 48h. We quote this result only in order to remind the reader that complicated as well as simple crystal structures can still have the same space group.

The cubic zinc-blende structure, considered here, is closely related to the hexagonal wurtzite structure. In fact several compounds can be found to occur in both structures. Problem 5, at the end of this chapter, discusses the wurtzite as well as the simpler hexagonal close-packed structures.

## 6-5 Symmetry Operations of the Space Groups

We have talked a great deal about symmetry operations of space groups. However, we have not explicitly shown how, in general, the appropriate number of symmetry operations for the space groups may be determined. This very large omission will be corrected in this section.

As mentioned several times, there is for every space group an infinite number of primitive lattice translations $\{1 \mid \mathbf{t}_n\}$. We should like to determine the h symmetry operations (h = order of the point group of the space group) of the form $\{R \mid \boldsymbol{\tau}\}$. There is a fundamental theorem, proved in Section 6-6, that tells us that the h symmetry operations R, belonging to the symmetry operations $\{R \mid \boldsymbol{\tau}\}$, are the same as the h operations in the point group of the space group. Thus, only the values of $\boldsymbol{\tau}$ need to be determined for each value of R. In this section we shall determine all the h $\{R \mid \boldsymbol{\tau}\}$ symmetry operations with respect to one origin. This is not absolutely necessary but certainly a great convenience. (Recall, in Section 5-5 that the space groups were described using only the International symbol as a guide. We found that, in general, different origins were required for the different symmetry operations.) It is important to remember that if attention is focused on a specific atom in a specific unit cell and one of the $\{R \mid \boldsymbol{\tau}\}$ symmetry operations takes the atoms out of this unit cell, then it can always be translated back into the original cell by one of the translation symmetry operations $\{1 \mid \mathbf{t}_n\}$.

There are several ways of determining the h symmetry operations, $\{R \mid \boldsymbol{\tau}\}$, of the space group. For a symmorphic space group it can be done by inspection. For a nonsymmorphic space group we recommend using one of the sets of tables that have appeared in the last few years and which list all the symmetry operations for all the 230 space groups. Although it takes a little effort to learn how to use these tables it is worthwhile and will be discussed briefly here. Much shorter tables of generating elements for all the space groups are also available and we shall mention these too. From the general equivalent positions, given in the International Tables for each space group, the symmetry operations can be determined. These can also be determined fairly easily from the space group diagrams. We shall discuss each of these approaches in turn.

**6-5a Symmorphic space groups** For symmorphic space groups it is very easy to find the h symmetry operations of the form $\{R\,|\,\mathbf{0}\}$. The h-values of R from the point group of the space group are clearly symmetry operations of the space group. The origin, the point that is fixed, for these symmetry operations, can be taken at any position with site symmetry the same as the point group.

As an example, consider the space group P4/m ($C_{4h}^{1}$) in Fig. 6-1a. The eight space group symmetry operations are in the International and Schoenflies notations:

$$\{1\,|\,\mathbf{0}\},\ \{4\,|\,\mathbf{0}\},\ \{2\,|\,\mathbf{0}\},\ \{4^3\,|\,\mathbf{0}\},\ \{\bar{1}\,|\,\mathbf{0}\},\ \{\bar{4}\,|\,\mathbf{0}\},\ \{m\,|\,\mathbf{0}\},\ \{\bar{4}^3\,|\,\mathbf{0}\}$$

$$\{E\,|\,\mathbf{0}\},\ \{C_4\,|\,\mathbf{0}\},\ \{C_2\,|\,\mathbf{0}\},\ \{C_4^{\,3}\,|\,\mathbf{0}\},\ \{i\,|\,\mathbf{0}\},\ \{S_4^{\,3}\,|\,\mathbf{0}\},\ \{\sigma_h\,|\,\mathbf{0}\},\ \{S_4\,|\,\mathbf{0}\}$$

By taking the origin at Wyckoff sites, a, b, c, or d, we immediately see that these eight symmetry operations reproduce the eight circles in the unit cell. The circles outside the unit cell are obtained by applying a primitive translation $\{1\,|\,\mathbf{t}_n\}$ to the circles inside the primitive cell. The circles outside the unit cell are included in the diagram for the convenience of showing the symmetry operations clearly, but for counting purposes it must be remembered that they belong to neighboring unit cells.

These same eight symmetry operations apply to the primitive cell of the I4/m($C_{4h}^{5}$) space group in Fig. 6-2a. However, as usual, the diagram in the International Tables shows the multiply-primitive conventional Bravais body-centered unit cell. Therefore, in this diagram we see that the eight circles grouped at the corner of the unit cell transform among themselves under all of the eight symmetry operations of the point group with respect to an origin at (0, 0, 0), which is one of the 2a positions. The other eight circles shown in this multiply-primitive unit cell are obtained from these first eight circles after adding the centering condition. For the conventional multiply-primitive I-unit cell one adds the quantity (1/2, 1/2, 1/2) remembering that (1, 0, 0), (0, 1, 0), etc., can always be added or subtracted for any position because of the translational symmetry.

Thus, the symmorphic space groups only really require the knowledge of point groups to understand them. Now we shall go on to nonsymmorphic space groups where it is a little more difficult to determine the h-symmetry operations.

**6-5b Nonsymmorphic space groups: Symmetry operations ascertained from the diagram** If in the International Tables a space group diagram is given and the lattice is primitive, the h-space group symmetry operations can be determined fairly easily for the nonsymmorphic space groups. Consider the space group P4/n ($C_{4h}^3$) in Fig. 6-1b. We wish to determine the eight-symmetry operations $\{R \mid \boldsymbol{\tau}\}$, where $\boldsymbol{\tau}$ must be non-zero for at least one R because the space group is nonsymmorphic. For convenience, take the origin to be at the top left-hand corner of the unit cell (the normal convention in the International Tables) and start with the circle just below it and to the right. The four symmorphic operations, $\{R_1 \mid \mathbf{0}\}$, namely, $\{1 \mid \mathbf{0}\}$, $\{\overline{4}^3 \mid \mathbf{0}\}$, $\{2 \mid \mathbf{0}\}$, and $\{\overline{4} \mid \mathbf{0}\}$, generate from it the four circles grouped around this origin, of course, leaving the original circle unchanged. How do we obtain the other four circles close to the face-center position (1/2, 1/2, 0) and yet keep the origin fixed? This can be done in the following way. Operate on the starting circle with operation $\overline{1}$ and follow this by a translation $\boldsymbol{\tau}(1/2, 1/2, 0)$. The result of this is the circle, with a comma, above and to the left of the (1/2, 1/2, 0) position. Operating on the starting circle with $\{4 \mid \boldsymbol{\tau}(1/2, 1/2, 0)\}$ one produces the circle above and to the right of the (1/2, 1/2, 0) position. The remaining two circles are obtained by $\{4^3 \mid \boldsymbol{\tau}(1/2, 1/2, 0)\}$ and $\{m[001] \mid \boldsymbol{\tau}(1/2, 1/2, 0)\}$. Notice, in this case, that the new set of operations $\{R_2 \mid \boldsymbol{\tau}\}$ are produced from the first set $\{R_1 \mid \mathbf{0}\}$ by

$$\{\overline{1} \mid \boldsymbol{\tau}(1/2, 1/2, 0)\}\, \{R_1 \mid \mathbf{0}\} = \{R_2 \mid \boldsymbol{\tau}\}$$

Thus, the eight symmetry operations of this nonsymmorphic space group taken with respect to one origin are (in two notations):

$$\{1 \mid \mathbf{0}\},\ \{4 \mid \boldsymbol{\tau}\},\ \{2 \mid \mathbf{0}\},\ \{4^3 \mid \boldsymbol{\tau}\},\ \{\overline{1} \mid \boldsymbol{\tau}\},\ \{\overline{4} \mid \mathbf{0}\},\ \{m[001] \mid \boldsymbol{\tau}\},\ \{\overline{4}^3 \mid \mathbf{0}\}$$

$$\{E \mid \mathbf{0}\},\ \{C_4 \mid \boldsymbol{\tau}\},\ \{C_2 \mid \mathbf{0}\},\ \{C_4^3 \mid \boldsymbol{\tau}\},\ \{i \mid \boldsymbol{\tau}\},\ \{S_4^3 \mid \mathbf{0}\},\ \{\sigma_h \mid \boldsymbol{\tau}\},\ \{S_4 \mid \mathbf{0}\}$$

with $\boldsymbol{\tau} = (\mathbf{a}/2)+(\mathbf{b}/2)$. Note that the same $\boldsymbol{\tau}$ appears in all of the nonsymmorphic symmetry operations.

Clearly, with some practice, this procedure can be repeated easily for any space group, even if a space group diagram is not available. The procedure is straightforward. We may pick an origin at any convenient place. For instance, the center of the unit cell might have been picked in the above example. We start with a circle to represent the identity symmetry operation. We then write down (h-1) other symmetry operations that relate this original circle to the (h-1) different circles in the unit cell, always remembering that we may also use translational symmetry to move the circle back into the unit cell.

We use this occasion to bring up a very interesting point about the symmetry operations given above. In Chapter 5 we talked about glide planes and screw axes. From the symbol P4/n and the diagram we see that there is a diagonal glide but no screw axes. However, some of the symmetry operations we have obtained are neither glide planes nor screw axes. $\{4^3 \mid \boldsymbol{\tau}(1/2, 1/2, 0)\}$ is not a screw axis because $\boldsymbol{\tau}$ is not in the direction of the 4-fold axis, and $\{\bar{1} \mid \boldsymbol{\tau}(1/2, 1/2, 0)\}$ is not even remotely like a glide or screw operation. Here again we run into the different approaches taken by crystallographers and other solid state scientists. By allowing rotation axes and reflection planes to be at various positions in the unit cell, the crystallographer has pure glide planes and screw axes. However, by causing all of the point operators to be taken with respect to one origin, we find general $\{R \mid \boldsymbol{\tau}\}$ operators that are not glide planes or screw axes. This latter approach, using one origin, is however a great convenience to the solid state scientist.

**6-5c Symmetry operations from the general equivalent positions** The International Tables list the coordinates of the general positions for all the 230 space groups, including the cubic ones. From these coordinates one can determine the symmetry operations of the space group, with respect to one origin, in much the same manner as from the diagram. Take the general equivalent position (x,y,z) as the starting point (identity operation). Then, the other (h-1) symmetry operations of the form $\{R \mid \boldsymbol{\tau}\}$, taken with respect to one origin, that give the other (h-1) positions may be written down almost by inspection in the same manner as in Section 6-5b. As above, the h symmetry operations R are known from the point group.

A procedure for determining the h symmetry operations $\{R \mid \boldsymbol{\tau}\}$ but with respect to different origins, as in the International Tables, has been given by Wondratschek and Neubüser, where tables giving the geometric characterizations of all space-group symmetry elements are provided. The same results can be obtained by using the methods discussed in Chapter 5 where the only tables that need to be consulted are those for the matrix operators in Appendix 1. For example, to deturmine what symmetry operation maps the point (x,y,z) to (y−x, y, 1/2−z), we write

$$\{R \mid \boldsymbol{\tau}\}\, r = \begin{bmatrix} -1 & 1 & 0 \\ 0 & 1 & 0 \\ 0 & 0 & -1 \end{bmatrix} \mathbf{r}' + \begin{bmatrix} 0 \\ 0 \\ 1/2 \end{bmatrix} \qquad (6\text{-}1)$$

which from Appendix 1 is simply $\{2[120] \mid \mathbf{0}\}$ passing through the point 1/2(0, 0, 1/2) = (0, 0, 1/4).

**6-5d Tables of symmetry operations**. There now exist several tables of the h symmetry operations $\{R \mid \boldsymbol{\tau}\}$ for each of the 230 space groups.

(Kovalev, Miller and Love, and Zak, Casher, Glüch and Gur. The full references are given in the Bibliography.) These books contain other tables of interest to solid state scientists such as information about the Brillouin zones and irreducible representations for different points and lines in the Brillouin zones; however we shall confine our attention here to the symmetry operations alone. We use some of the tables from Kovalev's book as examples.

Table 6-1 shows part of Kovalev's tables of symmetry operations. (A list of the symmetry operations of all 230 space groups, as well as a description of the notation used by Kovalev, can be found in Appendix 9.) The six space groups that have point group $C_{4h}$ are shown. The space groups are listed by their Schoenflies symbol and "Type" refers to the Bravais space lattice. In Kovalev's notation $\Gamma_q$ is a primitive lattice, and $\Gamma_q^v(a)$ is a body-centered lattice. These symbols are also given in Appendix 9. In Kovalev's notation the primitive lattice is given by $\mathbf{a} = (2\tau, 0, 0)$, $\mathbf{b} = (0, 2\tau, 0)$, and $\mathbf{c} = (0, 0, 2\tau_z)$. The primitive unit cell of the I-lattice $\Gamma_q^v(a)$ refers to the same orthogonal coordinate system and is given by $\mathbf{a} = (-\tau, \tau, \tau_z)$, $\mathbf{b} = (\tau, -\tau, \tau_z)$, and $\mathbf{c} = (\tau, \tau, -\tau_z)$ which is the conventional primitive cell used in this book. For the cubic, tetragonal, orthorhombic, monoclinic, and triclinic crystal systems the 48 possible point operations given by R in the symmetry operation $\{R\,|\,\boldsymbol{\tau}\}$ are labelled $h_1$, $h_2$, ..., $h_{48}$, and they are defined in the front of Kovalev's book. In Table 6-1 we have added above Kovalev's tables the meaning of the operation in terms of the two, more usual, notations employed in this book. (For the hexagonal and trigonal crystal systems the 24 possible point operations are also labelled $h_1$, $h_2$, ..., $h_{24}$, but with different meanings than above. These are also defined in Kovalev's book.) The symmetry operation $\{1\,|\,\mathbf{0}\}$ is not written but is always included. We can see for space group $C_{4h}^1$, which is the symmorphic space group P4/m, that the h-symmetry operations are given by $\{R\,|\,\mathbf{0}\}$ as expected. We also see that the symmetry operations for the space group $C_{4h}^3$(P4/n) given in Table 6-1 are the same as those derived here.

The two space groups with body-centered Bravais lattices are shown in Fig. 6-2. We see that the h symmetry operations in Table 6-1 are the same for the symmorphic space group I4/m($C_{4h}^5$) as for the symmorphic space group P4/m($C_{4h}^1$), and yet the primitive cell of the former is quite different from the latter. Nevertheless, if one cares to work with a multiply-primitive cell, the 2h=16 general equivalent positions in the conventional Bravais unit cell for I4/m($C_{4h}^5$) shown in Fig. 6-2, can be determined by the h symmetry operations of Kovalev with the addition of the centering condition. That is, to each of the

**Table 6-1** Part of Kovalev's book.

| Class $C_{4h}$ | | $\bar{4}$ | 2 | $\bar{4}^3$ | m | $4^3$ | $\bar{1}$ | 4 |
|---|---|---|---|---|---|---|---|---|
| | | $S_4^3$ | $C_2$ | $S_4$ | $\sigma_h$ | $C_4^3$ | i | $C_4$ |
| Group | Type | $h_{38}$ | $h_4$ | $h_{39}$ | $h_{28}$ | $h_{15}$ | $h_{25}$ | $h_{14}$ |
| $C_{4h}^1$ | $\Gamma_q$ | | | | | | | |
| $C_{4h}^2$ | $\Gamma_q$ | | | | $0, 0, \tau_z$ | $0, 0, \tau_z$ | $0, 0, \tau_z$ | $0, 0, \tau_z$ |
| $C_{4h}^3$ | $\Gamma_q$ | | | | $\tau, \tau, 0$ | $\tau, \tau, 0$ | $\tau, \tau, 0$ | $\tau, \tau, 0$ |
| $C_{4h}^4$ | $\Gamma_q$ | | | | $\tau, \tau, \tau_z$ | $\tau, \tau, \tau_z$ | $\tau, \tau, \tau_z$ | $\tau, \tau, \tau_z$ |
| $C_{4h}^5$ | $\Gamma_q^v(\alpha)$ | | | | | | | |
| $C_{4h}^6$ | $\Gamma_q^v(\alpha)$ | | | | $0, \tau, \frac{\tau_z}{2}$ | $0, \tau, \frac{\tau_z}{2}$ | $0, \tau, \frac{\tau_z}{2}$ | $0, \tau, \frac{\tau_z}{2}$ |

general equivalent positions obtained from the h symmetry operations given by Kovalev, add (1/2, 1/2, 1/2). The extension to F- and C-centering is obvious. Similarly, we can check the symmetry operations given in Table 6-1 for $I4_1/a$ ($C_{4h}^6$) using the diagram in Fig. 6-2b. Eight general equivalent positions for the primitive cell are obtained. The other eight shown in the multiply-primitive cell are obtained by the addition of (1/2, 1/2, 1/2).

Now, consider space group $P4_2/m$ ($C_{4h}^2$). From the diagram in the International Tables we can very easily write down the symmetry operations. They are, with $\boldsymbol{\tau} = (0, 0, 1/2)$,

$$\{1 \mid \mathbf{0}\}, \ \{4 \mid \boldsymbol{\tau}\}, \ \{2 \mid \mathbf{0}\} \ \ \{\bar{4}^3 \mid \boldsymbol{\tau}\}, \{m \mid \mathbf{0}\}, \ \{\bar{4} \mid \boldsymbol{\tau}\}, \ \ \{\bar{1} \mid \mathbf{0}\}, \ \{4^3 \mid \boldsymbol{\tau}\}.$$

These appear to be quite different from the symmetry operations given in Table 6-1, but actually they are the same. The unit cell in Kovalev is translated by an amount (0, 0, $\mathbf{c}/4$) with respect to that in the International Tables (the details about translations with respect to the International Tables are sometimes given in the tables of generating elements discussed in the next section, but unfortunately not in Kovalev's book).

The remainder of Kovalev's tables, shown in Appendix 9, is similar to the information shown in Table 6-1, except that for some of the space groups the group multiplication principle is used. For example, $D_{4h}^2$ is written by Kovalev in the following way, where $h_{25}$ is the inversion operation,

$$D_{4h}^2 = D_4^1 + D_4^1 \times t_{(0,0,\tau_z)} \cdot h_{25} \tag{6-2}$$

Thus, the 16 symmetry operations of the space group $D_{4h}^2$ are obtained by taking the eight symmetry operations of the space group $D_4^1$, which are given in Kovalev in tabular form. To these we add eight further symmetry operations, obtained by multiplying each operation in $D_4^1$ by inversion ($h_{25}$) followed by translation through an amount $\tau(0, 0, 1/2)$. It is always advisable when using these tables to check with the diagrams in the International Tables.

**6-5e Tables of generating elements for space groups** Besides tables of the symmetry operations of all 230 space groups, there also exist much shorter tables of the generating elements for each of the space groups. These tables are given by Bradley and Cracknell, Faddeyev, Koptsik and Lyubarskii. The complete references are given in the Bibliography.

We may define the **generating elements of a group** as a particular set of operations from which all of the operations of the group can be obtained by successive multiplications of one another. A simple example of a generating element is the symmetry operation $C_4$ for the point group $4(C_4)$. Every symmetry operation of this point group can be expressed in terms of successive multiplications of the generating element, i.e., $C_4$, $C_4^2 = C_2$, $C_4^3$, $C_4^4 = E$. For a given group the generating elements are not a unique set, in general. For the point group $4(C_4)$, we could equally well have chosen $C_4^3$ as the generating element.

As an example of generating elements for space groups, Bradley and Cracknell list for the space group $P4/n(C_{4h}^3)$, shown in Fig. 6-1b, the two generating elements $\{C_4 | \boldsymbol{\tau}\}$ and $\{i | \boldsymbol{\tau}\}$, where $\boldsymbol{\tau} = (1/2, 1/2, 0)$. Using the law of multiplication in Eq. (5-2) we can see that the following operations are generated:

$$\begin{array}{ll} \{i | \boldsymbol{\tau}\}^2 = \{E | \mathbf{0}\} & \{i | \boldsymbol{\tau}\} \\ \{C_4 | \boldsymbol{\tau}\} & \{i | \boldsymbol{\tau}\}\{C_4 | \boldsymbol{\tau}\} = \{S_4^3 | \mathbf{0}\} \\ \{C_4 | \boldsymbol{\tau}\}^2 = \{C_2 | \mathbf{0}\} & \{i | \boldsymbol{\tau}\}\{C_2 | \mathbf{0}\} = \{\sigma_h | \boldsymbol{\tau}\} \\ \{C_4 | \boldsymbol{\tau}\}^3 = \{C_4^3 | \boldsymbol{\tau}\} & \{C_4 | \boldsymbol{\tau}\}\{i | \boldsymbol{\tau}\}\{C_2 | \mathbf{0}\} = \{S_4 | \mathbf{0}\} \end{array} \quad (6\text{-}3)$$

These are the same operations as those given before.

## 6-6 **Point Group of a Space Group**

**6-6a Introduction**. We have defined the **point group of a space group** as the set of symmetry operations obtained when all the translations in the space group symmetry operations are taken to be zero. As usual, we take $\mathbf{t}_n$ as the primitive lattice translation vectors and $\boldsymbol{\tau}$ as a fraction of a primitive lattice vector. Thus $\boldsymbol{\tau}$ with a point operation R allows one to describe the glide, screw, or any general nonsymmorphic symmetry operation. We may symbolically describe the method of obtaining the operations of the point group of a space group as

$$\{R_i \mid \boldsymbol{\tau}_i + \mathbf{t}_n\} \rightarrow \{R_i \mid \mathbf{0}\} \tag{6-4}$$

where we have added the subscript i (=1 to h) to make it perfectly clear that a certain value of $\boldsymbol{\tau}$ goes with a certain R and that the identical $R_i$ appears on both sides of this expression.

For a symmorphic space group these h symmetry operations $\{R \mid \mathbf{0}\}$ are always symmetry operations of the space group. However, for a nonsymmorphic space group, at least one of the h operations cannot be a symmetry operation of the space group. Thus, one might wonder why we have made this definition and what use it is. We shall attempt to answer these questions in this section.

(Once again we emphasize that, as always, when we talk about a symmorphic crystal we consider the essential h space group symmetry operations $\{R_i \mid \mathbf{0}\}$ about one origin. We know that these operations can, and usually do, imply other symmetry operations, such as, glide planes or screw axes but these are not essential in describing the space group symmetry. These other symmetry operations are obtained by the product $\{R \mid \mathbf{0}\}\{1 \mid \boldsymbol{\tau}_n\} = \{R \mid R\boldsymbol{\tau}_n\}$. A nonsymmorphic space group is a space group in which some operations of the form $\{R \mid \boldsymbol{\tau}\}$ are required no matter which origin one uses.)

There are several very important reasons for defining the point group of a space group. In particular, it is intimately bound up with the relationship between macroscopic physical properties and symmetry (**Neumann's principle**). Possibly an even more important consequence of defining the point group of a space group is that it leads to a very fundamental theorem in solid state physics which allows one to handle the symmetry operations of a space group in terms of a point group. Let us briefly consider the connection between macroscopic physical properties and symmetry and then go on to discuss this fundamental theorem at some length.

(i) Neumann's principle This states that the macroscopic (tensor) properties of a crystal have at least the symmetry of the point group of the space group. The physical reason for this is that in measuring a macroscopic property one would not expect to be able to detect the effect of a translation that is only a fraction of a primitive unit cell. In other words, no distinction could be made between $\{R \mid \boldsymbol{\tau}\}$ and $\{R \mid \mathbf{0}\}$ using macroscopic physical properties alone. On the other hand, the rotational part of the symmetry operation will relate points within the crystal that are separated by macroscopic distances and hence will have an effect on the macroscopic properties. Actually, we are not strictly correct here, as certain physical properties, such as optical activity, can distinguish between different nonsymmorphic groups. This is because such a property adds in phase from one unit cell to the next to result in an overall macroscopic effect.

Note the use of the words at least in the statement of Neumann's principle. It is important to understand that the point group of the space group is generally of lower symmetry than the symmetry of the physical properties. For example, if we consider properties specified by second-rank tensors, we find that cubic crystals (those having cubic point groups) are isotropic, i.e., the diagonal elements of the tensor are equal and nonzero, while the nondiagonal elements are zero. This means that such properties are the same in all directions and therefore have spherical symmetry. Clearly, all of the symmetry elements of the cubic point groups are contained by such spherical symmetry, so that we can say that the cubic point groups are subgroups of a spherically symmetric group. With properties that are described by tensors of higher rank, the situation is more involved. Several books that discuss the use of Neumann's principal in considerable detail are listed in the Bibliography.

**(ii)** Theorem. There is an **isomorphism** (a one-to-one correspondence) between the operations of the point group of a space group and the operations of the factor group of a space group, where the factor group is taken with respect to the primitive lattice translation group.

In order to understand and prove this fundamental theorem we review briefly some concepts that are normally taught at the beginning of a group theory course. For a more detailed discussion of these concepts see the various group theory books mentioned in the Bibliography, in particular, the book by Burns, Chapter 2.

Subgroup. The group S is called a subgroup of the group G if all the elements of S are also contained in G. If there are h elements in G and s in S, then one can prove that h/s = an integer.

Complex. A complex is a set of elements of a group and this set need not be a subgroup. If $\alpha$ and $\beta$ are two complexes, then the product $\alpha\beta$ is the product of each element in $\alpha$ with every element in $\beta$, where the resulting product of two elements, if it occurs more than once, is only counted once.

Coset. If p is an element of the group G and is not contained in the subgroup S, then the complexes pS and Sp are the left and right cosets of

S. Cosets must be formed with respect to a subgroup. Thus, cosets can never be subgroups themselves, since the identity (E) is contained in S, and therefore pS cannot contain an identity. If p and q are different elements of G and are not in S, then the cosets pS and qS are distinct (have no overlapping elements). This can be proved by the so-called rearrangement theorem.

Factored Set. A finite group can be written in terms of a finite number of distinct cosets, G = S + pS + qS + ..., where p and q are in G but not in S and q is not in pS. In fact the number of distinct cosets is h/s.

Conjugate Elements. Let a, b, c, ..., x, ... be elements of a group. Groups A and B are conjugate if, for some element x in the group, $a = x^{-1}bx$. Every element is conjugate with itself because we may take x = E. It is very easy to prove that: if a is conjugate to b, then b is conjugate to a; if a is conjugate to b and to c, then b is conjugate to c.

Class. The set of elements of a group that are conjugate are said to form a class. The importance of the class concept is that the character is identical for the matrix representation of all the members of the same class. Thus, in character tables the group elements are gathered into the different classes.

Invariant Subgroup. A subgroup that consists of complete classes is called an invariant subgroup (or sometimes a normal divisor). By this we mean that T is an invariant subgroup of G if it is a subgroup of G and if, for any g in G and t in T, $g^{-1}tg$ is an element of T. From this we see that $g^{-1}Tg = T$ or $Tg = gT$. (T consists of complete classes.) Thus, for an invariant subgroup the left and right cosets are the same. We may also say that an invariant subgroup is self-conjugate.

Factor Group. A factor group of G is a set of elements obtained by considering an invariant subgroup S as one element and all the cosets of this invariant subgroup as the remaining elements. In order to form the factor group, take p, g, t, ... which are distinct elements of G not contained in S. Then, the factor group of G with respect to S has elements {S, pS, gS, tS, ... }. One may write G as a factored set G = S + pS + qS + tS + ..., where S plays the part of the identity element of the factor group as we see below. It is clear that the factor group is a group from the following:

Associativity – same as the original group
Closure – $(pS)(qS) = pSSq = pSq = (pq)S = tS$
Identity – $S(pS) = pSS = (pS)$
Inverse – $(pS)^{-1}(pS) = S^{-1}p^{-1}pS = S^{-1}S = S$

We shall use these properties to prove our fundamental theorem.

To make some of these concepts clearer, we consider a simple example of a factor group of the point group 4mm($C_{4v}$). The elements of this point group are: $\{E, C_4, C_4^3, C_2, \sigma_v, \sigma_v', \sigma_d, \sigma_d'\}$. When these are arranged by classes, one finds five classes: (E); ($C_2$); ($C_4$,$C_4^3$); ($\sigma_v$,$\sigma_v'$); ($\sigma_d$,$\sigma_d'$). Thus, we may take S = $\{E,C_2\}$ and since S is a subgroup and is made up of complete classes it is an invariant subgroup. Then $C_4S = (C_4,C_4^3)$, $\sigma_vS = (\sigma_v,\sigma_v')$, and $\sigma_dS = (\sigma_d,\sigma_d')$ as can be verified by the use of a group multiplication table, stereograms, or the matrix multiplication method. Thus, the factor group with respect to the invariant subgroup S = $\{E,C_2\}$ can be written as $\{S, C_4S, \sigma_vS, \sigma_dS\}$. We see the **homomorphism** (many-to-one correspondence) between the point group and the factor group. There is a two-to-one correspondence, where the elements E and $C_2$ of the point group correspond to the element S of the factor group, etc. Thus, the multiplication table of the point group $G_p$ and the factor group $G_p/S$ are identical so long as this correspondence is recognized. The invariant subgroup S always plays the role of the identity, as shown above. Also, we see that this factor group is smaller (has fewer elements) than the original, in fact one half the size in our example. Thus, by the use of the factor group concept we may deal with larger groups in terms of smaller groups. As we shall see for a space group, which is infinite, we may obtain a small finite factor group (at most, 48 elements).

6-6b **The factor group of a space group** We prove the fundamental theorem in this section. Let G be the space group. Let T be the subgroup of G that consists of all the pure primitive lattice translations $\{1 \mid \mathbf{t}_n\}$. It is clear that T is a subgroup of G; in fact in the case of the space group P1($C_1^1$) it is the same as G. It is easy to show that T is an invariant subgroup of G. In order to do this, take a typical element of T, $\{1 \mid \mathbf{t}_n\}$, and a typical element of G, $\{R \mid t_n + \tau\}$. We find the elements conjugate to $\{1 \mid \mathbf{t}_n\}$ by

$$\{R \mid t_n + \tau\}^{-1} \{1 \mid t_n\} \{R \mid t_n + \tau\} = \{R^{-1} \mid -R^{-1}t_n - R^{-1}\tau\} \{R \mid 2t_n + \tau\}$$
$$= \{1 \mid R^{-1}t_n\} \qquad (6\text{-}5)$$

The final result is just a pure translation since $R^{-1}\mathbf{t}_n$ is still a primitve lattice vector. Thus the subgroup T is conjugate to itself and it is an invariant subgroup.

We may now form the factor group of G with respect to the invariant subgroup T and this is labelled G/T. We may write the space group in a factored set

$$G = \{E\,|\,\mathbf{0}\}T + \{R_2\,|\,\tau_2\}T + \ldots + \{R_h\,|\,\tau_h\}T \qquad (6\text{-}6)$$

where we have taken the $i = 1$ term to be the identity. The corresponding factor group has the h elements T, $\{R_2\,|\,\tau_2\}T$, ..., $\{R_h\,|\,\tau_h\}T$.

Before we go on to prove our fundamental theorem let us examine this equation more closely. So far in this book we have always taken the lattice as infinite (an infinite number of symmetry operations in T). We could just as well have taken the lattice as finite with periodic boundary conditions. For the sake of a better understanding of this equation let us do just that and assume that the group T has some huge number of symmetry operations equal to m. Thus T is a large group of order m. This equation, then, is a short way of writing the hm symmetry operations of the space group G. Clearly each one of the elements of this factor group is "hiding" a huge number of operations. As we shall see presently, Eq. (6-6) contains, at most, 48 (= h) entries on the right-hand side.

In order to prove that G/T and the point group $G_p$ are isomorphic we must show two things.

(i) First, all elements of one coset have $R_i$ as the rotational part of the element. This is fairly easy to show since a typical element of one coset is $\{R_i\,|\,\tau\}\{E\,|\,t_n\} = \{R_i\,|\,R_i t_n + \tau\}$. Clearly the rotational part of the result is $R_i$.

(ii) Second, which is the converse, all the elements of G that have $R_i$ as the rotational part must be contained in the particular coset $\{R_i\,|\,\tau\}T$. Consider an element of G, $\{R_i\,|\,\mathbf{t}'\}$, and assume for the moment that it is not contained in the coset $\{R_i\,|\,\tau\}T$. Form

$$\{R_i\,|\,\tau_i\}\{R_i\,|\,\mathbf{t}'\}^{-1} = \{R_i\,|\,\tau_i\}\{R_i^{-1}\,|\,-R_i^{-1}\mathbf{t}'\} = \{E\,|\,-t'+\tau_i\} \qquad (6\text{-}7)$$

Because the result must be a member of G, it must also be a pure primitive lattice translation (the rotational part is the identity) and so $\mathbf{t}'$ may differ from $\tau$ only by a pure primitive lattice vector. If we take $\mathbf{t}' = \mathbf{t}_n + \tau_i$, then we see that the term $\{R_i\,|\,\mathbf{t}'\}$ is in the coset $\{R_i\,|\,\tau_i\}T$ because the general term of this coset is $\{R_i\,|\,\tau_i\}\{E\,|\,\mathbf{t}_n\} = \{R_i\,|\,\mathbf{t}_n + \tau_i\}$. Thus, our assumption is contradicted since $\{R_i\,|\,\mathbf{t}'\}$ must be contained in the product of $\{R\,|\,\tau\}$ and a primitive translation of T.

Therefore, there is a one-to-one correspondence (an isomorphism) between the elements of the factor group of G with respect to T, G/T, and the elements of the point group $G_p$. The corresponding elements of G/T are $\{R_i\,|\,\tau_i\}T$ and those of $G_p$ are $\{R_i\,|\,\mathbf{0}\}$ for $i = 1$ to h. By this we mean, for example, $\{R_3\,|\,\tau_3\}T$ corresponds to $\{R_3\,|\,\mathbf{0}\}$ in $G_p$. It is clear that elements of $G_p$ form a group since this set of elements is isomorphic to G/T which we have shown in Section 6-6a to form a group. Furthermore, the restrictions on the symmetry operations $R_i$ for a space group are for screw operations – rotations of order 1, 2, 3, 4, or 6 and for glide operations – a mirror reflection. (Note that in proving this isomorphism between $G_p$ and G/T we have also proved something that we proved geometrically in Chapter 5, namely, that the order of rotation in screw axes is confined to the same values as for proper rotations.) $G_p$ must be one of the 32 crystallographic point groups.

## Problems

**1.** Consider the space groups $P4_122$ and $P4_322$. Write out the coordinates of equivalent positions for all of the special and general points as well as the site symmetry for each point. These two space groups are an enantiomorphic pair.

**2.** Show that by using the short symbol Fd3m alone it is possible to deduce the presence of a $4_1$ axis along [100] and its position with respect to a chosen origin. Hint: take the combination of a d-glide perpendicular to [001] with a mirror perpendicular to $[01\bar{1}]$ and use the matrix-multiplication method of Chapter 5.

**3.** What are the point groups of the following space groups and what is the symmetry of the special position with the highest site symmetry in each case: $P\bar{4}m2$, $P\bar{4}c2$, P3m1, $R\bar{3}c$, and I23?

**4.** Consider the space group Pban given in the International Tables. Write out all the essential symmetry operations with respect to a fixed origin taken to be at (i) the intersection of the 2-fold axes and (ii) a center of inversion.

**5.** An important structure in which many simple metals, such as Be, Mg, Ti, Zr, Os, Zn and Cd, crystallize, is the **hexagonal close-packed structure**, with space group $P6_3/mmc$ ($D_{6h}{}^4$). The atoms are on the 2c sites at (0,0,0) and (1/3,2/3,1/2). With a different choice of origin, the atoms are at $\pm$(2/3,1/3,1/4). Each atom is surrounded by 12 neighbors, 6 in the same **ab**-plane, 3 above and 3 below. (a) Show that the 12 neighbors are equidistant if $c/a=(8/3)^{1/2}=1.633$. This value is known as the ideal c/a ratio. (b) In this structure, the 3 atoms above the plane are directly over the 3 atoms below the plane if you look down the **c**-axis. Consider a face-centered cubic lattice and look down a <111>. Then surrounding any one lattice point, which we call the origin, there are 12 equidistant lattice points (6 in the plane of the origin, 3 above and 3 below). Show that the 3 above are not directly over the 3 below. In fact, they are rotated by 60°. This is the reason one says there is a stacking sequence ABABAB... in a hexagonal close packed structure, while in a cubic close packed structure (face-centered cubic lattice) the sequence is ABCABC... along [111]. (c) ZnS, in the wurtzite phase, has space group $P6_3mc(C_{6v}^4)$ with the atoms at (0,0,u) and (1/3,2/3,1/2+u) where u=0 and ≈ 3/8 for Zn and S respectively. Show that, for u=3/8 and the ideal c/a ratio, the tetrahedron formed from the Zn and its four S neighbors is exactly the same as that found in the zinc-blende structure discussed in Section 6-4e.

# Chapter 7

# SOME APPLICATIONS

*But real adventures, I reflected, do not happen to people who remain at home: they must be sought abroad.*

*Joyce, "Dubliners"*

## 7-1 Introduction

In this final chapter, we should like to discuss a few additional items which are relevant to space groups. We shall start by giving the reader an idea of how one may go about recognizing to which space group a particular crystal structure belongs. Although this is a problem that does not usually arise for many solid state scientists since they normally work with materials that have already been well characterized, it is, nevertheless, useful to see how it is done. We shall then go on to discuss some more difficult problems relating to the concept of the irreducible representations of a space group. We shall illustrate this with reference to the analysis of normal modes of vibration both at $\mathbf{k} = 0$ and $\mathbf{k} \neq 0$.

The topics discussed in this chapter need not be read in the order given. Sections 7-2 and 7-3 are separate topics and are independent of each other. Also the $\mathbf{k} \approx 0$ normal lattice vibrational mode analysis, which is so important in infrared and Raman studies, is covered in Section 7-5a and can be read independently from the remainder of the chapter.

## 7-2 Recognition of the Space Group from the Crystal Structure

So far in this book, we have concentrated mainly on the understanding and development of space groups. We shall now address another problem; namely, given the crystal structure described either by a diagram or perhaps an atomic model or even a set of coordinates, how can we recognize to which space group the structure belongs? This is the kind of question that is familiar to crystallographers, since this must be considered at some stage in any crystal structure determination. However, it can be important to other solid state scientists when, for example, considering the possibility of modifications of a crystalline material to structures that have not been actually determined before. This is particularly common in the field of solid state phase transitions, where on altering the temperature a particular structure may change to one of a number of plausible structures different from the initial one. Another reason for wanting to be able to determine the space group of a material would be when some experiment suggests that the published structure may not be correct and, in fact, suggests an alternative one. In such a case, it is often necessary to find the space group of this alternative structure in order to see if it fits in with this or any other experimental measurement. The procedure that we shall use for recognizing a space group is as follows:

(i) Examine the lattice parameters for inequality of axes and angles. This may suggest the crystal system, but, as we have stressed several times before, we must be careful not to assume that equality of axes or angles is an absolute guide, since it may be that the experimental measurement of the lattice parameters is not sufficiently precise.

(ii) Look for centering in order to determine the lattice type. It is important here to understand that the centering must be true for all atoms and not for just certain atoms in order for the unit cell to be considered centered.

(iii) Look for symmetry elements. These taken with the results of (i) and (ii) will suggest the space group, or at least the point group. It is often helpful to look for a center of inversion first, since its presence places the structure into one of 90 centrosymmetric space groups.

It is difficult to give any hard-and-fast rules for recognizing a space group and so we shall consider a few examples, indicating as we go along how one may proceed. We first take an example of the structure of an organic material, anthracene, which crystallizes in a space group that is common to many aromatic organic compounds. We then consider the perovskite structure which, although very simple, is capable of many structural variations each with its own space group.

**7-2a The structure of Anthracene** Anthracene is an aromatic organic compound of formula $C_{14}H_{10}$. Figure 7-1 shows a drawing of an isolated molecule, which consists of three six-membered rings of carbon atoms joined together side by side. The crystal structure, determined by

X-ray diffraction studies, is shown in Fig. 7-2 where the molecules of anthracene in the unit cell can be seen. (The hydrogen atoms are not shown.) The first thing to note is that the unit-cell axes are not orthogonal. In fact, the lattice parameters are given as a = 8.561 Å, b = 6.036 Å, c = 11.153 Å, $\beta$ = 120°42′, and $\alpha = \gamma$ = 90°. The lattice parameters, then, suggest that the crystal system is probably monoclinic (2nd setting). We notice also from the diagram that with reference to a molecule situated at the origin of the unit cell, there is no other molecule related by any centering condition, and therefore the unit cell as drawn is primitive. Let us now consider the symmetry elements. It is obvious from Fig. 7-1 that the molecule is centrosymmetric, provided it is taken to be flat and this suggests that there is a center of inversion at the unit-cell origin in Fig. 7-2, taking atom A to atom A′, B to B′, and so on. This fact, together with the possibility of monoclinic symmetry suggests that the point group of the space group is $2/m(C_{2h})$, and hence the space group would be either $P2/m(C_{2h}{}^1)$, $P2_1/m(C_{2h}{}^2)$, $P2/c(C_{2h}{}^4)$, or $P2_1/c(C_{2h}{}^5)$. Thus we only have to ascertain whether there is a 2- or $2_1$-axis and a mirror or glide plane.

In Fig. 7-2, we see that one molecule is located with its center at the point (0,0,0) with a second one at (1/2,1/2,0) giving two molecules in the unit cell. Now, in the second setting of the monoclinic system, the 2 or $2_1$ axis must lie parallel to **b** and must relate these two molecules. Clearly the two are not related by a 2-fold axis since they are displaced through **b**/2 with respect to each other. The two can only be related by a $2_1$-axis and close scrutiny of the figure shows such an axis parallel to **b** and passing through (1/4,0,0). This narrows the space group to $P2_1/m(C_{2h}{}^2)$ or $P2_1/c(C_{2h}{}^5)$. In order to distinguish between these we now look for a mirror plane perpendicular to **b**. As before, we see that the two molecules cannot be related by a symmorphic mirror operation because they are displaced from each other in the plane perpendicular to **b** through a half translation along **a**. This is clearly a glide operation along **a** with the reflection plane perpendicular to **b** and passing through (0, 1/4, 0). Therefore, the space group must be $P2_1/a(C_{2h}{}^5)$, which is equivalent to $P2_1/c(C_{2h}{}^5)$ because the choice of **a**- or **c**-axis is arbitrary.

There is another feature of this structure that we should be aware of: the atoms all lie at general positions. Now, we have only two molecules per unit cell and yet there are four general equivalent positions per unit cell in $P2_1/a(C_{2h}{}^5)$. How does this apparent paradox come about? If we take as a unit one-half of the molecule, say atoms A, B, C, D, E, F, and G, and think of this as being at a general position, we see that three other halves are generated to give four in all, corresponding to the four

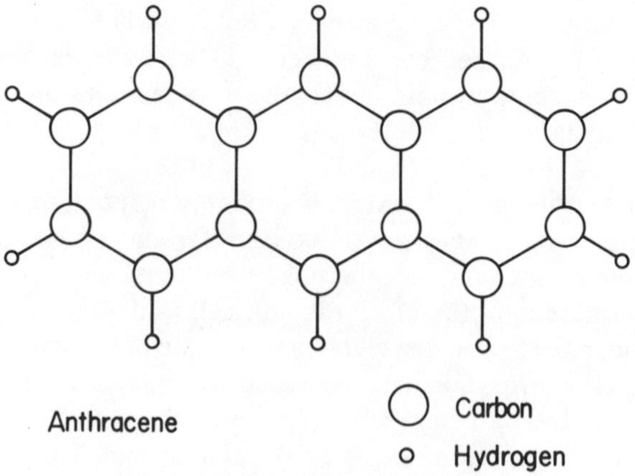


**Fig. 7-1** An anthracene molecule.

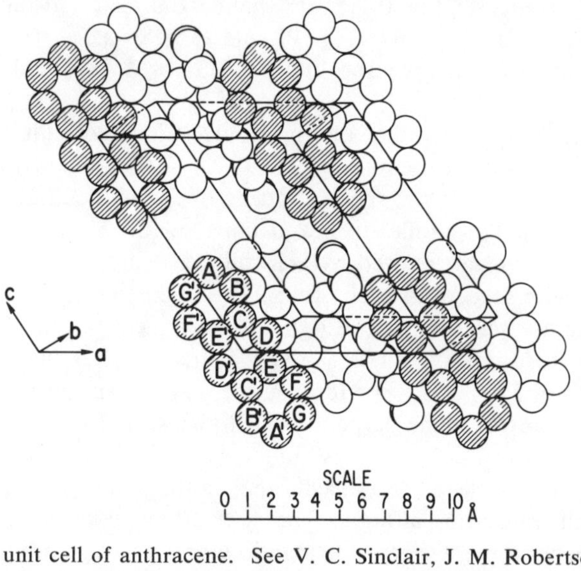


**Fig. 7-2** The unit cell of anthracene. See V. C. Sinclair, J. M. Robertson and A. M. Mathieson, Acta. Cryst. **3**, 251 (1950).

general equivalent positions. Clearly, four halves make two whole molecules and so we see that there is no paradox after all. This is quite an important idea to grasp since the crystallographer can often find it helpful in determining the crystal structure of a molecular compound. If we know in advance that the space group is $P2_1/a(C_{2h}{}^5)$, from an X-ray experiment say, and also that there are two molecules per unit cell as calculated from the measured density, we can say that the molecule has two symmetry-related halves (by the inversion, screw or glide operations). In the case of anthracene, the molecule in Fig. 7-1 is centrosymmetric and therefore these two halves are related by $\bar{1}$(i) with the center of the molecule coincident with the center of inversion of the unit cell. If we knew that there were four molecules per cell, on the other hand, we could not tell if the molecule is centrosymmetric nor where it is located, although the chances are that it is not centrosymmetric.

This space group is probably the most common one for organic molecules, and naphthalene, phenazine, tetracyanoquinone (TCNQ), and many others share this space group. The reasons for this are tied up with the problem of the packing together of flat, anisotropic molecules and have been discussed at great length by Kitaigorodskii in particular. The space group leads to a herringbone arrangement of the molecules, which turns out to be the most efficient way of packing this type of molecule into the smallest volume.

**7-2b The Structure of Perovskites** Perovskites are inorganic with general formula $ABX_3$ (A and B are cations and X anions). Some typical examples of perovskites are $BaTiO_3$, $SrTiO_3$, and $CaTiO_3$. Figure 7-3 shows a diagram of the ideal structure (usually the highest temperature form) where we see that it consists of a framework of corner linked octahedra with anions at the corners, the B cations at the centers of the octahedra, and the A cation at the center of the space between the octahedra. It is clear from the diagram that if we take axes **a**, **b**, and **c** as indicated with an origin at one of the B cations, we have

$$a = b = c \qquad \alpha = \beta = \gamma = 90^\circ$$

| | | |
|---|---|---|
| the A cation | at | (1/2, 1/2, 1/2) |
| the B cation | at | (0, 0, 0) |
| the X anions | at | (1/2, 0, 0), (0, 1/2, 0),and (0, 0, 1/2) |

The lattice parameters suggest cubic symmetry and the unit cell is clearly primitive. Certain symmetry elements are obvious. First, there are centers of inversion at the cation. Second, there are mirror planes perpendicular to $<100>$, e.g., perpendicular to **b** and passing through $(0, 0, 0)$ and $(0, 1/2, 0)$. Third, there are other mirror planes perpendicular to $<110>$ passing through the face diagonals. Finally, we see that along $<111>$ we have 3-fold axes, i.e., perpendicular to the triangular faces of the octahedra. This determines the space group to be $Pm3m(O_h^{\ 1})$. Once we know this, of course, other symmetry elements of this space group become apparent, such as 2-fold axes parallel to the face diagonals of the

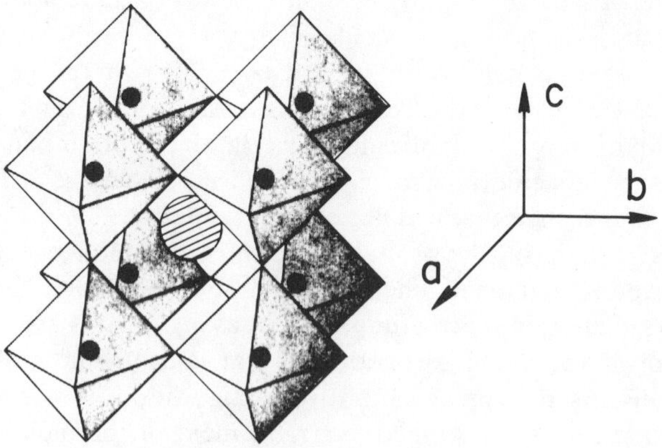


**Fig. 7-3** The perovskite structure.

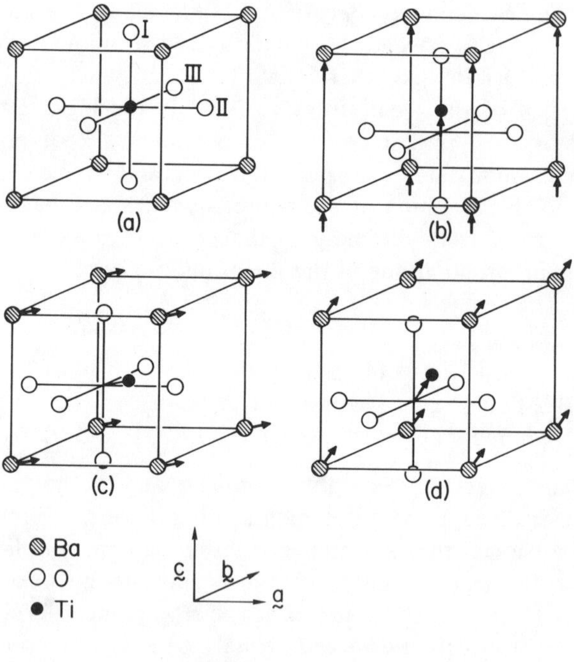


**Fig. 7-4** Cation displacements in the perovskite structure.

cubic unit cell. If we look at the appropriate page in the International Tables, as in Fig. 6-6, it is quite easy to see that all of the atoms lie on certain special positions of space group $Pm3m(O_h{}^1)$. Thus we have

| | | |
|---|---|---|
| A cation | on | 1 b site |
| B cation | on | 1 a site |
| X anion | on | 3 d sites |

Figure 7-4a shows an alternative diagram of the structure with the unit cell origin taken at the A cation. Close inspection will reveal that both diagrams are equivalent.

The interesting thing about perovskites is that this very simple structure can show many variations with phase transitions between the different structures. For most purposes we can divide the stuctural variations into three types:

(i) where the cations are displaced from their centers, either in a parallel or antiparallel fashion

(ii) where the anion octahedra tilt about various axes; and

(iii) where both effects occur.

The first type is particularly easy to deal with. Consider the material $BaTiO_3$, for example. At high temperatures it has the cubic Pm3m structure. However, when the temperature is lowered, it transforms to a structure in which the Ti and Ba ions are displaced, by different amounts, along [001] with respect to the oxygen framework. This is shown schematically in Fig. 7-4b. Notice that this results in a noncentrosymmetric structure with the **c**-axis different from **a** and **b**, and because the displacements are confined to one of the 4-fold directions of the originally cubic structure, this 4-fold axis is retained while those perpendicular are lost. This means that the structure is tetragonal. Another point to note is that, in principle, this structure could revert to the cubic one by decreasing the displacements continuously to zero, although, of course, the symmetry change must itself be discontinuous. This further means that the point group for the lower-temperature phase is a subgroup of the higher one. This structure still has a primitive cell and still retains two types of mirror plane but not those perpendicular to [001]. From this we find that the space group is $P4mm(C_{4v}{}^1)$ with

Ba on a 1a site, Ti on a 1b site
$O_I$ on a 1b site, and $O_{II}$ and $O_{III}$ on 2c sites

We see that all the symmetry operations of $P4mm(C_{4v}{}^1)$ are contained in $Pm3m(O_h{}^1)$. On lowering the temperature further, the displacements switch to the [110] direction (Fig. 7-4c). Examination of this diagram reveals that there are 2-fold axes along [110] with mirror

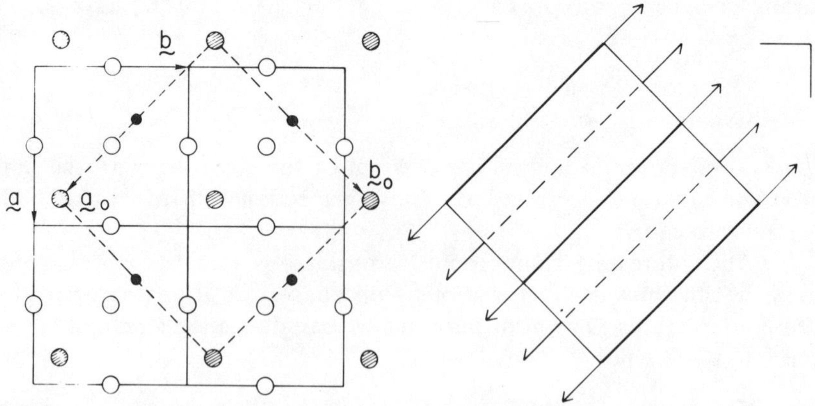


Fig. 7-5 A C-centered cell of the perovskite structure.

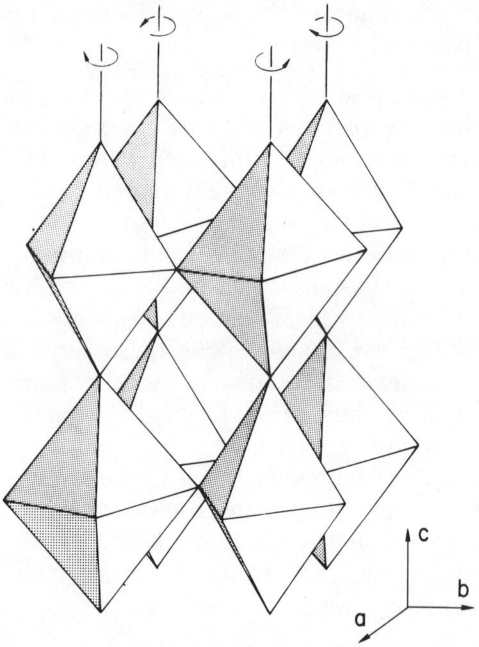


Fig. 7-6 A possible tilting in the perovskite structure.

planes perpendicular to [001] and parallel to [110]. That is, the point group symmetry is $mm2(C_{2v})$, and the crystal system is orthorhombic. However, because the 2-fold axis is along a face diagonal, in order to specify an orthorhombic space group a new cell has to be constructed with axes containing the 2-fold axis and a mirror plane. This new cell is outlined in Fig. 7-5 where we see that it is C-centered with the 2-fold axis along the new $\mathbf{a}_o$-axis and mirror planes perpendicular to the new $\mathbf{b}_o$ and $\mathbf{c}_o$-axes. Note that the new $\mathbf{c}_o$-axis is equivalent to the original $\mathbf{c}$-axis. The space group is therefore C2mm($C_{2v}{}^{14}$). Here again, because this structure can go to the cubic one by continuously decreasing the displacements to zero, all the elements of the point group of this space group must be contained in m3m($O_h$), i.e., it is a subgroup of m3m($O_h$). Note however, that it is not possible to go directly from the orthorhombic phase to the tetragonal phase by continuously changing the displacements (without passing first through the cubic phase), i.e., the point group of one is not a subgroup of the other in this case. Finally, in Fig. 7-4d we show the lowest-temperature phase of $BaTiO_3$ where the displacements are now along [111]. This too is a structure whose point group is a subgroup of the cubic m3m($O_h$) and in fact is rhombohedral R3m. The reader should by now be in a position to verify this for himself.

With regard to perovskites with tilted octahedra let us look briefly at just one case, that of $SrTiO_3$, where there is a transition from the ideal cubic structure to one where there is a tilting of the octahedra about the $\mathbf{c}$-axis. This is shown in Fig. 7-6 where we see that the tilting results in a doubling of the unit cell axes. Since the axis of tilt is along $\mathbf{c}$, this direction becomes unique and the structure is tetragonal. You should be able to convince yourself that the space group is F4/mmc($D_{4h}{}^{18}$). Again note that by slowly untilting the octahedra we approach the ideal cubic structure and so this too must be a subgroup of the cubic space group; examination of the symmetry operations for F4/mmc($D_{4h}{}^{18}$) shows that they are all contained in Pm3m($O_h{}^1$).

## 7-3 Irreducible Representations of the Translation Group

One of the very important aspects of group theory for solid state scientists is the use of the irreducible representations as labels for the eigenfunctions of the Hamiltonian. This labelling describes the way that the eigenfunctions transform under all the symmetry operations of the group and gives a considerable amount of information about the degeneracies. Let us review, very briefly, some of the most important aspects of the irreducible representations of a group and apply them to the translation group T.

Returning to the definition of a group, as in Section 4-1, let us concentrate on the closure concept. You will recall that this means that the product of any two elements (a, b, c,..., m, n) of the group must be equal to another element of the group (i.e., ab = m, etc). This can be summarized conveniently in terms of a multiplication table. If there are h elements in the group, then the multiplication table is an h × h array expressing all the binary products of the elements. A set of square matrices for which there is a correspondence with the elements of the group is said to form a **representation of the group**. Thus, for all elements of the group there are matrices [Γ(a), Γ(b), ..., Γ(m), Γ(n)] such that the set of matrices has the same multiplication table (under matrix multiplication) as the elements of the group

$$\Gamma(a)\,\Gamma(b) = \Gamma(m) \qquad \text{if } ab = m \tag{7-1}$$

Another important feature of representations is that, given an $l$-dimensional representation (consisting of h square $l \times l$ square matrices), one may always find an equivalent representation by means of a **similarity transformation**

$$\Gamma'(a) = S^{-1}\,\Gamma(a)\,S \tag{7-2}$$

where S is an $l$-dimensional nonsingular matrix. If Eq. (7-1) is true, it is easy to show, using Eq. (7-2), that $\Gamma'(a)\,\Gamma'(b) = \Gamma'(m)$. Furthermore, given two representations of a group $\Gamma_1(i)$, ..., and $\Gamma_2(i)$, ..., for i = 1 to h, we may always obtain a new representation $\Gamma_1(i) + \Gamma_2(i)$, i = 1 to h, where the binary operator + means

$$\begin{bmatrix} \Gamma_1(a) & 0 \\ 0 & \Gamma_2(a) \end{bmatrix}, \quad \begin{bmatrix} \Gamma_1(b) & 0 \\ 0 & \Gamma_2(b) \end{bmatrix} \quad \text{, etc.} \tag{7-3}$$

(This plus sign is not the normal addition of matrices.) The representation in Eq. (7-3) is said to be in block form. Such a representation, or a representation that arises from Eq. (7-3) but where the block form is obscured by a similarity transform, Eq. (7-2), is said to be a **reducible representation**. A representation that cannot be put into block form is said to be an **irreducible representation**.

Just as the elements in the group can be gathered together according to classes, as in Section 6-6, so can the matrix representations. If certain elements of the group are in the same class, then the corresponding matrices of the representation must also be in the same class, as can be proved by means of Eq. (7-1) and (7-2). This leads to a very useful theorem in group theory, namely, that there are as many irreducible representations as there are classes in a given group. Examples of the determination of the classes for a given group can be found in almost any group theory book, and so we shall not give any at this point. However, we note that the tables of the 32 point groups shown in Appendix 8 have the symmetry operations already gathered together in classes. The equality between the number of classes and irreducible representations may be seen there.

Now, consider the translation group, taking for convenience a 1-dimensional lattice. The symmetry operations are given by $\{1 \mid \mathbf{t}_n\}$, where $\mathbf{t}_n = n\mathbf{a}$. For this group each operation is in a class by itself, because

$$\{1 \mid \mathbf{t}_m\}^{-1} \{1 \mid \mathbf{t}_n\} \{1 \mid \mathbf{t}_m\} = \{1 \mid \mathbf{t}_{-m}\} \{1 \mid \mathbf{t}_{n+m}\} = \{1 \mid \mathbf{t}_n\} \qquad (7\text{-}4)$$

Thus, there are as many irreducible representations as there are elements of the group. It is convenient to consider a finite lattice with periodic boundary conditions. Putting N equal to the number of lattice points, this is expressed as

$$\{1 \mid \mathbf{t}_{n+N}\} = \{1 \mid \mathbf{t}_n\} \qquad (7\text{-}5)$$

We may now express the entire group in terms of powers of the generating element $\{1 \mid \mathbf{a}\}$ since

$$\{1 \mid \mathbf{t}_n\} = \{1 \mid \mathbf{a}\}^n = \{1 \mid \mathbf{a}\}^{n+N} \qquad (7\text{-}6)$$

For this generating element we have $\{1 \mid \mathbf{a}\}^N = \{1 \mid \mathbf{0}\}$. Thus, a representation of the group generated by $\{1 \mid \mathbf{a}\}$ consists of the N roots of unity since these roots have the same multiplication table as the elements of the group.

$$\Gamma\{1 \mid \mathbf{a}\} = [1]^{1/N} = [e^{2\pi i m}]^{1/N} = e^{2\pi i m/N} \qquad m = \text{an integer} \qquad (7\text{-}7)$$

While m may be an integer, its values must be restricted since there are only as many irreducible representations as there are classes, which in this case is equal to N. Conventionally, one picks $0 \leq m \leq N - 1$. It is easy to write out all the representations of the translation group and since they are all 1-dimensional, the representations and characters (sums of the diagonal elements of the matrix representations) are identical. Table 7-1 shows the resulting character table. The first column under $\{1 \mid \mathbf{a}\}$ lists the N roots of unity as in Eq. (7-7) for our allowed values of m. The other columns, $\{1 \mid \mathbf{a}\}^2$, etc., are obtained by squaring, etc., the results of the first column. In the last column we have $\{1 \mid \mathbf{a}\}^N = \{1 \mid \mathbf{0}\}$ and unity for all of the representations. This last column, therefore, gives the result of applying the identity symmetry operation and it is usually placed as the first column in most character tables. Notice that the number m serves as a label for the irreducible representations.

**Table 7-1** The irreducible representations of the translation group.

| | $\{1\mid\underset{\sim}{a}\}$ | $\{1\mid\underset{\sim}{a}\}^2$ | ... | $\{1\mid\underset{\sim}{a}\}^{N-1}$ | $\{1\mid\underset{\sim}{a}\}^N=\{1\mid\underset{\sim}{0}\}$ |
|---|---|---|---|---|---|
| m=0 | 1 | 1 | | 1 | 1 |
| 1 | $\epsilon$ | $\epsilon^2$ | | $\epsilon^{N-1}$ | $\epsilon^N=1$ |
| 2 | $\epsilon^2$ | $\epsilon^4$ | | $\epsilon^{2N-2}$ | $\epsilon^{2N}=1$ |
| . | . | . | | | . |
| . | . | . | | | . |
| N−1 | $\epsilon^{N-1}$ | $\epsilon^{2N-2}$ | | | $\epsilon^{2N-N}=1$ |

where $[\epsilon = \exp(2\pi i/N)]$

For the 3-dimensional lattice the translations in the three directions commute and therefore the resultant irreducible representation is just the direct product of 1-dimensional representations. Thus, noting that $\{1\mid \mathbf{a}\}^n = \{1\mid n\mathbf{a}\}$, we may write the result for the mth irreducible representation for 1- and 3-dimensional cases as

$$\Gamma_m\,\{1\mid n\mathbf{a}\} = e^{i2\pi mn/N} \tag{7-8a}$$

and

$$\Gamma_{m_1,m_2,m_3}\{1\mid \mathbf{t}_n\}=e^{i2\pi m_1n_1/N_1}\,e^{i2\pi m_2n_2/N_2}\,e^{i2\pi m_3n_3/N_3} \tag{7-8b}$$

where $N_i$ refers to the number of lattice points in a particular direction.

By introducing the concept of reciprocal space and Brillouin zones, we may give Eq. (7-8) an important and simple geometric interpretation. Reciprocal lattice vectors, $\mathbf{a}^*$, $\mathbf{b}^*$, and $\mathbf{c}^*$, can be defined in terms of the lattice vectors in direct space, **a**, **b**, and **c**, by

$$\begin{aligned}\mathbf{a}^* &= 2\pi\, \mathbf{b}\times\mathbf{c}/\mathbf{a}\cdot(\mathbf{b}\times\mathbf{c})\\ \mathbf{b}^* &= 2\pi\, \mathbf{c}\times\mathbf{a}/\mathbf{b}\cdot(\mathbf{c}\times\mathbf{a})\\ \mathbf{c}^* &= 2\pi\, \mathbf{a}\times\mathbf{b}/\mathbf{c}\cdot(\mathbf{a}\times\mathbf{b})\end{aligned} \tag{7-9}$$

These equations lead to the following results:

$$\mathbf{a}\cdot\mathbf{a}^* = \mathbf{b}\cdot\mathbf{b}^* = \mathbf{c}\cdot\mathbf{c}^* = 2\pi$$

and
$$\mathbf{a}\cdot\mathbf{b}^* = \mathbf{b}\cdot\mathbf{c}^* = \mathbf{c}\cdot\mathbf{a}^* = 0 \tag{7-10}$$

Note in particular from Eq. (7-10) that a direct axis always has two reciprocal axes perpendicular to itself. Moreover, if the direct lattice is made up of orthogonal vectors (orthorhombic, tetragonal or cubic crystal systems), then the reciprocal axes are parallel to their corresponding direct axes with magnitudes given by

$$|a^*| = 2\pi/a, \quad |b^*| = 2\pi/b, \quad |c^*| = 2\pi/c \tag{7-11}$$

We may define a lattice of points in reciprocal space given by $\mathbf{K}_n$, the **reciprocal lattice vector**,

$$\mathbf{K}_n = n_1\mathbf{a}^* + n_2\mathbf{b}^* + n_3\mathbf{c}^*, \quad n_i = \text{any integer} \tag{7-12}$$

Figure 7-7 shows a 2-dimensional rectangular lattice of points (large dots) defined by Eq. (7-12). **Reciprocal space** or **reciprocal lattice space** is the space defined by these points. Within this space we may define a set of vectors

$$\mathbf{k} = p_1\mathbf{a}^* + p_2\mathbf{b}^* + p_3\mathbf{c}^* \tag{7-13}$$

This looks like Eq. (7-12) but the $|p_i|$ will, in general, be restricted to much smaller values than unity. With $p_i$ very small, we find that the points defined by the end points of **k** form a very high density lattice in reciprocal space. The definition of **k** in Eq. (7-13) is designed to eliminate $m_i$ from Eq. (7-8). We note that

$$\mathbf{k}\cdot\mathbf{t}_n = p_1n_1\, \mathbf{a}\cdot\mathbf{a}^* + \ldots = 2\pi p_1 n_1 + \ldots \tag{7-14}$$

Now, we set $p_i = -m_i/N_i$ and the restriction on $m_i$ is carried over to $p_i$, i.e.,

$$0 \le -p_i \le (N_i-1)/N_i \tag{7-15}$$

This necessitates that $|p_i|$ be smaller than 1 as mentioned above. Now **k** becomes the **label for the irreducible representations** instead of m. The **k**th irreducible representation is given by

$$\Gamma(\mathbf{k};\{1\,|\,\mathbf{t}_n\}) = e^{-i\mathbf{k}\cdot\mathbf{t}_n} \tag{7-16}$$

Figure 7-7 shows the allowed values of **k** in reciprocal space for a 2-dimensional lattice composed of ten by ten unit cells. In real crystals the number of unit cells is very much larger and so the density of points is very much higher. Since

$$e^{-i\mathbf{K}_s\cdot\mathbf{t}_n} = e^{-i(s_1n_1\mathbf{a}^*\cdot\mathbf{a}+\ldots)} = e^{-i2\pi(s_1n_1+\ldots)} = 1 \tag{7-17}$$

the allowed values of **k** in reciprocal space may be drawn within a more convenient primitive cell as shown in Fig. 7-7, namely, the one denoted by the primed numbers. This is obtained by subtracting $\mathbf{K} = \mathbf{a}^*$, $\mathbf{b}^*$ or $\mathbf{a}^*+\mathbf{b}^*$ from the different parts of the space as indicated. The addition of **K** to **k** will make no difference in the irreducible representations, Eq.

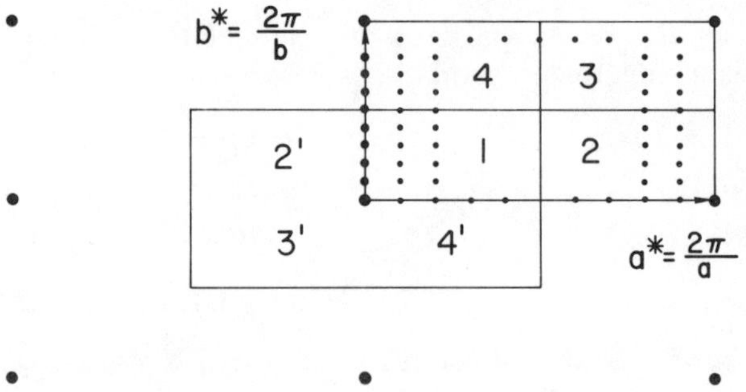


**Fig. 7-7** The large dots show a 2-dimensional reciprocal lattice. The smaller dots show the end ponts of possible k vectors.

(7-16), as shown by Eq. (7-17). The resulting cell in reciprocal space is the conventional **first Brillouin zone** and is symmetrically placed about a reciprocal lattice point. In general this can be derived by the Wigner-Seitz construction in reciprocal space. However, it is important to realize that this is a matter of convenience. The Brillouin zone is simply a unit cell in reciprocal space and can therefore be selected arbitrarily. The Wigner-Seitz construction ensures that the resultant reciprocal unit cell is primitive (it contains only one reciprocal lattice point) and, at the same time, displays the maximum symmetry of the Bravais lattice. This is convenient when trying to carry out calculations based on a Brillouin zone.

The Brillouin zone, therefore, contains the allowed values of **k** that label the irreducible representations of the translation group. The allowed values are bounded by $-\mathbf{a}^*/2$ and $+\mathbf{a}^*/2$, etc., and the previous restriction, $p_i = -m_i/N_i$ from Eq. (7-15), now becomes

$$-1/2 \leq -p_i \leq +1/2 \tag{7-18}$$

The cell defined by Eq. (7-18) has slightly more allowed values than the cell defined by Eq. (7-15). The extra values are at the boundary of the cell but they present no difficulty since they differ from one another by a reciprocal lattice vector and may be considered identical according to Eq. (7-17).

By considering the wave equation for electrons in a solid one may show that **k**, the label of the irreducible representations of the translation group, also has a physical interpretation; it is the wave vector ($\mathbf{k} = 2\pi/\lambda$) of a wave propagating in the crystal. It is a simple matter to show that wave vectors ending at the Brillouin zone boundary correspond to waves satisfying the Bragg reflection law and thus such waves do not propagate without scattering.

For a given value of the wave vector **k**, the eigenfunction of the Hamiltonian that involves translational symmetry alone transforms as the **k**th irreducible representation, i.e., **k** is a label for this eigenfunction. Actually, the Hamiltonian transforms into itself under **all** the symmetry operations of the space group and not only under those of the translation group. Thus, the labels of the eigenfunctions, which describe transformation properties of these functions, involve a particular **k** as well as particular irreducible representation labels of the factor group of the space group taken with respect to the translation group for the given **k** (the group of **k** or little group, see below).

## 7-4 Representations at $\mathbf{k} \neq 0$

When dealing with group theoretical problems at $\mathbf{k} = 0$, use can be made of the factor group G/T which is isomorphic to the point group $G_p$. Thus one can use the same representations as those of the point group when carrying out such an analysis. However when $\mathbf{k} \neq 0$, the problems become more complicated. We summarize some of the results here.

There are two different approaches to the $\mathbf{k} \neq 0$ problem. The method due to Herring, which is the earlier of the two, relies on the construction of the factor group $G_k/T_k$. $G_k$ is a subgroup of the space group G and consists of all the elements $\{R \,|\, \mathbf{t}_n + \boldsymbol{\tau}\}$, which either do not change **k** or change it by adding a reciprocal lattice vector; $\mathbf{t}_n$ is a lattice translation vector of the crystal and $\boldsymbol{\tau}$ is a nonsymmorphic translation vector. $G_k$ is known as the **group of k** or **little group**. $T_k$ is the subgroup of the lattice translations for which $\exp(-i\mathbf{k}\cdot\mathbf{t}) = 1$. Since we are "dividing out" only some of the translations, i.e., we ignore those translations for which $\exp(-i\mathbf{k}\cdot\mathbf{t}) = -1$, the resultant factor group is very large.

The second more recent approach is the method of **multiplier (ray or projective) representations**, introduced into solid state problems by Lyubarskii and later applied to normal mode analysis by Maradudin and Vosko. This method allows one to deal with the non-zero **k** problem by handling small groups with, at most, h elements. It is thus possible to have a complete set of tables of irreducible multiplier representations which can be treated in much the same manner as point group representations. (Kovalev's tables are, in fact, tables of irreducible multiplier representations.) Because of the convenience of the latter method we shall confine ourselves to the discussion of multiplier representations. We shall only sketch the arguments here as full details can be found in the book by Lyubarskii.

As before, we denote the space group as G and let Γ be a representation of the subgroup T of all translations of G. Therefore, Γ can be decomposed into 1-dimensional representations of T characterized by wave vectors **k**. The set of vectors $\mathbf{k}_1$, $\mathbf{k}_2$, ... characterizing the representations of T that are contained in Γ is called the **star of the representation** and can be shown to be invariant with respect to the elements of G. This means that each vector of the star of the representation is transformed by any element of G to another vector of the star.

Consider the subgroup $G_k$ of G as defined above, i.e., the group of vector **k**. The representations of $G_k$ are known as **small representations**, denoted $\Gamma(\mathbf{k}; \{R \mid \mathbf{t}_n+\boldsymbol{\tau}\})$. It can be shown that the vector **k** and the representation $\Gamma(\mathbf{k};\{R \mid \mathbf{t}_n+\boldsymbol{\tau}\})$ uniquely define the representation Γ. Moreover, if $\Gamma(\mathbf{k};\{R \mid \mathbf{t}_n+\boldsymbol{\tau}\})$ is unitary, so too is Γ. Again, if $\Gamma(\mathbf{k};\{R \mid \mathbf{t}_n+\boldsymbol{\tau}\})$ is irreducible, the representation Γ is also irreducible, and vice-versa.

Let us examine the representation $\Gamma(\mathbf{k};\{R \mid \mathbf{t}_n+\boldsymbol{\tau}\})$ in more detail. As stated earlier, any element of the group $G_k$ is given as $\{R \mid \mathbf{t}_n+\boldsymbol{\tau}\}$. It is also possible to define a group $\overline{G}_k$ consisting of all the elements R, which we call the **point group of vector k** or **little co-group**. With each element R of the point group $\overline{G}_k$, we associate an operator T(**k**;R) which is defined by

$$T(\mathbf{k};R) = \Gamma(\mathbf{k};\{R \mid \mathbf{t}_n+\boldsymbol{\tau}\})\, e^{-i\mathbf{k}\cdot(\mathbf{t}_n+\boldsymbol{\tau})} \qquad (7\text{-}19)$$

This definition is unique despite the fact that to every element, R, there corresponds an infinite number of different operations in the group $G_k$. We see therefore that the matrix operator T(**k**;R) completely defines the representation $\Gamma(\mathbf{k};\{R \mid \mathbf{t}_n+\boldsymbol{\tau}\})$. There is a one-to-one correspondence between the elements of the point group of **k**, $\overline{G}_k$, and the matrices T(**k**;R). However, the latter do not, generally, provide a representation of $\overline{G}_k$ in the usual sense. To see this consider two operations $\{R_1 \mid \mathbf{t}_{(1)}\}$ and $\{R_2 \mid \mathbf{t}_{(2)}\}$ contained in $G_k$, where for short-hand we have put $\mathbf{t}_{(1)} = \mathbf{t}_n + \boldsymbol{\tau}_1$ and $\mathbf{t}_{(2)} = \mathbf{t}_n + \boldsymbol{\tau}_2$. We have

$$\{R_1 \mid \mathbf{t}_{(1)}\}\, \{R_2 \mid \mathbf{t}_{(2)}\} = \{R_1R_2 \mid \mathbf{t}_{(1)} + R_1\, \mathbf{t}_{(2)}\} \qquad (7\text{-}20)$$

Thus, using Eq. (7-19), we obtain

$$T(\mathbf{k};R_1R_2) = \Gamma(\mathbf{k};\{R_1 \mid \mathbf{t}_{(1)}\}\, \{R_2 \mid \mathbf{t}_{(2)}\})\, e^{-i\mathbf{k}\cdot(\mathbf{t}_{(1)}+R_1\mathbf{t}_{(2)})} \qquad (7\text{-}21a)$$

Now consider the term, $\mathbf{k}\cdot R_1\, \mathbf{t}_{(2)}$, in Eq. (7-21a). In Fig. 7-8a we show what this means. The operator $R_1$ rotates the vector $\mathbf{t}_{(2)}$ counterclockwise through an angle ψ to form a new vector $\mathbf{t}'_{(2)}$ of the same magnitude. Then, the scalar product with **k** projects **k** onto $\mathbf{t}'_{(2)}$ through an angle θ to

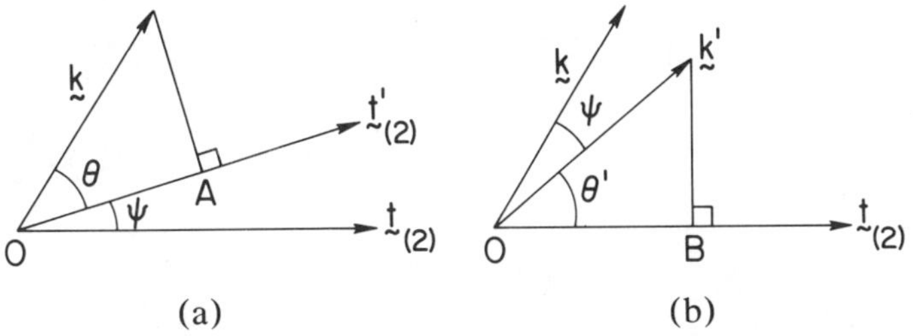


Fig. 7-8

form the length OA. In Fig. 7-8b we show the equivalent diagram for $R_1^{-1}\mathbf{k}\cdot\mathbf{t}_{(2)}$. Here, $R_1^{-1}$ rotates the vector **k** clockwise through the angle $\psi$ to form vector $\mathbf{k}'$. This is then projected through an angle $\theta'$ to form the length OB. As in both diagrams the angle between **k** and $\mathbf{t}_{(2)}$ is the same, $\theta + \psi = \theta' + \psi$ and therefore $\theta = \theta'$. This means that $\mathbf{k}\cdot R_1\,\mathbf{t}_{(2)}$ is equivalent to $R_1^{-1}\,\mathbf{k}\cdot\mathbf{t}_{(2)}$. Therefore, we can write

$$\begin{aligned} T(\mathbf{k};R_1R_2) &= \Gamma(\mathbf{k};\{R_1\,|\,\mathbf{t}_{(1)}\})\,\Gamma(\mathbf{k};\{R_2\,|\,\mathbf{t}_{(2)}\})\,e^{[-i\mathbf{k}\cdot\mathbf{t}_{(1)}-i\,R_1^{-1}\mathbf{k}\cdot\mathbf{t}_{(2)}]} \\ &= T(\mathbf{k};R_1)\,T(\mathbf{k};R_2)\,e^{i(\mathbf{k}-R_1^{-1}\mathbf{k})\cdot\mathbf{t}_{(2)}} \end{aligned} \tag{7-21b}$$

By definition of $G_k$, the element $R_1^{-1}$ either does not change **k** or transforms it into an equivalent vector by adding to it a vector **K** of the reciprocal lattice:

$$R_1^{-1}\,\mathbf{k} = \mathbf{k} + \mathbf{K} \tag{7-22}$$

and therefore,

$$T(\mathbf{k};R_1R_2) = T(\mathbf{k};R_1)\,T(\mathbf{k};R_2)\,e^{-i\mathbf{K}\cdot\boldsymbol{\tau}_2} \tag{7-23}$$

where we have used the fact that $\mathbf{K}\cdot\mathbf{t}_n = 2\pi \times$ integer. The quantity $\phi(\mathbf{k};R_1,R_2) = e^{-i\mathbf{K}\cdot\boldsymbol{\tau}_2}$ is known as a **multiplier** and the matrices $T(\mathbf{k};R)$ are said to provide a **unitary multiplier representation** of the point group $\overline{G}_k$ of wave vector **k**. From Eq. (7-19), it follows that to each irreducible representation of $G_k$ there corresponds an irreducible multiplier representation, $\hat{\tau}^i$ of the point group, $\overline{G}_k$, with the same dimension. Note that if **k** lies within the Brillouin zone the reciprocal lattice vector **K** is identically zero and the multiplier equals unity. It is also always unity for symmorphic space groups. For these two cases, therefore, the matrices $T(\mathbf{k};R)$ provide an ordinary representation of the point group, $\overline{G}_k$. It is only when **k** is on the Brillouin zone boundary for a crystal belonging to a nonsymmorphic space group that the representation of $\overline{G}_k$ provided by $T(\mathbf{k};R)$ can be different from an ordinary representation (although it is not necessarily different).

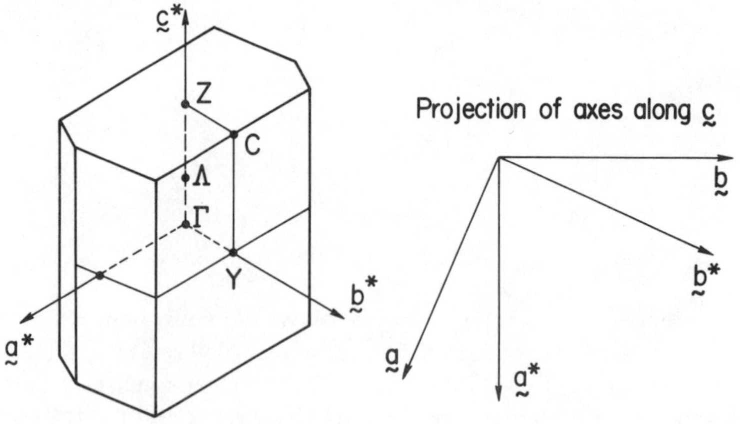


**Fig. 7-9** The Brillouin zone for a primitive monoclinic crystal.

Let us now try to understand how the irreducible multiplier representations $\hat{r}^i$ of $\overline{G}_k$ can be calculated. The easiest way of seeing this is with a specific example. Consider the space group $P2_1/b(C_{2h}{}^5)$ (1st setting) and, in particular, wave vector **k** given by (0, b*/2, c*/2). Figure 7-9 shows the Brillouin zone for a primitive monoclinic crystal and the **k** in question ends at the point marked C. By examining the symmetry of the environment of this point in reciprocal space we easily determine that the point group of the wave vector, $\overline{G}_k$, is $2/m(C_{2h})$, with symmetry elements {1, 2[001], $\overline{1}$, m[001]}. The corresponding elements of G are, as we shall see in the next section, $\{1 \mid \mathbf{0}\}$, $\{2[001] \mid \tau(0,0,1/2)\}$ $\{\overline{1} \mid \tau(0,1/2,1/2)\}$ and $\{m[001] \mid \tau(0,1/2,0)\}$. We have ignored the infinite number of translations $\mathbf{t}_n$ here since Eq. (7-23) shows that they do not enter explicitly into the multipliers. We now make use of the fact that in a group

$$R_pR_q = R_r \tag{7-24}$$

and then from Eq. (7-23)

$$T(\mathbf{k};R_r) = T(\mathbf{k};R_p)\, T(\mathbf{k};R_q)\, e^{i[\mathbf{k}-\mathbf{R}_p{}^{-1}\mathbf{k}]\bullet\tau_q} \tag{7-25}$$

Hence for the irreducible representations,

$$\begin{aligned}\hat{r}^i(r) &= \hat{r}^i(p)\hat{r}^i(q)\, e^{i[\mathbf{k}-\mathbf{R}_p{}^{-1}\mathbf{k}]\bullet\tau_q} \\ &= \hat{r}^i(p)\hat{r}^i(q)\, \phi\, (\mathbf{k};\, R_p,\, R_q)\end{aligned} \tag{7-26}$$

where $\hat{r}^i(p)$ means the matrix for operation $R_p$ in the *i*th irreducible representation $\hat{r}^i$, and similarly for $\hat{r}^i(q)$ and $\hat{r}^i(r)$. We start by composing the multiplier $\phi(\mathbf{k};R_p, R_q)$ for each combination of operations. For example, for $\{\bar{1}\,|\,\tau\ (0,1/2,1/2)\}$ and $\{m\,|\,\tau\ (0,1/2,0)\}$, whose rotational parts for convenience we shall denote as $R_3$ and $R_4$, we have

$$\begin{aligned}\phi(\mathbf{k};R_3,R_4) &= e^{\,i[\mathbf{k} - \{\bar{1}\}^{-1}\mathbf{k}]\bullet\tau(0,1/2,0)} \\ &= e^{\,i\,2\mathbf{k}\bullet\tau(0,1/2,0)} \\ &= e^{\,i\,2\,(\mathbf{b}^*/2\,+\,\mathbf{c}^*/2)\,\bullet\,\mathbf{b}/2} \\ &= -1 \end{aligned} \qquad (7\text{-}27)$$

In Table 7-2 we list all of the multipliers for this value of **k** together with the multiplication table of $\hat{\Gamma}^i(p)\ \hat{\Gamma}^i(q)$. Because the point group $\overline{G}_k$ is $2/m(C_{2h})$ (and the sum of the squares of the dimensions must equal the number of elements in the group) it either consists of four 1-dimensional representations or one of two dimensions. We see that

$$\hat{\Gamma}^i(p)\hat{\Gamma}^i(q) = \hat{\Gamma}^i(q)\hat{\Gamma}^i(p) \qquad (7\text{-}28)$$

so that the representations must be 1-dimensional. The table of irreducible multiplier representations (Table 7-2) is easily obtained by inspection of the multiplication table.

Consider now the case of $\mathbf{k} = (0,0,c^*/2)$. In this case, the Z-point, the point group $\overline{G}_k$ is again $2/m(C_{2h})$. Table 7-3 lists the multipliers $\phi(R_p,R_q)$ and corresponding multiplication table. In this case we see that

$$\hat{\Gamma}^i(3)\hat{\Gamma}^i(4) = -\hat{\Gamma}^i(4)\hat{\Gamma}^i(3) \qquad (7\text{-}29)$$

which is only possible if there is a single 2-dimensional representation for this $\overline{G}_k$. We can derive the representation as follows. Consider the representation decomposed into the 1-dimensional representations of the subgroup $2(C_2)$. In order to achieve this decomposition, the matrix, $\hat{\Gamma}^i(2)$, of operation $\{\,2[001]\,|\,\mathbf{0}\}$ must be equal to one of the following matrices:

$$\begin{bmatrix}1 & 0\\ 0 & -1\end{bmatrix},\quad \begin{bmatrix}1 & 0\\ 0 & 1\end{bmatrix},\quad \begin{bmatrix}-1 & 0\\ 0 & -1\end{bmatrix} \qquad (7\text{-}30)$$

because the diagonal elements must be made up from the characters under operation $\{2\,|\,\mathbf{0}\}$ in point group $2(C_2)$. However, the last two matrices can be rejected as they commute with all the matrices. Thus,

$$\hat{\Gamma}^i(2) = \begin{bmatrix}1 & 0\\ 0 & -1\end{bmatrix} \qquad (7\text{-}31)$$

Now define

$$\hat{\Gamma}^i(3) = \begin{bmatrix}a & b\\ c & d\end{bmatrix} \qquad (7\text{-}32)$$

**Table 7-2** (a) Multipliers $\phi(k;R_i,R_j)$ for the operations $R_1=\{1\,|\,\mathbf{0}\}$, $R_2=\{2\,|\,\tau(0,0,1/2)\}$, $R_3=\{\bar{1}\,|\,\tau(0,1/2,1/2)\}$; $R_4=\{m\,|\,\tau(0,1/2,0)\}$ at $k=(0,b^*/2,c^*/2)$ in $P2_1/b$ ($C_{2h}{}^5$). (b) Multiplication table and character table for the irreducible representations.

(a)

| $\phi(\underset{\sim}{k};R_i,R_j)$ | $R_1$ | $R_2$ | $R_3$ | $R_4$ |
|---|---|---|---|---|
| $R_1$ | 1 | 1 | 1 | 1 |
| $R_2$ | 1 | 1 | −1 | −1 |
| $R_3$ | 1 | −1 | 1 | −1 |
| $R_4$ | 1 | −1 | −1 | 1 |

(b)

| | $\hat{\tau}^i(1)$ | $\hat{\tau}^i(2)$ | $\hat{\tau}^i(3)$ | $\hat{\tau}^i(4)$ |
|---|---|---|---|---|
| $\hat{\tau}^i(1)$ | $\hat{\tau}^i(1)$ | $\hat{\tau}^i(2)$ | $\hat{\tau}^i(3)$ | $\hat{\tau}^i(4)$ |
| $\hat{\tau}^i(2)$ | $\hat{\tau}^i(2)$ | $\hat{\tau}^i(1)$ | $-\hat{\tau}^i(4)$ | $-\hat{\tau}^i(3)$ |
| $\hat{\tau}^i(3)$ | $\hat{\tau}^i(3)$ | $-\hat{\tau}^i(4)$ | $\hat{\tau}^i(1)$ | $-\hat{\tau}^i(2)$ |
| $\hat{\tau}^i(4)$ | $\hat{\tau}^i(4)$ | $-\hat{\tau}^i(3)$ | $-\hat{\tau}^i(2)$ | $\hat{\tau}^i(1)$ |

(c)

| | $\{1\,|\,\underset{\sim}{0}\}$ | $\{2\,|\,\underset{\sim}{0}\}$ | $\{\bar{1}\,|\,\underset{\sim}{0}\}$ | $\{m\,|\,\underset{\sim}{0}\}$ |
|---|---|---|---|---|
| $\hat{\tau}1$ | 1 | 1 | 1 | −1 |
| $\hat{\tau}2$ | 1 | 1 | −1 | 1 |
| $\hat{\tau}3$ | 1 | −1 | 1 | 1 |
| $\hat{\tau}4$ | 1 | −1 | −1 | −1 |

From Table 7-3 we find that

$$\hat{\tau}^i(2)\hat{\tau}^i(3) = -\hat{\tau}^i(3)\hat{\tau}^i(2) \tag{7-33}$$

and therefore

$$\begin{bmatrix} 1 & 0 \\ 0 & -1 \end{bmatrix}\begin{bmatrix} a & b \\ c & d \end{bmatrix} = -\begin{bmatrix} a & b \\ c & d \end{bmatrix}\begin{bmatrix} 1 & 0 \\ 0 & -1 \end{bmatrix} \tag{7-34}$$

or

$$\begin{bmatrix} a & b \\ -c & -d \end{bmatrix} = \begin{bmatrix} -a & b \\ -c & d \end{bmatrix} \tag{7-35}$$

Hence we find that a and d = 0. In addition,

$$\hat{\tau}^i(3)\hat{\tau}^i(3) = -\hat{\tau}^i(1) \tag{7-36}$$

**Table 7-3** Same as previous table but for k=(0,0,c*/2).

(a)

| $\phi(\underset{\sim}{k}; R_i, R_j)$ | $R_1$ | $R_2$ | $R_3$ | $R_4$ |
|---|---|---|---|---|
| $R_1$ | 1 | 1 | 1 | 1 |
| $R_2$ | 1 | 1 | 1 | 1 |
| $R_3$ | 1 | −1 | −1 | 1 |
| $R_4$ | 1 | −1 | −1 | 1 |

(b)

| | $\hat{\tau}^i(1)$ | $\hat{\tau}^i(2)$ | $\hat{\tau}^i(3)$ | $\hat{\tau}^i(4)$ |
|---|---|---|---|---|
| $\hat{\tau}^i(1)$ | $\hat{\tau}^i(1)$ | $\hat{\tau}^i(2)$ | $\hat{\tau}^i(3)$ | $\hat{\tau}^i(4)$ |
| $\hat{\tau}^i(2)$ | $\hat{\tau}^i(2)$ | $\hat{\tau}^i(1)$ | $\hat{\tau}^i(4)$ | $\hat{\tau}^i(3)$ |
| $\hat{\tau}^i(3)$ | $\hat{\tau}^i(3)$ | $-\hat{\tau}^i(4)$ | $-\hat{\tau}^i(1)$ | $\hat{\tau}^i(2)$ |
| $\hat{\tau}^i(4)$ | $\hat{\tau}^i(4)$ | $-\hat{\tau}^i(3)$ | $-\hat{\tau}^i(2)$ | $\hat{\tau}^i(1)$ |

(c)

| | $\{1\,\vert\,\underset{\sim}{0}\}$ | $\{2\,\vert\,\underset{\sim}{0}\}$ | $\{\bar{1}\,\vert\,\underset{\sim}{0}\}$ | $\{m\,\vert\,\underset{\sim}{0}\}$ |
|---|---|---|---|---|
| $\hat{\tau}^1$ | $\begin{bmatrix} 1 & 0 \\ 0 & 1 \end{bmatrix}$ | $\begin{bmatrix} 1 & 0 \\ 0 & -1 \end{bmatrix}$ | $\begin{bmatrix} 0 & 1 \\ -1 & 0 \end{bmatrix}$ | $\begin{bmatrix} 0 & 1 \\ 1 & 0 \end{bmatrix}$ |

or

$$\begin{bmatrix} 0 & b \\ c & 0 \end{bmatrix}\begin{bmatrix} 0 & b \\ c & 0 \end{bmatrix} = -\begin{bmatrix} 1 & 0 \\ 0 & 1 \end{bmatrix} \tag{7-37}$$

which leads to the result that $b\,c = -1$. We arbitrarily put $b = 1$ and $c = -1$ so that

$$\hat{\tau}^i(3) = \begin{bmatrix} 0 & 1 \\ -1 & 0 \end{bmatrix} \tag{7-38}$$

It is now a simple matter to find $\hat{\tau}^i(4)$ and the resulting table of representations is given in Table 7-3. Because there is only one representation in this case, the index i only takes the value 1. Note that our result implies that at the Z-point there is 2-fold degeneracy. This is a consequence of Z being at a special point on the Brillouin zone boundary of a nonsymmorphic space group and gives rise to a "sticking together" of species such as electronic bands or normal modes at this particular value of **k**.

The tables of irreducible multiplier representations obtained in the way described here are precisely the same as those in Kovalev's tables, so that in principle, the reader should now be in a position to be able to produce any of the tables for himself.

## 7-5 Normal Mode Analysis

In this section we shall describe how one can apply what we have learnt about space groups and irreducible representations to the problem of finding the symmetries of vibrational waves or phonons propagating in a crystalline solid. We shall not go into any great detail here since full details may be found in many articles and books on group theory.

We shall start by discussing a fairly common problem, namely, the analysis of normal modes of vibration with $\mathbf{k} \approx 0$ and then go on to deal briefly with modes with $\mathbf{k} \neq 0$. As we have said earlier, the latter subject is very rarely dealt with in the literature and even when it is, the treatment is often obscured by very heavy mathematics. We shall try and deal with this topic in a very simple manner which, of course, will not be rigorous nor complete. We hope, however, that our discussion will put the reader in a better position to understand the literature on this subject.

**7-5a Lattice Vibrations, $\mathbf{k} \approx 0$** Waves in solids with $\mathbf{k} \approx 0$ have very long wavelengths ($k = 2\pi/\lambda$) and therefore can couple directly to incident light. This coupling can be used in the determination of the normal modes of vibration since it means that light of an appropriate wavelength can be absorbed (in the infrared region) or else it can be scattered inelastically (Raman scattering). Spectroscopic resolution of both processes can be achieved fairly easily in the laboratory and the number and frequencies of the normal modes can be found. The analysis of these normal modes is usually achieved by standard group theory techniques and has been discussed extensively in the literature, particularly with regard to isolated molecules.

The analysis for molecules can be summarized quite simply, starting from the fact that for a molecule the symmetry group is the point group of the molecule. If the molecule has p atoms, there are 3p normal modes of vibration, because in 3-dimensional space there are three degrees of vibrational freedom for each atom. These 3p normal modes can be described in terms of arbitrary displacements of the p atoms. We affix to each atom a coordinate system given by three axes, x, y, z. Thus, we have 3p coordinates $x_1, y_1, z_1; x_2, y_2, z_2; ...; x_p, y_p, z_p$. We must now ask how these 3p coordinates transform among themselves under all the symmetry operations of the point group. For each symmetry operation, a 3p × 3p matrix describing that transformation is obtained. These h matrices, where h = order of the group, then form a representation of the group. In the solution of this problem, one needs only to know the character of this representation. (The **character**, **trace** or **spur**, is the sum of the diagonal elements of a matrix.) This makes the problem rather easy since, for a given symmetry operation, it is only possible to have a contribution to the character if the atom transforms into itself under the symmetry operation. The characters of this representation may be reduced, by standard group theory techniques, in order to determine under which irreducible representations the normal modes of vibration transform. We do not give an example of this technique applied to molecules since essentially the same method can be applied to crystals and the example that follows should suffice.

For the case of crystals the same approach is used except that the symmetry group clearly is the space group and not the point group. Since we shall consider only the very long wavelength limit, each unit cell vibrates in phase with the next and so the full translational symmetry of the crystal is also applied to the normal modes. Thus, for the very long wavelength limit any arbitrary displacement in any one unit cell may be translated back to the cell we choose as our origin, and we need only consider the space group operations of the type $\{R \mid \tau\}$, where $\tau$ is a fraction of a unit cell distance. Naturally, these operations are simply the symmetry operations of the factor group of the space group. Using these symmetry operations on the p atoms in the primitive cell, we obtain a 3p × 3p matrix for each operation (again we need only work with the characters of the representation). Since the symmetry operations of the factor group of the space group are isomorphic to the operations of the point group, we may reduce this representation of the factor group in terms of the irreducible representations of the point group. This reduction is accomplished in the same way as in the molecule problem and shows the number of normal modes of vibration that transform as each irreducible representation.

An example should make this procedure absolutely clear and also show, in an elementary manner, the use of symmetry operations of the space group and their relation to those of the point group of the space group. For this we shall consider the nonsymmorphic space group $P2_1/b(C_{2h}^5)$. Figure 7-10 shows the space group diagram for this with

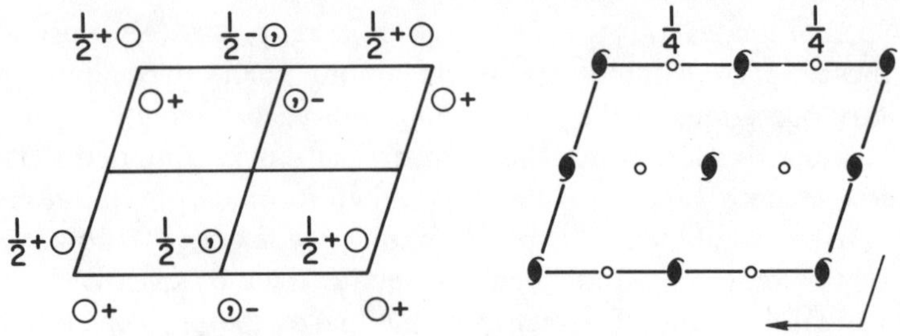


P$2_1$/b; ORIGIN AT $2_1$ AND b-GLIDE

| SITE | SITE SYMMETRY | |
|---|---|---|
| 4e | 1 | $x,y,z;\ -x,-y,\frac{1}{2}+z;\ x,\frac{1}{2}+y,-z;-x,\frac{1}{2}-y,\frac{1}{2}-z$ |
| 2d | $\bar{1}$ | $\frac{1}{2},\frac{1}{4},\frac{1}{4};\ \frac{1}{2},\frac{3}{4},\frac{3}{4}$ |
| 2c | $\bar{1}$ | $0,\frac{1}{4},\frac{1}{4};\ 0,\frac{3}{4},\frac{3}{4}$ |
| 2b | $\bar{1}$ | $\frac{1}{2},\frac{3}{4},\frac{1}{4};\ \frac{1}{2},\frac{1}{4},\frac{3}{4}$ |
| 2a | $\bar{1}$ | $0,\frac{3}{4},\frac{1}{4};\ 0,\frac{1}{4},\frac{3}{4}$ |

**Fig. 7-10.**

the origin taken at the intersection of the $2_1$ axis and the b-glide plane. We do this simply in order to be consistent with Kovalev. (While choice of origin does not matter in the $\mathbf{k} \approx 0$ case, it is important for $\mathbf{k} \neq 0$ as it determines which irreducible representation is used for a specific normal mode of vibration. Since Kovalev lists all the tables of irreducible multiplier representations for the point group of vector $\mathbf{k}$, $\overline{G}_k$, it is useful therefore to use Kovalev's origin particularly when we come to deal with the $\mathbf{k} \neq 0$ problem.) Imagine that at each general position, the 4e sites, a coordinate system of axes is attached. The problem, then, is to identify what happens to these positions and to their attached coordinate axes under the symmetry operations of the factor group of P$2_1$/b. In the point group of this space group there are four operations and these are isomorphic to the four space group operations, which with respect to a fixed origin as chosen here are

$$\{1\,|\,\mathbf{0}\},\{2[001]\,|\,\tau(0,0,1/2)\},\{\bar{1}\,|\,\tau(0,1/2,1/2)\},\text{and}\{m[001]\,|\,\tau(0,1/2,0)\}.$$

These are the same as Kovalev's operations, except that, for convenience, we have taken the glide direction to be along **b** rather than **a** (this makes no difference to this part of the analysis). Let us consider the effect of each operation in turn on the four general equivalent positions and their attached axes.

Under the identity operation $\{1 \mid \mathbf{0}\}$, of course, the positions do not change, as shown in Table 7-4, nor do the attached coordinate axes. The character under this operation is therefore $4 \times 3 = 12$ and this is entered in Table 7-5. Under the next three operations each general position is taken into another as shown in Table 7-4 and therefore there are no contributions to the characters under these operations. Hence in Table 7-5 we see 0 writen under these three operations for 4e sites. In the special positions we find that the situation is somewhat different. In Table 7-4 we see that the special positions are taken into themselves under $\{\bar{1} \mid \tau(0, 1/2, 1/2)\}$. Thus position 5 (1/2, 1/4, 1/4) is taken by this operation to (−1/2, 1/4, 1/4), which by a primitive lattice translation along **a** is equal to (1/2, 1/4, 1/4). Thus each special position contributes to the character. Since the inversion part of this operation takes each attached coordinate axes to its inverse, i.e., $x_1 \rightarrow -x_1$, $y_1 \rightarrow -y_1$, $z_1 \rightarrow -z_1$,..., there is a contribution of −3 to the character for each position. Thus we find in Table 7-5 the character −6 for the two symmetry-related special positions.

In Table 7-6 we show the character table of the point group $2/m(C_{2h})$ which is isomorphic to the factor group of the space group $P2_1/b(C_{2h}{}^5)$. The isomorphic correspondence between the elements of the two groups is shown. Then, by standard group theory techniques we may reduce the character of the representation of the factor group in terms of the irreducible representations of the point group. This leads to the following reduction:

for the 4e sites $\Gamma = 3A_g + 3B_g + 3A_u + 3B_u$

for the 2a, 2b, 2c, and 2d sites $\Gamma = 3A_u + 3B_u$

We use here the standard chemical symbols for the irreducible representations. We should point out that the solution found above applies to all crystals with space group $P2_1/b(C_{2h}{}^5)$, no matter how complicated. The 4e sites may be occupied by many different types of atoms, although naturally each group of four must have a different value of (x,y,z). For each group of four the same set of irreducible representations is found. The vibration problem may be solved for any space group for all the possible positions in precisely the same way. To do this for all the space groups is a large but clearly finite problem.

**Table 7-4** Effect of symmetry operations on the equivalent posiions of $P2_1/b(C_{2h}{}^5)$.

| | | $\{1 \mid \underset{\sim}{0}\}$ | $\{2\,[001] \mid \underset{\sim}{\tau}(0,0,½)\}$ | $\{\bar{1} \mid \underset{\sim}{\tau}(0,½,½)\}$ | $\{m\,[001] \mid \underset{\sim}{\tau}(0,½,0)\}$ |
|---|---|---|---|---|---|
| 4e | 1 | 1 | 2 | 4 | 3 |
| | 2 | 2 | 1 | 3 | 4 |
| | 3 | 3 | 4 | 2 | 1 |
| | 4 | 4 | 3 | 1 | 2 |
| 2d | 5 | 5 | 6 | 5 | 6 |
| | 6 | 6 | 5 | 6 | 5 |
| 2c | 7 | 7 | 8 | 7 | 8 |
| | 8 | 8 | 7 | 8 | 7 |
| 2b | 9 | 9 | 10 | 9 | 10 |
| | 10 | 10 | 9 | 10 | 9 |
| 2a | 11 | 11 | 12 | 11 | 12 |
| | 12 | 12 | 11 | 12 | 11 |

Position
1 x,y,z
2 −x,−y, ½+z
3 x, ½ + y, −z
4 −x, ½−y, ½−z

Position
5 ½,¼,¼
6 ½,¾,¾

Position
7 0,¼,¼
8 0,¾,¾

Position
9 ½,¾,¼
10 ½,¼,¾

Position
11 0,¾,¼
12 0,¼,¾

**Table 7-5** Reducible representations of $P2_1/b(C_{2h}{}^5)$ at k=0.

| | $\{1 \mid \underset{\sim}{0}\}$ | $\{2 \mid \underset{\sim}{\tau}(0,0,½)\}$ | $\{\bar{1} \mid \underset{\sim}{\tau}(0,½,½)\}$ | $\{m \mid \underset{\sim}{\tau}(0,½,0)\}$ |
|---|---|---|---|---|
| 4e | 12 | 0 | 0 | 0 |
| 2d | 6 | 0 | −6 | 0 |
| 2c | 6 | 0 | −6 | 0 |
| 2b | 6 | 0 | −6 | 0 |
| 2a | 6 | 0 | −6 | 0 |

**Table 7-6** The character table for the point group2/m($C_{2h}$).

| $P2_1/b(C_{2h}^5)$ <br> $2/m(C_{2h})$ | $\{1\|\tilde{0}\}$ <br> 1 | $\{2\|\tilde{\tau}(0,0,\frac{1}{2})\}$ <br> 2 | $\{\bar{1}\|\tilde{\tau}(0,\frac{1}{2},\frac{1}{2})\}$ <br> $\bar{1}$ | $\{m\|\tilde{\tau}(0,\frac{1}{2},0)\}$ <br> m |
|---|---|---|---|---|
| $\hat{\tau}^1$, $A_g$ | 1 | 1 | 1 | 1 |
| $\hat{\tau}^2$, $B_g$ | 1 | −1 | 1 | −1 |
| $\hat{\tau}^3$, $A_u$ | 1 | 1 | −1 | −1 |
| $\hat{\tau}^4$, $B_u$ | 1 | −1 | −1 | 1 |

Finally, note one special item. Because in a molecule there is complete freedom of translation and rotation, the representations of the vibrational modes are found after subtracting the three representations that transform as rotations $R_x$, $R_y$, and $R_z$ (two for a linear molecule) and the three representations that transform as a bulk translation $T_x$, $T_y$, and $T_z$. In a crystalline solid, however, there is no complete rotational or translational freedom and therefore both types of representations must be considered. However, the translational modes or acoustic modes have zero energy at infinite wavelength (**k** = 0) and hence are not found in the inelastically scattered light spectrum of a normal Raman experiment. Therefore, the three translational representations ($A_u + 2B_u$) are subtracted out of the set of irreducible representations in order to leave only the long-wavelength optic modes.

**7-5b Lattice Vibrations, k ≠ 0** In this section we should like to sketch briefly the steps needed to analyze the symmetries of representations for modes with nonzero wave vector. This is typical of the kind of problem met with in inelastic neutron studies of phonon dispersion relations, where the wavelength of the neutrons (around 1 – 2 Å) is small enough to allow the neutrons to couple to the short-wavelength phonons at nonzero **k**.

Let us once again take the case of the space group $P2_1/b(C_{2h}^5)$ and consider the Brillouin zone shown in Fig. 7-9. As we have explained earlier, points in the Brillouin zone represent waves with different wave vectors given by the distance from the center of the zone, at Γ, to these points. (Special points are marked by a letter.) The directions of the wave vectors are also the directions of propagation of the waves.

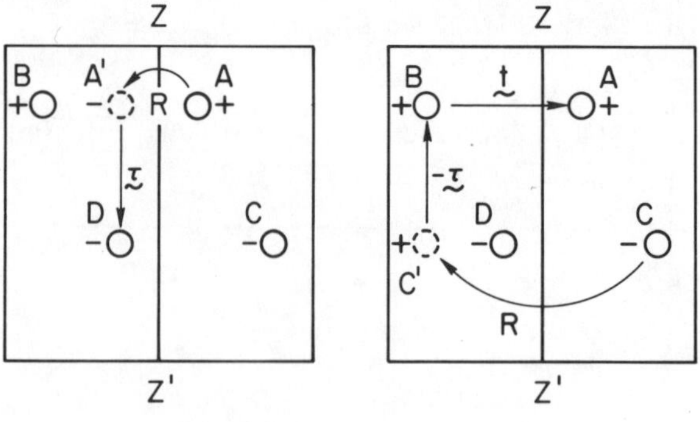


(a) (b)

**Fig. 7-11.**

Now, in order to carry out the analysis we must consider the effects of symmetry operations $\{R \mid \boldsymbol{\tau}\}$ on the various positions and attached coordinate axes, as in the previous section. However, this time it is not generally true to assume that equivalent positions in neighboring unit cells vibrate in phase with those in the chosen cell and we must now make use of the multiplier representations defined by Eq. (7-19).

That is, we form matrices $T(\mathbf{k};R)$ with elements $T_{\alpha\beta}$ $(i,j,\mathbf{k};R)$ which can be shown (see Maradudin and Vosko) to be given by

$$T_{\alpha\beta}(i,j,\mathbf{k};R) = \delta_{ij}e^{\{i\mathbf{k}\cdot[\mathbf{r}_i - R\mathbf{r}_j]\}} R_{\alpha\beta} \tag{7-39}$$

where $R_{\alpha\beta}$ form the elements of the matrix representation of the rotation R. $\delta_{ij} = 1$ if a position given by $r_i$ is transformed to one given by $r_j$ under the operation $\{R \mid \boldsymbol{\tau}\}$ and $\delta_{ij} = 0$ otherwise.

Let us look more closely at Eq. (7-39) and see exactly what it means. Figure 7-11a shows two unit cells each with two atoms. Consider, for example, a symmetry operation $\{R \mid \boldsymbol{\tau}\}$ operating about the line $ZZ'$ such that the atom A given by position vector $\mathbf{r}_A$ is taken by R to A′, which is in the neighboring cell, and then by $\boldsymbol{\tau}$ to D. D is the same as C by translational symmetry. Figure 7-11b shows the effect of the exponent term in Eq. (7-39). The atom C with position vector $\mathbf{r}_C$ is taken by R to C′, i.e., $\mathbf{r}_{C'} = R\mathbf{r}_C$. It can be seen that C′ is related to B through a translation of $-\boldsymbol{\tau}$, and B is subsequently related to A (given by $\mathbf{r}_A$) by a unit translation $\mathbf{t}$. Thus by forming $\mathbf{r}_A - R\mathbf{r}_C$, we obtain a phase factor for the representation of

$$e^{\{i\mathbf{k}\cdot(\mathbf{r}_A - \mathbf{r}_{C'})\}} = e^{\{i\mathbf{k}\cdot(\mathbf{t}-\boldsymbol{\tau})\}} \quad \text{where} \quad \mathbf{r}_{C'} = R\mathbf{r}_C \tag{7-40}$$

**Table 7-7** Phase factors.

| | i | j | $\{1\,|\,\underset{\sim}{0}\}$ | $\{\bar{1}\,|\,\underset{\sim}{\tau}(0,½,½)\}$ |
|---|---|---|---|---|
| 2d | 5 | 5 | 1 | $\exp\left[½i(2k_xa' + k_yb' + k_zc)\right]$ |
| | 6 | 6 | 1 | $\exp\left[½i(2k_xa' - k_yb' - k_zc)\right]$ |
| 2c | 7 | 7 | 1 | $\exp\left[½i(k_yb' + k_zc)\right]$ |
| | 8 | 8 | 1 | $\exp\left[-½i(k_yb' + k_zc)\right]$ |
| 2b | 9 | 9 | 1 | $\exp\left[½i(2k_xa' - k_yb' + k_zc)\right]$ |
| | 10 | 10 | 1 | $\exp\left[½i(2k_xa' + k_yb' - k_zc)\right]$ |
| 2a | 11 | 11 | 1 | $\exp\left[-½i(k_yb' - k_zc)\right]$ |
| | 12 | 12 | 1 | $\exp\left[½i(k_yb' - k_zc)\right]$ |

$a' = a\cos(\gamma - 90)$; $b' = b\cos(\gamma - 90)$

$\gamma$ = angle between $\underset{\sim}{a}$ and $\underset{\sim}{b}$

Note that this phase factor, which we may denote as $\Delta_{ij}$, only contains terms in wave vector **k** and translations. $\boldsymbol{\tau}$ arises from the non-symmorphic nature of the symmetry operation and **t** represents the fact that the atom A is taken into another unit cell by the operation.

Thus the analysis of normal modes proceeds as with the $\mathbf{k} = 0$ case except that we multiply the matrix representations of R for the group $\overline{G}_k$ by a phase factor $\Delta_{ij}$ to form the $T_{\alpha\beta}(i,j,\mathbf{k};R)$. Naturally, in order to form the reducible representations of the normal modes, we need only consider the diagonal elements $T_{\alpha\alpha}(i,i,\mathbf{k};R)$ of the multiplier representations, since these are the only ones that contribute to the characters, $\chi(\mathbf{k};R)$.

In our example of space group $P2_1/b(C_{2h}^5)$, we shall not consider the general equivalent positions this time since the characters for them are all zero, except under the identity operation, because the diagonal elements $T_{\alpha\alpha}$ (i,i,**k**;R) are all zero. However, let us look at the special positions. For instance, take position 5 (1/2,1/2,1/4) and, for simplicity, consider the relevant characters alone. Under operations $\{2\,|\,\boldsymbol{\tau}(0,0,1/2)\}$ and $\{m\,|\,\boldsymbol{\tau}(0,1/2,0)\}$ the character is zero as shown in Table 7-5. However, under $\{\bar{1}\,|\,\boldsymbol{\tau}(0,1/2,1/2)\}$ the position (1/2,1/4,1/4) is taken to (−1/2,1/4,1/4). For $\mathbf{k} = 0$, we used the principle of translational invariance to say that these two positions were equivalent, thus giving a contribution to the character of $1 \times -3$ ($-3$ for $\{\bar{1}\,|\,\mathbf{0}\}$ operating on the attached coordinate axes). For $\mathbf{k} \neq 0$ we must multiply by $\Delta_{55}$. This is seen to be

$$\Delta_{55} = e^{i\mathbf{k}\cdot[\mathbf{r}_5 - \mathbf{R}\mathbf{r}_5]} = e^{i\mathbf{k}\cdot[(1/2,1/4,1/4) - \{\bar{1}\}\,(1/2,1/4,1/4)]} \tag{7-41}$$

which gives

$$\Delta_{55} = e^{i\{k_x a \cos(\gamma - 90°) + 1/2\, k_y b \cos(\gamma - 90°) + 1/2 k_z c\}} \tag{7-42}$$

The phase factors found in this way are given in Table 7-7 for all the special positions. (In monoclinic space groups, with the first setting, **a** and **b** are not orthogonal. $\mathbf{k}_x$ and **a** are inclined by $\gamma - 90°$ to each other because $\mathbf{k}_x$ is perpendicular to **b**. Similar considerations apply to $\mathbf{k}_y$ and **b**.)

We can now draw up a table of characters of reducible representations for positions of each type of site and these are shown in Table 7-8. The reduction of these representations must now be accomplished with respect to the particular point group of **k** required. For instance, we might wish to work out the reduction for the 2d sites at the points Γ, Λ, Z, C, and Y in Fig. 7-9. Let us start with the Γ point, which is at $\mathbf{k} = 0$ and which has the full point group symmetry $2/m(C_{2h})$. The reduction here naturally gives the same result as in the previous section, and is repeated in Table 7-9. The Λ point has point symmetry $2(C_2)$ and so the operations of the appropriate character table will be $\{1\,|\,\mathbf{0}\}$ and $\{2\,|\,\mathbf{0}\}$ (E and $C_2$). However since this is at nonzero **k**, we cannot necessarily use the same character table as for point groups at $\mathbf{k} = 0$. Kovalev lists all the character tables of the irreducible multiplier representations for different **k** and we show the appropriate tables in Table 7-9. We see that from the Γ point to Λ, we have the result

$$A_u \longrightarrow \hat{\tau}^1$$

$$B_u \longrightarrow \hat{\tau}^2$$

The complete sequence ΓΛZCYΓ forms a closed loop around the Brillouin zone and all the reductions are given in Table 7-9 where it is possible to see the correlation between representations with differing **k**. Note that as mentioned in Section 7-4 the special point Z on the zone boundary always has doubly degenerate representations, meaning that there is a "sticking" together of modes at this point. This extra degeneracy is only possible on

**Table 7-8** The characters of reducible representations for $k \neq 0$ for $P2_1/b(C_{2h}^5)$.

| | $\{1\|\underset{\sim}{0}\}$ | $\{2[001]\|\underset{\sim}{\tau}(0,0,\frac{1}{2})\}$ | $\{\bar{1}\|\underset{\sim}{\tau}(0,\frac{1}{2},\frac{1}{2})\}$ | $\{m[001]\|\underset{\sim}{\tau}(0,\frac{1}{2},0)\}$ |
|---|---|---|---|---|
| $\Gamma$ (4e) | 12 | 0 | 0 | 0 |
| $\Gamma$ (2d) | 6 | 0 | $-3\{\exp[\frac{1}{2}i(2k_xa' + k_yb' + k_zc)] + \exp[\frac{1}{2}i(2k_xa' - k_yb' - k_zc)]\}$ | 0 |
| $\Gamma$ (2c) | 6 | 0 | $-3\{\exp[\frac{1}{2}i(k_yb' + k_zc)] + \exp[-\frac{1}{2}i(k_yb' + k_zc)]\}$ | 0 |
| $\Gamma$ (2b) | 6 | 0 | $-3\{\exp[\frac{1}{2}i(2k_xa' - k_yb' + k_zc)] + \exp[\frac{1}{2}i(2k_xa' + k_yb' - k_zc)]\}$ | 0 |
| $\Gamma$ (2a) | 6 | 0 | $-3\{\exp[-\frac{1}{2}i(k_yb' - k_zc)] + \exp[\frac{1}{2}i(k_yb' - k_zc)]\}$ | 0 |

the Brillouin zone surface of nonsymmorphic space groups. Within the Brillouin zone, for these space groups, there can be no extra degeneracies.

The same general techniques that we have discussed in this section can be used for any positions in any space group and for any value of **k**. Another example of this method is given in a very readable paper on normal modes in crystalline carbon disulphide and chlorine by Grout, Leech, and English which we recommend to the reader. A full account of all the theories can be found in the papers by Maradudin and Vosko, Warren, and the books by Lyubarskii, and Bradley and Cracknell. Basically the same techniques described here can be used with electronic band theory where the operators act on wave functions.

**Addendum to Chapter 7**

Bloch Theorem: Consider a function space operator S operating on the function exp $i\mathbf{k}\cdot\mathbf{r}$. We can write that

$$Se^{i\mathbf{k}\cdot\mathbf{r}} \equiv e^{iS\mathbf{k}\cdot\mathbf{r}}$$

from the definition of an operator.

As shown by Fig. 7-8, this can be written as

$$e^{iS\mathbf{k}\cdot\mathbf{r}} = e^{i\mathbf{k}\cdot S^{-1}\mathbf{r}}$$

It is, in fact, true to say that generally

$$Sf(\mathbf{r}) = f(S^{-1}\mathbf{r})$$

if S is a function space operator.

Now consider the operator $\{1 \mid \mathbf{t}_n\}$

$$\begin{aligned} \{1 \mid \mathbf{t}_n\}e^{i\mathbf{k}\cdot\mathbf{r}} &= e^{i\mathbf{k}\cdot(\mathbf{r}-\mathbf{t}_n)} \\ &= e^{-\mathbf{k}\cdot\mathbf{t}_n} e^{i\mathbf{k}\cdot\mathbf{r}} \\ &= \Gamma(\mathbf{k};\{1 \mid \mathbf{t}_n\})e^{i\mathbf{k}\cdot\mathbf{r}} \end{aligned}$$

Therefore the basis functions for the irreducible representations of the translation group can be taken to be $e^{i\mathbf{k}\cdot\mathbf{r}}$. This leads to the general basis function given by

$$\Psi_{\mathbf{k}}(\mathbf{r}) = u_{\mathbf{k}}(\mathbf{r})e^{i\mathbf{k}\cdot\mathbf{r}}$$

where

$$u_{\mathbf{k}}(\mathbf{r}) = u_{\mathbf{k}}(\mathbf{r}+\mathbf{t}_n) \quad \text{for all } \mathbf{t}_n.$$

**Table 7-9** (a) Irreducible representations at special points of the Brillouin zone for the 2d site of $P2_1/b(C_{2h}^5)$. (b) Appropriate tables of irreducible multiplier representations.

(a)

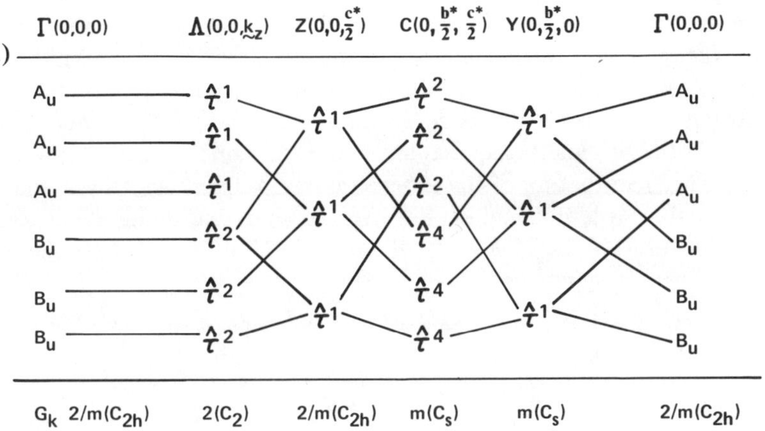


(b)

| Λ | $\{1\|\underset{\sim}{0}\}$ | $\{2\|\underset{\sim}{0}\}$ |
|---|---|---|
| $\hat{\tau}^1$ | 1 | 1 |
| $\hat{\tau}^2$ | 1 | −1 |

| Z | $\{1\|\underset{\sim}{0}\}$ | $\{2\|\underset{\sim}{0}\}$ | $\{\bar{1}\|\underset{\sim}{0}\}$ | $\{m\|\underset{\sim}{0}\}$ |
|---|---|---|---|---|
| $\hat{\tau}^1$ | $\begin{bmatrix}1 & 0\\ 0 & 1\end{bmatrix}$ | $\begin{bmatrix}1 & 0\\ 0 & -1\end{bmatrix}$ | $\begin{bmatrix}0 & 1\\ -1 & 0\end{bmatrix}$ | $\begin{bmatrix}0 & 1\\ 1 & 0\end{bmatrix}$ |

| Y | $\{1\|\underset{\sim}{0}\}$ | $\{2\|\underset{\sim}{0}\}$ | $\{\bar{1}\|\underset{\sim}{0}\}$ | $\{m\|\underset{\sim}{0}\}$ |
|---|---|---|---|---|
| $\hat{\tau}^1$ | $\begin{bmatrix}1 & 0\\ 0 & 1\end{bmatrix}$ | $\begin{bmatrix}1 & 0\\ 0 & -1\end{bmatrix}$ | $\begin{bmatrix}0 & -1\\ 1 & 0\end{bmatrix}$ | $\begin{bmatrix}0 & 1\\ 1 & 0\end{bmatrix}$ |

| C | $\{1\|\underset{\sim}{0}\}$ | $\{2\|\underset{\sim}{0}\}$ | $\{\bar{1}\|\underset{\sim}{0}\}$ | $\{m\|\underset{\sim}{0}\}$ |
|---|---|---|---|---|
| $\hat{\tau}^1$ | 1 | 1 | 1 | −1 |
| $\hat{\tau}^2$ | 1 | 1 | −1 | 1 |
| $\hat{\tau}^3$ | 1 | −1 | 1 | 1 |
| $\hat{\tau}^4$ | 1 | −1 | −1 | −1 |

The Bloch theorem states that the wave function of a particle moving in a periodic potential $V(\mathbf{r})$ with periodicity given by the symmetry of the translation group T is

$$\Psi_{\mathbf{k}}(\mathbf{r}) = u_{\mathbf{k}}\, e^{i\mathbf{k}\cdot\mathbf{r}}$$

It was in order to be consistent with the standard form of the Bloch theorem that we chose $p_i$ to be negative in Eq. 7-14.

**Problems**

**1.** Consider a collection of spherical atoms of the same kind arranged in a hexagonal array so that they are in close contact with one another. Draw a diagram of this and outline the unit cell. What is the space group and where are the symmetry elements? Now add atoms of the same kind at (2/3, 1/3, 1/2) positions. This is the so-called hexagonal close-packed (h.c.p) structure. What is its space group and where are the symmetry elements? To the original hexagonal array add the same type of atoms at ±(2/3, 1/3, 1/3) so that all of the atoms are in close contact. Show that this forms a cubic structure (cubic close-packed) and determine the space group and location of the symmetry elements. (Hint: recall that these rather special centering positions give a rhombohedral lattice.)

**2.** A crystal with $a \neq b \neq c$, $\alpha = \beta = \gamma = 90°$ has atoms of the same kind in the following positions:

| | | | | | |
|---|---|---|---|---|---|
| (0.29 | 0.04 | 0.22) | (−0.29 | −0.04 | −0.22) |
| (0.79 | 0.46 | 0.28) | (0.21 | 0.54 | 0.72) |
| (−0.29 | 0.54 | −0.22) | (0.29 | 0.46 | 0.22) |
| (0.21 | −0.04 | 0.72) | (0.79 | 0.04 | 0.28) |

Identify the space group.

**3.** In the cubic perovskite structure the atoms are at the positions:

A 1/2, 1/2, 1/2
B 0, 0, 0
X 0, 0, 1/2; 0, 1/2, 0; 1/2, 0, 0

Find the reducible representations for normal modes at $\mathbf{k} = 0$. Repeat this for the special points on the Brillouin zone: M(a*/2, b*/2, 0) and R(a*/2, b*/2, c*/2). (Note that the Brillouin zone is a cube of side $2\pi/a$.) Reduce these representations to sums of irreducible representations. Note that because the appropriate space group is symmorphic, one can use the ordinary character tables for the point group $\overline{G}_k$, i.e., 4/mmm ($D_{4h}$) for the M-point and m3m ($O_h$) for the R-point.

**4.** For the space group P4/mbm $(D_{4h})^5$ determine under which irreducible representations the $k = 0$ normal modes of vibration transform for atoms on positions 2c and 4g. (The answers are $A_{2u} + B_{1u} + 2E_u$ and $A_{1g} + A_{2g} + B_{1g} + B_{2g} + E_g + A_{2u} + B_{1u} + 2E_u$ respectively.)

**5.** For the space group $P2_1/b(C_{2h}{}^5)$ derive the tables of irreducible multiplier representations for the points in the Brillouin zone given by (0,b*/2,c*/2); (a*/2,0,c*/2); (a*/2,b*/2,c*/2); (0,b*/2,0); (a*/2,0,0) and (a*/2,b*/2,0). Hence, find the irreducible representations at each point for the 2d sites.

Appendix 1

# MATRIX OPERATIONS FOR THE SYMMETRY ELEMENTS

The matrices given here are those for the active operation **r'** = **Rr**. Thus multiplication of any coordinate position r ≡ (x,y,z) by the matrix, R, will give the symmetry-related coordinate. The matrix operations are grouped together according to the directions about which they operate. The directions used are those that are usually needed in problems related to crystal symmetry. The matrices applying specifically to the hexagonal (and trigonal) systems are marked with the letter H. The determinant of any of these matrices is always ± 1, +1 for the proper operations and -1 for improper (or inversion) operations. This number taken together with the trace of each matrix (sum of diagonal elements) is characteristic of a particular point symmetry:

| | | | | | | | | | | |
|---|---|---|---|---|---|---|---|---|---|---|
| element: | 1 | 2 | 3 | 4 | 6 | $\bar{1}$ | $\bar{2}$=m | $\bar{3}$ | $\bar{4}$ | $\bar{6}$ |
| trace: | 3 | -1 | 0 | 1 | 2 | -3 | 1 | 0 | -1 | -2 |
| determinant: | 1 | 1 | 1 | 1 | 1 | -1 | -1 | -1 | -1 | -1 |

If these two quantities are calculated for a particular matrix, it then makes it easier to find the operation in the following list.

**Direction** [0 0 0]

1(E) $\begin{bmatrix} 1 & 0 & 0 \\ 0 & 1 & 0 \\ 0 & 0 & 1 \end{bmatrix}$ $\bar{1}$(i) $\begin{bmatrix} -1 & 0 & 0 \\ 0 & -1 & 0 \\ 0 & 0 & -1 \end{bmatrix}$

**Direction** [1 0 0]

$2(C_2)$ $\begin{bmatrix} 1 & 0 & 0 \\ 0 & -1 & 0 \\ 0 & 0 & -1 \end{bmatrix}$ $\bar{2} \equiv m(\sigma)$ $\begin{bmatrix} -1 & 0 & 0 \\ 0 & 1 & 0 \\ 0 & 0 & 1 \end{bmatrix}$

H $2(C_2)$ $\begin{bmatrix} 1 & -1 & 0 \\ 0 & -1 & 0 \\ 0 & 0 & -1 \end{bmatrix}$ $\bar{2} \equiv m\ (\sigma)$ $\begin{bmatrix} -1 & 1 & 0 \\ 0 & 1 & 0 \\ 0 & 0 & 1 \end{bmatrix}$

$4(C_4)$ $\begin{bmatrix} 1 & 0 & 0 \\ 0 & 0 & 1 \\ 0 & -1 & 0 \end{bmatrix}$ $\bar{4}(S_4{}^3)$ $\begin{bmatrix} -1 & 0 & 0 \\ 0 & 0 & -1 \\ 0 & 1 & 0 \end{bmatrix}$

$4^2(C_4{}^2) = 2(C_2)$ $\bar{4}^2(S_4{}^2) = 2(C_2)$

$4^3(C_4{}^3)$ $\begin{bmatrix} 1 & 0 & 0 \\ 0 & 0 & -1 \\ 0 & 1 & 0 \end{bmatrix}$ $\bar{4}^3(S_4)$ $\begin{bmatrix} -1 & 0 & 0 \\ 0 & 0 & 1 \\ 0 & -1 & 0 \end{bmatrix}$

**Direction** [0 1 0]

$2(C_2)$ $\begin{bmatrix} -1 & 0 & 0 \\ 0 & 1 & 0 \\ 0 & 0 & -1 \end{bmatrix}$ $\bar{2} \equiv m(\sigma)$ $\begin{bmatrix} 1 & 0 & 0 \\ 0 & -1 & 0 \\ 0 & 0 & 1 \end{bmatrix}$

H $2(C_2)$ $\begin{bmatrix} -1 & 0 & 0 \\ -1 & 1 & 0 \\ 0 & 0 & -1 \end{bmatrix}$ $\bar{2} \equiv m(\sigma)$ $\begin{bmatrix} 1 & 0 & 0 \\ 1 & -1 & 0 \\ 0 & 0 & 1 \end{bmatrix}$

$4(C_4)$ $\begin{bmatrix} 0 & 0 & -1 \\ 0 & 1 & 0 \\ 1 & 0 & 0 \end{bmatrix}$ $\bar{4}(S_4{}^3)$ $\begin{bmatrix} 0 & 0 & 1 \\ 0 & -1 & 0 \\ -1 & 0 & 0 \end{bmatrix}$

$4^2(C_4{}^2) = 2(C_2)$ $\bar{4}^2(S_4{}^2) = 2(C_2)$

$4^3(C_4{}^3)$ $\begin{bmatrix} 0 & 0 & 1 \\ 0 & 1 & 0 \\ -1 & 0 & 0 \end{bmatrix}$ $\bar{4}^3(S_4)$ $\begin{bmatrix} 0 & 0 & -1 \\ 0 & -1 & 0 \\ 1 & 0 & 0 \end{bmatrix}$

**Direction** [0 0 1]

$2(C_2)$ $\begin{bmatrix} -1 & 0 & 0 \\ 0 & -1 & 0 \\ 0 & 0 & 1 \end{bmatrix}$ $\bar{2} \equiv m(\sigma)$ $\begin{bmatrix} 1 & 0 & 0 \\ 0 & 1 & 0 \\ 0 & 0 & -1 \end{bmatrix}$

H $3(C_3)$ $\begin{bmatrix} 0 & -1 & 0 \\ 1 & -1 & 0 \\ 0 & 0 & 1 \end{bmatrix}$ $\bar{3}(S_6{}^5)$ $\begin{bmatrix} 0 & 1 & 0 \\ -1 & 1 & 0 \\ 0 & 0 & -1 \end{bmatrix}$

H $3^2(C_3{}^2)$ $\begin{bmatrix} -1 & 1 & 0 \\ -1 & 0 & 0 \\ 0 & 0 & 1 \end{bmatrix}$ $\bar{3}^5(S_6)$ $\begin{bmatrix} 1 & -1 & 0 \\ 1 & 0 & 0 \\ 0 & 0 & -1 \end{bmatrix}$

H $\bar{3}^2(S_6{}^4) = 3^2(C_3{}^2)$

H $\bar{3}^3(S_6{}^3) = \bar{1}(i)$

H $\bar{3}^4(S_6{}^2) = 3(C_3)$

| | | | | |
|---|---|---|---|---|
| | $4(C_4)$ | $\begin{bmatrix} 0 & -1 & 0 \\ 1 & 0 & 0 \\ 0 & 0 & 1 \end{bmatrix}$ | $\overline{4}(S_4^3)$ | $\begin{bmatrix} 0 & 1 & 0 \\ -1 & 0 & 0 \\ 0 & 0 & -1 \end{bmatrix}$ |
| | $4^2(C_4^2) = 2(C_2)$ | | $\overline{4}^2(S_4^2) = 2(C_2)$ | |
| | $4^3(C_4^3)$ | $\begin{bmatrix} 0 & 1 & 0 \\ -1 & 0 & 0 \\ 0 & 0 & 1 \end{bmatrix}$ | $\overline{4}^3(S_4)$ | $\begin{bmatrix} 0 & -1 & 0 \\ 1 & 0 & 0 \\ 0 & 0 & -1 \end{bmatrix}$ |
| H | $6(C_6)$ | $\begin{bmatrix} 1 & -1 & 0 \\ 1 & 0 & 0 \\ 0 & 0 & 1 \end{bmatrix}$ | $\overline{6}(S_3^5)$ | $\begin{bmatrix} -1 & 1 & 0 \\ -1 & 0 & 0 \\ 0 & 0 & -1 \end{bmatrix}$ |
| H | $6^2(C_6^2) = 3(C_3)$ | | $\overline{6}^2(S_3^4) = 3(C_3)$ | |
| H | $6^3(C_6^3) = 2(C_2)$ | | $\overline{6}(S_3^3) = m(\sigma)$ | |
| H | $6^4(C_6^4) = 3^2(C_3^2)$ | | $\overline{6}^4(S_3^2) = 3^2(C_3^2)$ | |
| H | $6^5(C_6^5)$ | $\begin{bmatrix} 0 & 1 & 0 \\ -1 & 1 & 0 \\ 0 & 0 & 1 \end{bmatrix}$ | $\overline{6}^5(S_3)$ | $\begin{bmatrix} 0 & -1 & 0 \\ 1 & -1 & 0 \\ 0 & 0 & -1 \end{bmatrix}$ |

**Direction** [1 1 0]

| | | | |
|---|---|---|---|
| $2(C_2)$ | $\begin{bmatrix} 0 & 1 & 0 \\ 1 & 0 & 0 \\ 0 & 0 & -1 \end{bmatrix}$ | $\overline{2} \equiv m(\sigma)$ | $\begin{bmatrix} 0 & -1 & 0 \\ -1 & 0 & 0 \\ 0 & 0 & 1 \end{bmatrix}$ |

**Direction** [1 0 1]

| | | | |
|---|---|---|---|
| $2(C_2)$ | $\begin{bmatrix} 0 & 0 & 1 \\ 0 & -1 & 0 \\ 1 & 0 & 0 \end{bmatrix}$ | $\overline{2} \equiv m(\sigma)$ | $\begin{bmatrix} 0 & 0 & -1 \\ 0 & 1 & 0 \\ -1 & 0 & 0 \end{bmatrix}$ |

**Direction** [0 1 1]

$2(C_2)$ $\begin{bmatrix} -1 & 0 & 0 \\ 0 & 0 & 1 \\ 0 & 1 & 0 \end{bmatrix}$ $\bar{2} \equiv m(\sigma)$ $\begin{bmatrix} 1 & 0 & 0 \\ 0 & 0 & -1 \\ 0 & -1 & 0 \end{bmatrix}$

**Direction** [1 $\bar{1}$ 0]

$2(C_2)$ $\begin{bmatrix} 0 & -1 & 0 \\ -1 & 0 & 0 \\ 0 & 0 & -1 \end{bmatrix}$ $\bar{2} \equiv m(\sigma)$ $\begin{bmatrix} 0 & 1 & 0 \\ 1 & 0 & 0 \\ 0 & 0 & 1 \end{bmatrix}$

**Direction** [$\bar{1}$ 0 1]

$2(C_2)$ $\begin{bmatrix} 0 & 0 & -1 \\ 0 & -1 & 0 \\ -1 & 0 & 0 \end{bmatrix}$ $\bar{2} \equiv m(\sigma)$ $\begin{bmatrix} 0 & 0 & 1 \\ 0 & 1 & 0 \\ 1 & 0 & 0 \end{bmatrix}$

**Direction** [0 1 $\bar{1}$]

$2(C_2)$ $\begin{bmatrix} -1 & 0 & 0 \\ 0 & 0 & -1 \\ 0 & -1 & 0 \end{bmatrix}$ $\bar{2} \equiv m(\sigma)$ $\begin{bmatrix} 1 & 0 & 0 \\ 0 & 0 & 1 \\ 0 & 1 & 0 \end{bmatrix}$

**Direction** [1 1 1]

$3(C_3)$ $\begin{bmatrix} 0 & 0 & 1 \\ 1 & 0 & 0 \\ 0 & 1 & 0 \end{bmatrix}$ $\bar{3}(S_6{}^5)$ $\begin{bmatrix} 0 & 0 & -1 \\ -1 & 0 & 0 \\ 0 & -1 & 0 \end{bmatrix}$

$3^2(C_3{}^2)$ $\begin{bmatrix} 0 & 1 & 0 \\ 0 & 0 & 1 \\ 1 & 0 & 0 \end{bmatrix}$ $\bar{3}^5(S_6)$ $\begin{bmatrix} 0 & -1 & 0 \\ 0 & 0 & -1 \\ -1 & 0 & 0 \end{bmatrix}$

$$\bar{3}^2(S_6^4) = 3^2(C_3^2)$$
$$\bar{3}^3(S_6^3) = \bar{1}(i)$$
$$\bar{3}^4(S_6^2) = 3(C_3)$$

**Direction** $[\bar{1}\ 1\ 1]$

$$3(C_3) \quad \begin{bmatrix} 0 & -1 & 0 \\ 0 & 0 & 1 \\ -1 & 0 & 0 \end{bmatrix} \qquad \bar{3}(S_6^5) \quad \begin{bmatrix} 0 & 1 & 0 \\ 0 & 0 & -1 \\ 1 & 0 & 0 \end{bmatrix}$$

$$3^2(C_3^2) \quad \begin{bmatrix} 0 & 0 & -1 \\ -1 & 0 & 0 \\ 0 & 1 & 0 \end{bmatrix} \qquad \bar{3}^5(S_6) \quad \begin{bmatrix} 0 & 0 & 1 \\ 1 & 0 & 0 \\ 0 & -1 & 0 \end{bmatrix}$$

$$\bar{3}^2(S_6^4) = 3^2(C_3^2)$$
$$\bar{3}^3(S_6^3) = \bar{1}(i)$$
$$\bar{3}^4(S_6^2) = 3(C_3)$$

**Direction** $[1\ \bar{1}\ 1]$

$$3(C_3) \quad \begin{bmatrix} 0 & -1 & 0 \\ 0 & 0 & -1 \\ 1 & 0 & 0 \end{bmatrix} \qquad \bar{3}(S_6^5) \quad \begin{bmatrix} 0 & 1 & 0 \\ 0 & 0 & 1 \\ -1 & 0 & 0 \end{bmatrix}$$

$$3^2(C_3^2) \quad \begin{bmatrix} 0 & 0 & 1 \\ -1 & 0 & 0 \\ 0 & -1 & 0 \end{bmatrix} \qquad \bar{3}^5(S_6) \quad \begin{bmatrix} 0 & 0 & -1 \\ 1 & 0 & 0 \\ 0 & 1 & 0 \end{bmatrix}$$

$$\bar{3}^2(S_6^4) = 3^2(C_3^2)$$
$$\bar{3}^3(S_6^3) = \bar{1}(i)$$
$$\bar{3}^4(S_6^2) = 3(C_3)$$

**Direction** $[1\ 1\ \overline{1}]$

$3(C_3)$ $\begin{bmatrix} 0 & 1 & 0 \\ 0 & 0 & -1 \\ -1 & 0 & 0 \end{bmatrix}$ $\overline{3}(S_6{}^5)$ $\begin{bmatrix} 0 & -1 & 0 \\ 0 & 0 & 1 \\ 1 & 0 & 0 \end{bmatrix}$

$3^2(C_3{}^2)$ $\begin{bmatrix} 0 & 0 & -1 \\ 1 & 0 & 0 \\ 0 & -1 & 0 \end{bmatrix}$ $\overline{3}^5(S_6)$ $\begin{bmatrix} 0 & 0 & 1 \\ -1 & 0 & 0 \\ 0 & 1 & 0 \end{bmatrix}$

$\overline{3}^2(S_6{}^4) = 3^2(C_3{}^2)$
$\overline{3}^3(S_6{}^3) = \overline{1}(i)$
$\overline{3}^4(S_6{}^2) = 3(C_3)$

**Direction**[210]

H $2(C_2)$ $\begin{bmatrix} 1 & 0 & 0 \\ 1 & -1 & 0 \\ 0 & 0 & -1 \end{bmatrix}$ $\overline{2} = m(\sigma)$ $\begin{bmatrix} -1 & 0 & 0 \\ -1 & 1 & 0 \\ 0 & 0 & 1 \end{bmatrix}$

**Direction** [120]

H $2(C_2)$ $\begin{bmatrix} -1 & 1 & 0 \\ 0 & 1 & 0 \\ 0 & 0 & -1 \end{bmatrix}$ $\overline{2} \equiv m(\sigma)$ $\begin{bmatrix} 1 & -1 & 0 \\ 0 & -1 & 0 \\ 0 & 0 & 1 \end{bmatrix}$

## JONES' FAITHFUL REPRESENTATION SYMBOLS

The Jones symbol for the operator R is the vector r' formed by Rr, and is recognisable as one of the coordinates of the equivalent positions. It is easily obtained from any of the above matrices by multiplying with the vector r = (x,y,z). For example, the inverse operator would be represented by (-x, -y, -z), and 2[100] ($C_2$[100]) would be (x, -y, -z) and so on. The Jones' symbol is then simply an abbreviated form of the matrix operator. Multiplication of these symbols is similar to that for matrices. For example if we wish to find 2[001] m[001] ($C_2$[001]$\sigma_h$) we can write the Jones' symbols:

$$2[001]\ m[001] \equiv (-x, -y, z)(x, y, -z) = (-x', -y', z')$$

where (x', y', z') = (x, y, -z). Therefore (-x', -y', z') = (-x, -y, -z) and hence 2[001] m[001] = $\bar{1}$.

Appendix 2

# THE SEVEN CRYSTAL SYSTEMS

| Symmetry Condition | Crystal System | Properties | Types of Bravais Lattices |
|---|---|---|---|
| 1(E) or $\overline{1}$(i) | **Triclinic** | $a \neq b \neq c$<br>$\alpha \neq \beta \neq \gamma$ | P |
| 2($C_2$) or $\overline{2}$(m) | **Monoclinic** | $a \neq b \neq c$<br>$\alpha = \beta = \pi/2 \neq \gamma$ (1st setting)<br>$\alpha = \gamma = \pi/2 \neq \beta$ (2nd setting) | <br>P,B<br><br>P,C |
| two 2-fold axes or two mirror planes | **Orthorhombic** | $a \neq b \neq c$<br>$\alpha = \beta = \gamma = \pi/2$ | P, I,<br>F,C, |
| 4($C_4$) or $\overline{4}$($S_4{}^3$) | **Tetragonal** | $a = b \neq c$<br>$\alpha = \beta = \gamma = \pi/2$ | P, I |

| | | | |
|---|---|---|---|
| $3(C_3)$ or $\overline{3}(S_6^5)$ | **Trigonal** | $a = b \neq c$ <br> $\alpha = \beta = \pi/2;$ <br> $\gamma = 2\pi/3$ | P |
| | Rhombohedral: | | |
| | i) on Rhomb. axes | $a = b = c$ <br> $\alpha = \beta = \gamma$ | R |
| | ii) on Hex. axes | $a = b \neq c$ <br> $\alpha = \beta = \pi/2;$ <br> $\gamma = 2\pi/3$ | R |
| $6(C_6)$ or $\overline{6}(S_3^5)$ | **Hexagonal** | $a = b \neq c$ <br> $\alpha = \beta = \pi/2;$ <br> $\gamma = 2\pi/3$ | P |
| four 3-fold axes | **Cubic** | $a = b = c$ <br> $\alpha = \beta = \gamma = \pi/2$ | P, I, F |

Rhombohedral : Trigonal cell centered at (2/3, 1/3, 1/3) - obverse or at (1/3, 2/3, 1/3) - reverse

Note: The symbol $\neq$ should be read as 'not necessarily equal to'.

Appendix 3

# THE 14 BRAVAIS LATTICES

The conventional unit cells of the 14 Bravais lattices are shown. For the hexagonal lattice the unit cell is outlined in black, but a hexagonal prism is also shown, dotted. The prism is drawn only to help indicate the angles of the unit cell. For the monoclinic lattice a B-centered cell is shown. This is for the 1st setting where the **c**-axis is taken as the unique 2-fold axis. For the 2nd setting the **b**-axis is the unique 2-fold axis and then the cell is C-centered.

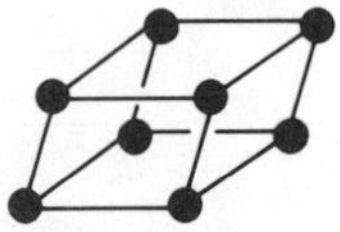
TRICLINIC-P

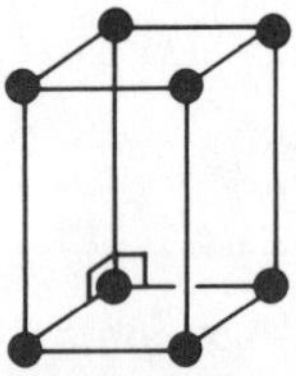
MONOCLINIC-P

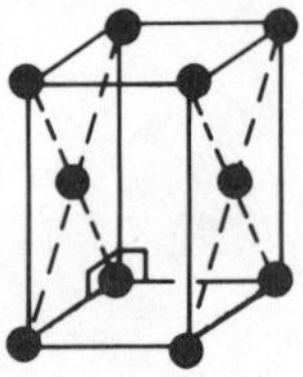
MONOCLINIC-B

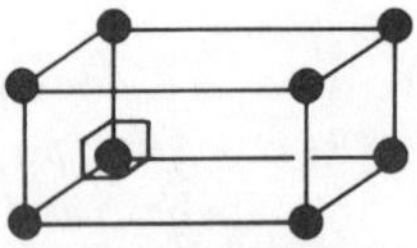
ORTHORHOMBIC-P

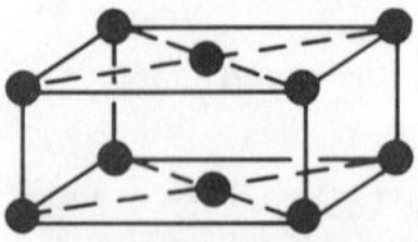
ORTHORHOMBIC-C

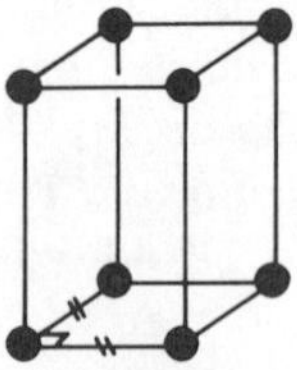
TETRAGONAL-P

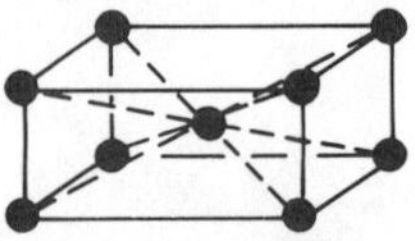
ORTHORHOMBIC-I

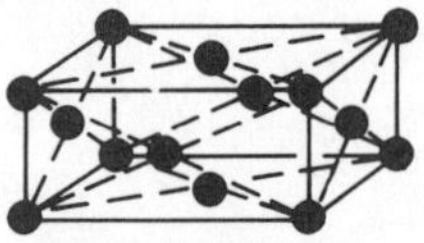
ORTHORHOMBIC-F

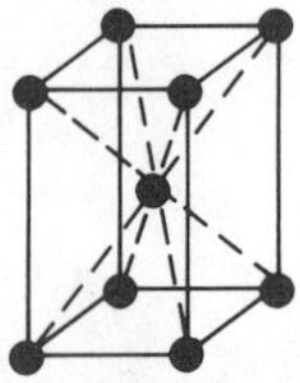
TETRAGONAL-I

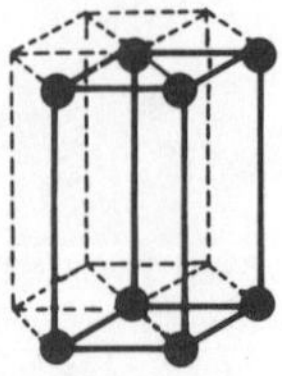
HEXAGONAL-P

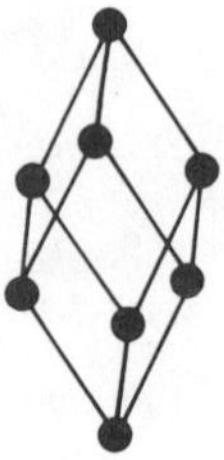
TRIGONAL-R

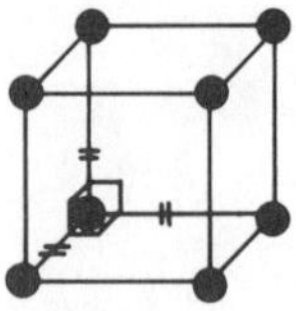
CUBIC-P

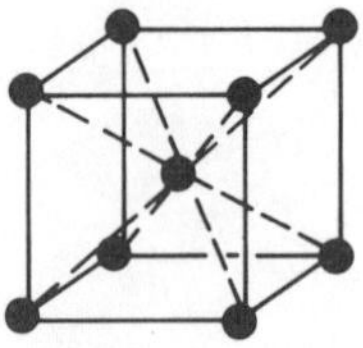
CUBIC-I

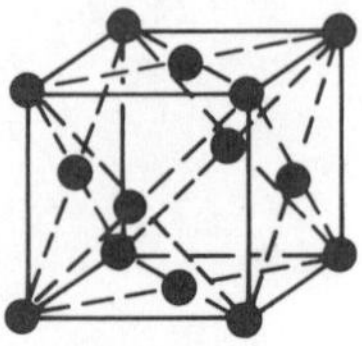
CUBIC-F

Appendix 4

# THE 32 CRYSTALLOGRAPHIC POINT GROUPS

The 32 crystallographic point groups are listed using the Schoenflies, International and Full International notation. The symmetry elements, grouped by classes, are shown and the space groups with factor groups that correspond to each point group.

| Schoenflies | International | Full Int. | Symmetry Elements | Space Groups |
|---|---|---|---|---|
| Triclinic | | | | |
| $C_1$ | 1 | 1 | E | 1 |
| $S_2$ ($C_i$) | $\bar{1}$ | $\bar{1}$ | E i | 2 |
| Monoclinic | | | | |
| $C_2$ | 2 | 2 | E $C_2$ | 3-5 |
| $C_{1h}$ ($C_s$) | m | m | E $\sigma_h$ | 6-9 |
| $C_{2h}$ | 2/m | $\frac{2}{m}$ | E $C_2$ i $\sigma_h$ | 10-15 |
| Orthorhombic | | | | |
| $D_2$ (V) | 222 | 222 | E $C_2$ $C_2'$ $C_2'$ | 16-24 |
| $C_{2v}$ | mm2 | mm2 | E $C_2$ $\sigma_v$ $\sigma_v$ | 25-46 |
| $D_{2h}$ ($V_h$) | mmm | $\frac{222}{mmm}$ | E $C_2$ $C_2'$ $C_2'$ i $\sigma_h$ $\sigma_v$ $\sigma_v$ | 47-74 |
| Tetragonal | | | | |
| $C_4$ | 4 | 4 | E $2C_4$ $C_2$ | 75-80 |
| $S_4$ | $\bar{4}$ | $\bar{4}$ | E $2S_4$ $C_2$ | 81-82 |
| $C_{4h}$ | 4/m | $\frac{4}{m}$ | E $2C_4$ $C_2$ i $2S_4$ $\sigma_h$ | 83-88 |
| $D_4$ | 422 | 422 | E $2C_4$ $C_2$ $2C_2'$ $2C_2''$ | 89-98 |
| $C_{4v}$ | 4mm | 4mm | E $2C_4$ $C_2$ $2\sigma_v$ $2\sigma_d$ | 99-110 |
| $D_{2d}$($V_d$) | $\bar{4}$2m | $\bar{4}$2m | E $C_2$ $2C_2'$ $2\sigma_d$ $2S_4$ | 111-122 |
| $D_{4h}$ | 4/mmm | $\frac{422}{mmm}$ | E $2C_4$ $C_2$ $2C_2'$ $2C_2''$ | 123-142 |
| | | | i $2S_4$ $\sigma_h$ $2\sigma_v$ $2\sigma_d$ | |
| Trigonal (Rhombohedral) | | | | |
| $C_3$ | 3 | 3 | E $2C_3$ | 143-146 |
| $S_6$($C_{3i}$) | $\bar{3}$ | $\bar{3}$ | E $2C_3$ i $2S_6$ | 147-148 |
| $D_3$ | 32 | 32 | E $2C_3$ $3C_2$ | 149-155 |
| $C_{3v}$ | 3m | 3m | E $2C_3$ $3\sigma_v$ | 156-161 |
| $D_{3d}$ | $\bar{3}$m | $\bar{3}\frac{2}{m}$ | E $2C_3$ $3C_2$ i $2S_6$ $3\sigma_v$ | 162-167 |
| Hexagonal | | | | |
| $C_6$ | 6 | 6 | E $2C_6$ $2C_3$ $C_2$ | 168-173 |
| $C_{3h}$ | $\bar{6}$ | $\bar{6}$ | E $2C_3$ $\sigma_h$ $2S_3$ | 174 |
| $C_{6h}$ | 6/m | $\frac{6}{m}$ | E $2C_6$ $2C_3$ $C_2$ i $2S_3$ $2S_6$ $\sigma_h$ | 175-176 |
| $D_6$ | 622 | 622 | E $2C_6$ $2C_3$ $C_2$ $3C_2'$ $3C_2''$ | 177-182 |
| $C_{6v}$ | 6mm | 6mm | E $2C_6$ $2C_3$ $C_2$ $3\sigma_v$ $3\sigma_d$ | 183-186 |
| $D_{3h}$ | $\bar{6}$m2 | $\bar{6}$m2 | E $2C_3$ $3C_2$ $\sigma_h$ $2S_3$ $3\sigma_v$ | 187-190 |
| $D_{6h}$ | 6/mmm | $\frac{622}{mmm}$ | E $2C_6$ $2C_3$ $C_2$ $3C_2'$ $3C_2''$ | 191-194 |
| | | | i $2S_3$ $2S_6$ $\sigma_h$ $3\sigma_v$ $3\sigma_d$ | |
| Cubic | | | | |
| T | 23 | 23 | E $8C_3$ $3C_2$ | 195-199 |
| $T_h$ | m3 | $\frac{2}{m}\bar{3}$ | E $8C_3$ $3C_2$ i $8S_6$ $3\sigma_h$ | 200-206 |
| O | 432 | 432 | E $8C_3$ $3C_2$ $6C_2$ $6C_4$ | 207-214 |
| $T_d$ | $\bar{4}$3m | $\bar{4}$3m | E $8C_3$ $3C_2$ $6\sigma_d$ $6S_4$ | 215-220 |
| $O_h$ | m3m | $\frac{4}{m}\bar{3}\frac{2}{m}$ | E $8C_3$ $3C_2$ $6C_2$ $6C_4$ | 221-230 |
| | | | i $8S_6$ $3\sigma_h$ $6\sigma_d$ $6S_4$ | |

## Appendix 5

# STEREOGRAMS OF THE 32 POINT GROUPS

Stereograms of the 32 point groups are given. Notice that the stereograms for the monoclinic 1st and 2nd setting look different at first glance but really are nothing more than different projections of the same arrangement of points. (Taken from the International Tables, p. 26.)

A stereographic projection is a useful and clear way of visualizing and understanding the effects of symmetry operations on molecules and crystals. It is usually defined as follows. A unit sphere is described around the crystal. A point in the +z hemisphere is projected on the xy-plane by determining the intersection of that plane and the line connecting the point with the south pole of the unit sphere. If the point to be projected is in the −z hemisphere, then the north pole is used. A stereogram is usually drawn with the z-axis (principal axis) projected onto the xy-plane. A general point or general equivalent position (this might be called an arbitrary point) on the unit sphere is projected onto the xy-plane and is labelled by a dot (•) or circle (o) if it is in the +z or −z hemisphere, respectively.

# SHAPES FOR THE 32 POINT GROUPS

Also shown in this appendix is a collection of shapes each having the point symmetry of one of the 32 crystallographic point groups. (Taken from Weinreich, p. 25.)

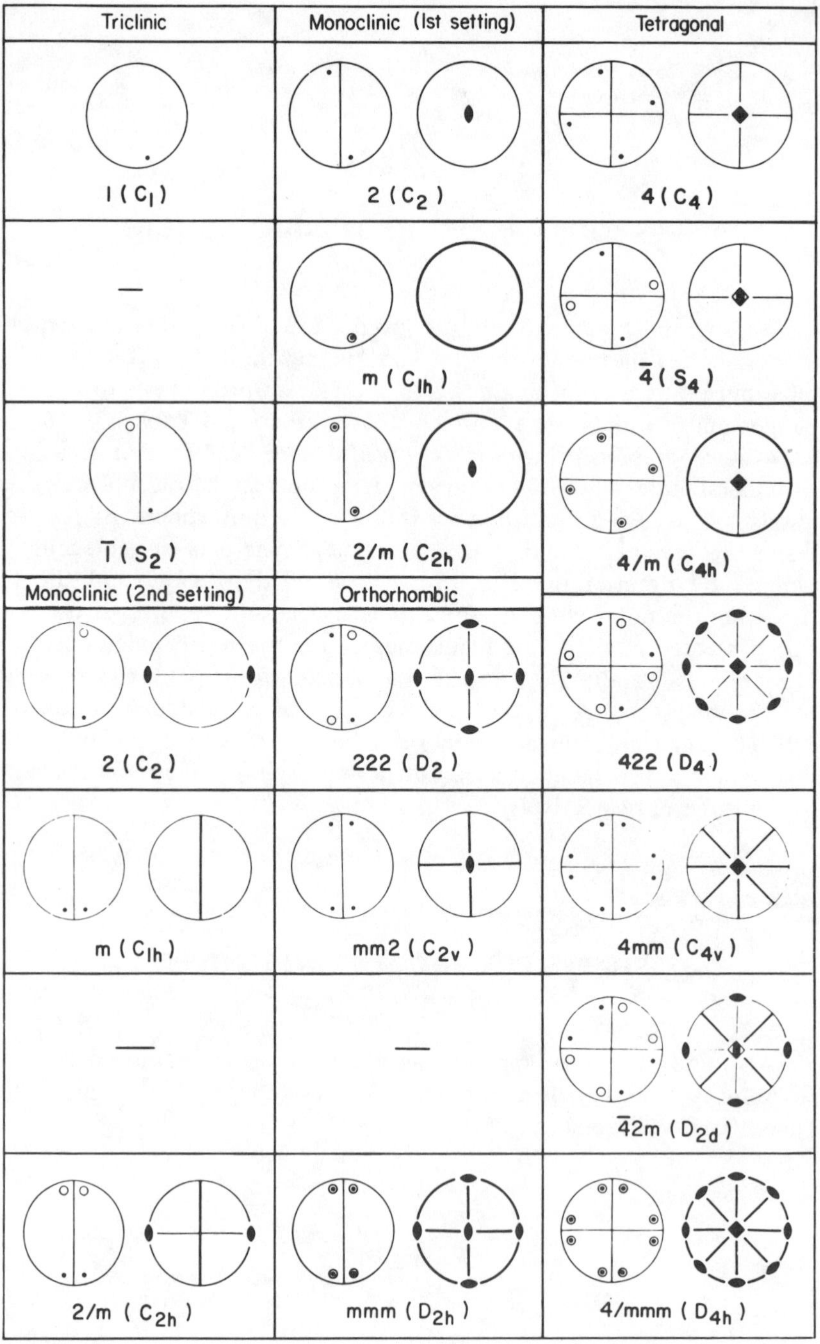

| Triclinic | Monoclinic (1st setting) | Tetragonal |
|---|---|---|
| $1(C_1)$ | $2(C_2)$ | $4(C_4)$ |
| — | $m(C_{1h})$ | $\bar{4}(S_4)$ |
| $\bar{1}(S_2)$ | $2/m(C_{2h})$ | $4/m(C_{4h})$ |
| Monoclinic (2nd setting) | Orthorhombic | |
| $2(C_2)$ | $222(D_2)$ | $422(D_4)$ |
| $m(C_{1h})$ | $mm2(C_{2v})$ | $4mm(C_{4v})$ |
| — | — | $\bar{4}2m(D_{2d})$ |
| $2/m(C_{2h})$ | $mmm(D_{2h})$ | $4/mmm(D_{4h})$ |

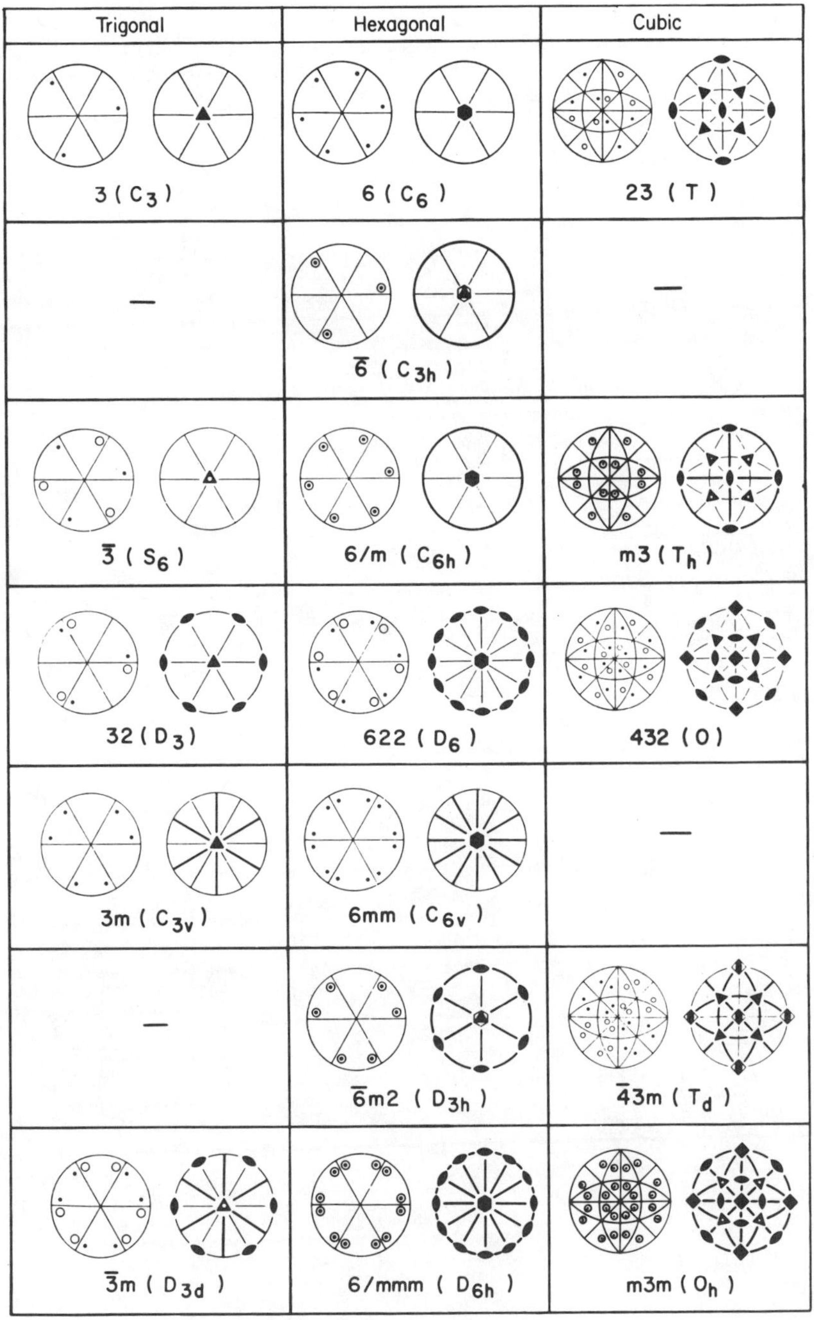

| Trigonal | Hexagonal | Cubic |
|---|---|---|
| 3 ( $C_3$ ) | 6 ( $C_6$ ) | 23 ( T ) |
| — | $\bar{6}$ ( $C_{3h}$ ) | — |
| $\bar{3}$ ( $S_6$ ) | 6/m ( $C_{6h}$ ) | m3 ( $T_h$ ) |
| 32 ( $D_3$ ) | 622 ( $D_6$ ) | 432 ( O ) |
| 3m ( $C_{3v}$ ) | 6mm ( $C_{6v}$ ) | — |
| — | $\bar{6}$m2 ( $D_{3h}$ ) | $\bar{4}$3m ( $T_d$ ) |
| $\bar{3}$m ( $D_{3d}$ ) | 6/mmm ( $D_{6h}$ ) | m3m ( $O_h$ ) |

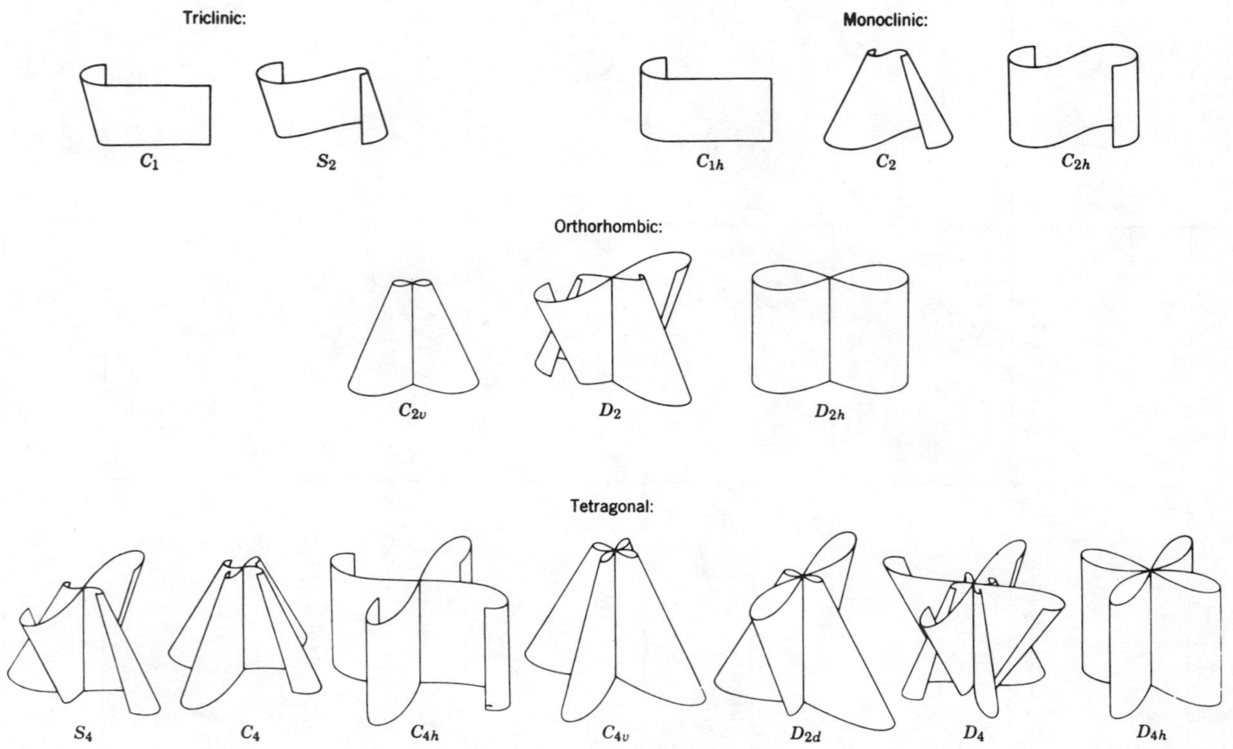
Triclinic:
$C_1$
$S_2$
Monoclinic:
$C_{1h}$
$C_2$
$C_{2h}$
Orthorhombic:
$C_{2v}$
$D_2$
$D_{2h}$
Tetragonal:
$S_4$
$C_4$
$C_{4h}$
$C_{4v}$
$D_{2d}$
$D_4$
$D_{4h}$

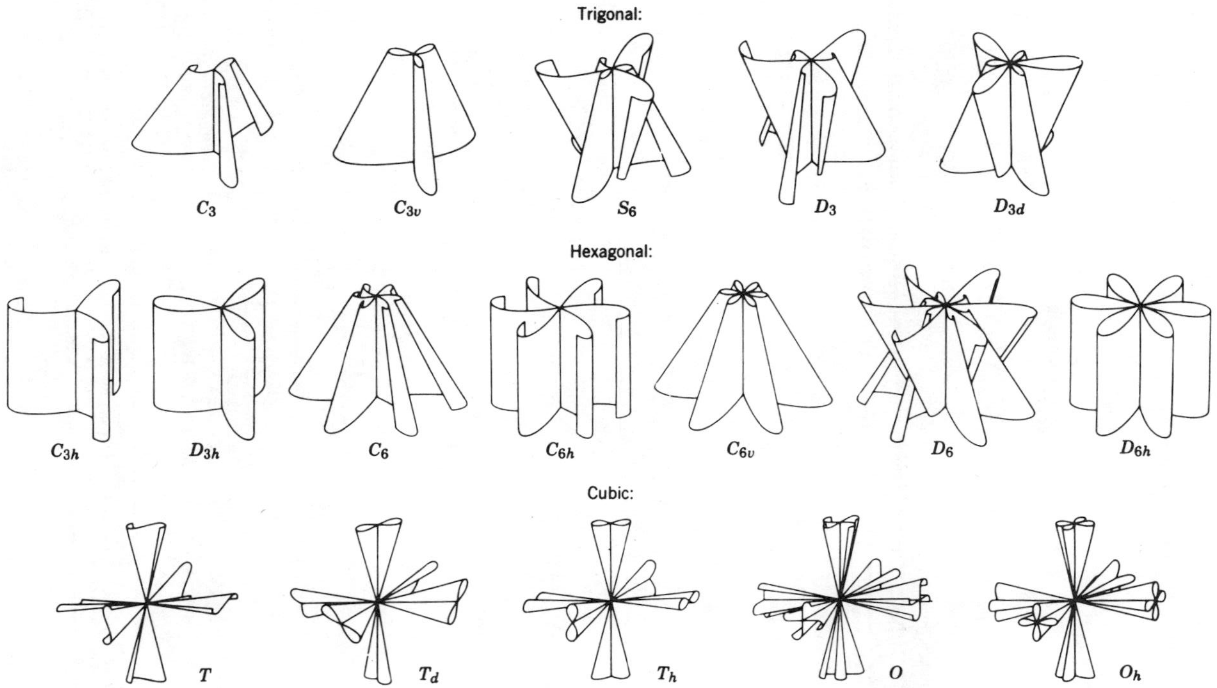

Trigonal:
C3
C3v
S6
D3
D3d
Hexagonal:
C3h
D3h
C6
C6h
C6v
D6
D6h
Cubic:
T
Td
Th
O
Oh

# Appendix 6

## SYMBOLS OF SYMMETRY PLANES

This figure, taken from the International Tables p. 49, shows the symbol and nature of the various symmetry planes.

TABLE 4.1.6. **Symbols of Symmetry Planes**

| Symbol | Symmetry plane | Graphical symbol | | Nature of glide translation |
|---|---|---|---|---|
| | | Normal to plane of projection | Parallel to plane of projection | |
| *m* | Reflection plane (mirror) | ———— | 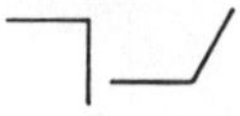 | None (NOTE. If the plane is at $z=\frac{1}{4}$ this is shown by printing $\frac{1}{4}$ beside the symbol.) |
| *a*, *b* | Axial glide plane | - - - - - - - |  | $a/2$ along [100] or $b/2$ along [010]; or along ⟨100⟩. |
| *c* | Axial glide plane | . . . . . . . . . . . . | None | $c/2$ along $z$-axis; or $(a+b+c)/2$ along [111] on rhombohedral axes. |
| *n* | Diagonal glide plane (net) | —·—·—·—·— |  | $(a+b)/2$ or $(b+c)/2$ or $(c+a)/2$; or $(a+b+c)/2$ (tetragonal and cubic). |
| *d* | "Diamond" glide plane | 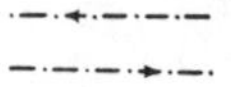 |  | $(a\pm b)/4$ or $(b\pm c)/4$ or $(c\pm a)/4$; or $(a\pm b\pm c)/4$ (tetragonal and cubic). See note below. |

NOTE. In the "diamond" glide plane the glide translation is half of the resultant of the two possible axial glide translations. The arrows in the first diagram show the direction of the horizontal component of the translation when the $z$-component is positive. In the second diagram the arrow shows the actual direction of the glide translation; there is always another diamond-glide reflection plane parallel to the first with a height difference of $\frac{1}{4}$ and with the arrow pointing along the other diagonal of the cell face.

## SYMBOLS OF SYMMETRY AXES

This figure, also from the International Tables p. 50, shows the symbols for the various symmetry axes.

TABLE 4.1.7

**Symbols of Symmetry Axes**

| Symbol | Symmetry axis | Graphical symbol | Nature of right-handed screw translation along the axis | Symbol | Symmetry axis | Graphical symbol (normal to plane of paper) | Nature of right-handed screw translation along the axis |
|---|---|---|---|---|---|---|---|
| 1 | Rotation monad | None | None | 4 | Rotation tetrad |  | None |
| $\bar{1}$ | Inversion monad | ○ | None | $4_1$ | Screw tetrads |  | $c/4$ |
| | | | | $4_2$ | |  | $2c/4$ |
| 2 | Rotation diad |  (normal to paper) | None | $4_3$ | |  | $3c/4$ |
| | |  (parallel to paper) | | $\bar{4}$ | Inversion tetrad |  | None |
| $2_1$ | Screw diad |  (normal to paper) | $c/2$ | 6 | Rotation hexad |  | None |
| | |  (parallel to paper) | Either $a/2$ or $b/2$ | $6_1$ | Screw hexads |  | $c/6$ |
| | | Normal to paper | | $6_2$ | |  | $2c/6$ |
| | | | | $6_3$ | |  | $3c/6$ |
| 3 | Rotation triad |  | None | $6_4$ | |  | $4c/6$ |
| $3_1$ | Screw triads |  | $c/3$ | $6_5$ | |  | $5c/6$ |
| $3_2$ | |  | $2c/3$ | | | | |
| $\bar{3}$ | Inversion triad |  | None | $\bar{6}$ | Inversion hexad |  | None |

## ORDER OF SYMBOLS

This Table summarizes the order of positions in the space group symbols (see Appendix 7) or point group symbols (see Appendix 4). Thus, for example in the orthorhombic system, mm2 refers to mirror planes perpendicular to **a** and **b**, and a 2-fold axis along **c**. Similarly, in the hexagonal system $\bar{6}$m2 means a $\bar{6}$ axis along **c**, mirror planes perpendicular to **a**, **b** and **a** + **b** ([110]), and 2-fold axes along **a**, **b** and **a** + **b**. Finally, in the cubic system, $\bar{4}$3m means $\bar{4}$ axes along the three cube axes, **a**, **b** and **c**, four 3-fold axes along the body diagonals <111> and diagonal mirror planes perpendicular to <110>. In m3 the first position tells us that there are mirror planes perpendicular to the cube axes and the second position that these are 3-fold axes along the body-diagonals. There is nothing in the third position, as in this case there is no symmetry element along the <110> directions, except, of course, for the identity element.

## ORDER OF SYMBOLS

| System | Position in International Symbol | | |
|---|---|---|---|
| | 1 | 2 | 3 |
| Triclinic | Only one symbol used | | |
| Monoclinic | 1st setting: $\underset{\sim}{c}$ - axis unique<br>2nd setting: $\underset{\sim}{b}$ - axis unique | | |
| Orthorhombic | 2 or $\bar{2}$ along $\underset{\sim}{a}$ | 2 or $\bar{2}$ along $\underset{\sim}{b}$ | 2 or $\bar{2}$ along $\underset{\sim}{c}$ |
| Tetragonal | 4 or $\bar{4}$ along $\underset{\sim}{c}$ | 2 or $\bar{2}$ along $\underset{\sim}{a}$ and $\underset{\sim}{b}$ | 2 or $\bar{2}$ along [110] and [1$\bar{1}$0] |
| Trigonal | 3 or $\bar{3}$ along $\underset{\sim}{c}$ | 2 or $\bar{2}$ along $\underset{\sim}{a}$, $\underset{\sim}{b}$ and [110] | 2 or $\bar{2}$ perpendicular to $\underset{\sim}{a}$, $\underset{\sim}{b}$ and [110] |
| Hexagonal | 6 or $\bar{6}$ along $\underset{\sim}{c}$ | 2 or $\bar{2}$ along $\underset{\sim}{a}$, $\underset{\sim}{b}$ and [110] | 2 or $\bar{2}$ perpendicular to $\underset{\sim}{a}$, $\underset{\sim}{b}$ and [110] |
| Cubic | 4, $\bar{4}$, 2 or $\bar{2}$ along $\underset{\sim}{a}$, $\underset{\sim}{b}$ and $\underset{\sim}{c}$ | 3 or $\bar{3}$ along <111> | 2 or $\bar{2}$ along <110> |

Remember: $\bar{2}$ is equivalent to a mirror plane m perpendicular to $\bar{2}$ axis.

## Appendix 7

## THE 11 ENANTIAMORPHIC SPACE GROUP PAIRS

The 11 enantiamorphic space group pairs are listed in the international and Schoenflies notation. (Naturally these space groups cannot contain a mirror plane.)

| | | | |
|---|---|---|---|
| $P3_1$ | $P3_2$ | $C_3^2$ | $C_3^3$ |
| $P4_1$ | $P4_3$ | $C_4^2$ | $C_4^4$ |
| $P6_1$ | $P6_5$ | $C_6^2$ | $C_6^3$ |
| $P6_2$ | $P6_4$ | $C_6^4$ | $C_6^5$ |
| $P3_112$ | $P3_212$ | $D_3^3$ | $D_3^5$ |
| $P3_121$ | $P3_221$ | $D_3^4$ | $D_3^6$ |
| $P4_122$ | $P4_322$ | $D_4^3$ | $D_4^7$ |
| $P4_12_12$ | $P4_32_12$ | $D_4^4$ | $D_4^8$ |
| $P6_122$ | $P6_522$ | $D_6^2$ | $D_6^3$ |
| $P6_422$ | $P6_222$ | $D_6^5$ | $D_6^6$ |
| $P4_322$ | $P4_132$ | $O^6$ | $O^7$ |

## THE 230 SPACE GROUPS

The 230 space groups are listed with a number and the Schoenflies, international standard short and international standard full symbol. A line under the number indicates that the space group is symmorphic. (Taken from the International Tables, p. 545.)

## TRICLINIC SYSTEM

| No. of space group | Schoenflies symbol | |
|---|---|---|
| $\underline{1}$ | $C_1^1$ | $P1$ |
| $\underline{2}$ | $C_i^1$ | $P\bar{1}$ |

## MONOCLINIC SYSTEM

| No. of space group | Schoen-flies symbol | z-axis unique (1st setting) | | y-axis unique (2nd setting) | |
|---|---|---|---|---|---|
| | | Short symbol | Full symbol | Short symbol | Full symbol |
| $\underline{3}$ | $C_2^1$ | $P2$ | $P112$ | $P2$ | $P121$ |
| 4 | $C_2^2$ | $P2_1$ | $P112_1$ | $P2_1$ | $P12_11$ |
| $\underline{5}$ | $C_2^3$ | $B2$ | $B112$ | $C2$ | $C121$ |
| $\underline{6}$ | $C_s^1$ | $Pm$ | $P11m$ | $Pm$ | $P1m1$ |
| 7 | $C_s^2$ | $Pb$ | $P11b$ | $Pc$ | $P1c1$ |
| $\underline{8}$ | $C_s^3$ | $Bm$ | $B11m$ | $Cm$ | $C1m1$ |
| 9 | $C_s^4$ | $Bb$ | $B11b$ | $Cc$ | $C1c1$ |
| $\underline{10}$ | $C_{2h}^1$ | $P2/m$ | $P11\frac{2}{m}$ | $P2/m$ | $P1\frac{2}{m}1$ |
| 11 | $C_{2h}^2$ | $P2_1/m$ | $P11\frac{2_1}{m}$ | $P2_1/m$ | $P1\frac{2_1}{m}1$ |
| $\underline{12}$ | $C_{2h}^3$ | $B2/m$ | $B11\frac{2}{m}$ | $C2/m$ | $C1\frac{2}{m}1$ |
| 13 | $C_{2h}^4$ | $P2/b$ | $P11\frac{2}{b}$ | $P2/c$ | $P1\frac{2}{c}1$ |
| 14 | $C_{2h}^5$ | $P2_1/b$ | $P11\frac{2_1}{b}$ | $P2_1/c$ | $P1\frac{2_1}{c}1$ |
| 15 | $C_{2h}^6$ | $B2/b$ | $B11\frac{2}{b}$ | $C2/c$ | $C1\frac{2}{c}1$ |

## ORTHORHOMBIC SYSTEM

| No. of space group | Schoenflies symbol | Short symbol | Full symbol |
|---|---|---|---|
| 16 | $D_2^1=V^1$ | *P*222 | *P*222 |
| 17 | $D_2^2=V^2$ | $P222_1$ | $P222_1$ |
| 18 | $D_2^3=V^3$ | $P2_12_12$ | $P2_12_12$ |
| 19 | $D_2^4=V^4$ | $P2_12_12_1$ | $P2_12_12_1$ |
| 20 | $D_2^5=V^5$ | $C222_1$ | $C222_1$ |
| 21 | $D_2^6=V^6$ | *C*222 | *C*222 |
| 22 | $D_2^7=V^7$ | *F*222 | *F*222 |
| 23 | $D_2^8=V^8$ | *I*222 | *I*222 |
| 24 | $D_2^9=V^9$ | $I2_12_12_1$ | $I2_12_12_1$ |
| 25 | $C_{2v}^1$ | *Pmm*2 | *Pmm*2 |
| 26 | $C_{2v}^2$ | $Pmc2_1$ | $Pmc2_1$ |
| 27 | $C_{2v}^3$ | *Pcc*2 | *Pcc*2 |
| 28 | $C_{2v}^4$ | *Pma*2 | *Pma*2 |
| 29 | $C_{2v}^5$ | $Pca2_1$ | $Pca2_1$ |
| 30 | $C_{2v}^6$ | *Pnc*2 | *Pnc*2 |
| 31 | $C_{2v}^7$ | $Pmn2_1$ | $Pmn2_1$ |
| 32 | $C_{2v}^8$ | *Pba*2 | *Pba*2 |
| 33 | $C_{2v}^9$ | $Pna2_1$ | $Pna2_1$ |
| 34 | $C_{2v}^{10}$ | *Pnn*2 | *Pnn*2 |
| 35 | $C_{2v}^{11}$ | *Cmm*2 | *Cmm*2 |

## ORTHORHOMBIC SYSTEM

| No. of space group | Schoenflies symbol | Short symbol | Full symbol |
|---|---|---|---|
| 36 | $C_{2v}^{12}$ | $Cmc2_1$ | $Cmc2_1$ |
| 37 | $C_{2v}^{13}$ | *Ccc*2 | *Ccc*2 |
| 38 | $C_{2v}^{14}$ | *Amm*2 | *Amm*2 |
| 39 | $C_{2v}^{15}$ | *Abm*2 | *Abm*2 |
| 40 | $C_{2v}^{16}$ | *Ama*2 | *Ama*2 |
| 41 | $C_{2v}^{17}$ | *Aba*2 | *Aba*2 |
| 42 | $C_{2v}^{18}$ | *Fmm*2 | *Fmm*2 |
| 43 | $C_{2v}^{19}$ | *Fdd*2 | *Fdd*2 |
| 44 | $C_{2v}^{20}$ | *Imm*2 | *Imm*2 |
| 45 | $C_{2v}^{21}$ | *Iba*2 | *Iba*2 |
| 46 | $C_{2v}^{22}$ | *Ima*2 | *Ima*2 |
| 47 | $D_{2h}^1=V_h^1$ | *Pmmm* | $P\frac{2}{m}\frac{2}{m}\frac{2}{m}$ |
| 48 | $D_{2h}^2=V_h^2$ | *Pnnn* | $P\frac{2}{n}\frac{2}{n}\frac{2}{n}$ |
| 49 | $D_{2h}^3=V_h^3$ | *Pccm* | $P\frac{2}{c}\frac{2}{c}\frac{2}{m}$ |
| 50 | $D_{2h}^4=V_h^4$ | *Pban* | $P\frac{2}{b}\frac{2}{a}\frac{2}{n}$ |
| 51 | $D_{2h}^5=V_h^5$ | *Pmma* | $P\frac{2_1}{m}\frac{2}{m}\frac{2}{a}$ |

## ORTHORHOMBIC SYSTEM

| No. of space group | Schoenflies symbol | Short symbol | Full symbol |
|---|---|---|---|
| 52 | $D_{2h}^{6}=V_h^{6}$ | *Pnna* | $P\frac{2}{n}\frac{2_1}{n}\frac{2}{a}$ |
| 53 | $D_{2h}^{7}=V_h^{7}$ | *Pmna* | $P\frac{2}{m}\frac{2}{n}\frac{2_1}{a}$ |
| 54 | $D_{2h}^{8}=V_h^{8}$ | *Pcca* | $P\frac{2_1}{c}\frac{2}{c}\frac{2}{a}$ |
| 55 | $D_{2h}^{9}=V_h^{9}$ | *Pbam* | $P\frac{2_1}{b}\frac{2_1}{a}\frac{2}{m}$ |
| 56 | $D_{2h}^{10}=V_h^{10}$ | *Pccn* | $P\frac{2_1}{c}\frac{2_1}{c}\frac{2}{n}$ |
| 57 | $D_{2h}^{11}=V_h^{11}$ | *Pbcm* | $P\frac{2}{b}\frac{2_1}{c}\frac{2_1}{m}$ |
| 58 | $D_{2h}^{12}=V_h^{12}$ | *Pnnm* | $P\frac{2_1}{n}\frac{2_1}{n}\frac{2}{m}$ |
| 59 | $D_{2h}^{13}=V_h^{13}$ | *Pmmn* | $P\frac{2_1}{m}\frac{2_1}{m}\frac{2}{n}$ |
| 60 | $D_{2h}^{14}=V_h^{14}$ | *Pbcn* | $P\frac{2_1}{b}\frac{2}{c}\frac{2_1}{n}$ |
| 61 | $D_{2h}^{15}=V_h^{15}$ | *Pbca* | $P\frac{2_1}{b}\frac{2_1}{c}\frac{2_1}{a}$ |
| 62 | $D_{2h}^{16}=V_h^{16}$ | *Pnma* | $P\frac{2_1}{n}\frac{2_1}{m}\frac{2_1}{a}$ |
| 63 | $D_{2h}^{17}=V_h^{17}$ | *Cmcm* | $C\frac{2}{m}\frac{2}{c}\frac{2_1}{m}$ |
| 64 | $D_{2h}^{18}=V_h^{18}$ | *Cmca* | $C\frac{2}{m}\frac{2}{c}\frac{2_1}{a}$ |
| 65 | $D_{2h}^{19}=V_h^{19}$ | *Cmmm* | $C\frac{2}{m}\frac{2}{m}\frac{2}{m}$ |
| 66 | $D_{2h}^{20}=V_h^{20}$ | *Cccm* | $C\frac{2}{c}\frac{2}{c}\frac{2}{m}$ |
| 67 | $D_{2h}^{21}=V_h^{21}$ | *Cmma* | $C\frac{2}{m}\frac{2}{m}\frac{2}{a}$ |
| 68 | $D_{2h}^{22}=V_h^{22}$ | *Ccca* | $C\frac{2}{c}\frac{2}{c}\frac{2}{a}$ |
| 69 | $D_{2h}^{23}=V_h^{23}$ | *Fmmm* | $F\frac{2}{m}\frac{2}{m}\frac{2}{m}$ |

## ORTHORHOMBIC SYSTEM

| No. of space group | Schoenflies symbol | Short symbol | Full symbol |
|---|---|---|---|
| 70 | $D_{2h}^{24}=V_h^{24}$ | *Fddd* | $F\frac{2}{d}\frac{2}{d}\frac{2}{d}$ |
| 71 | $D_{2h}^{25}=V_h^{25}$ | *Immm* | $I\frac{2}{m}\frac{2}{m}\frac{2}{m}$ |
| 72 | $D_{2h}^{26}=V_h^{26}$ | *Ibam* | $I\frac{2}{b}\frac{2}{a}\frac{2}{m}$ |
| 73 | $D_{2h}^{27}=V_h^{27}$ | *Ibca* | $I\frac{2}{b}\frac{2}{c}\frac{2}{a}$ |
| 74 | $D_{2h}^{28}=V_h^{28}$ | *Imma* | $I\frac{2}{m}\frac{2}{m}\frac{2}{a}$ |

## TETRAGONAL SYSTEM

| No. of space group | Schoenflies symbol | Symbols: a b c (standard) | Symbols: (a±b) (b∓a) c | No. of space group | Schoenflies symbol | Symbols: a b c (standard) | Symbols: (a±b) (b∓a) c |
|---|---|---|---|---|---|---|---|
| 75 | $C_4^1$ | $P4$ | $C4$ | 99 | $C_{4v}^1$ | $P4mm$ | $C4mm$ |
| 76 | $C_4^2$ | $P4_1$ | $C4_1$ | 100 | $C_{4v}^2$ | $P4bm$ | $C4mb$ |
| 77 | $C_4^3$ | $P4_2$ | $C4_2$ | 101 | $C_{4v}^3$ | $P4_2cm$ | $C4_2mc$ |
| 78 | $C_4^4$ | $P4_3$ | $C4_3$ | 102 | $C_{4v}^4$ | $P4_2nm$ | $C4_2mn$ |
| 79 | $C_4^5$ | $I4$ | $F4$ | 103 | $C_{4v}^5$ | $P4cc$ | $C4cc$ |
| 80 | $C_4^6$ | $I4_1$ | $F4_1$ | 104 | $C_{4v}^6$ | $P4nc$ | $C4cn$ |
| 81 | $S_4^1$ | $P\bar{4}$ | $C\bar{4}$ | 105 | $C_{4v}^7$ | $P4_2mc$ | $C4_2cm$ |
| 82 | $S_4^2$ | $I\bar{4}$ | $F\bar{4}$ | 106 | $C_{4v}^8$ | $P4_2bc$ | $C4_2cb$ |
| 83 | $C_{4h}^1$ | $P4/m$ | $C4/m$ | 107 | $C_{4v}^9$ | $I4mm$ | $F4mm$ |
| 84 | $C_{4h}^2$ | $P4_2/m$ | $C4_2/m$ | 108 | $C_{4v}^{10}$ | $I4cm$ | $F4mc$ |
| 85 | $C_{4h}^3$ | $P4/n$ | $C4/n$ | 109 | $C_{4v}^{11}$ | $I4_1md$ | $F4_1dm$ |
| 86 | $C_{4h}^4$ | $P4_2/n$ | $C4_2/n$ | 110 | $C_{4v}^{12}$ | $I4_1cd$ | $F4_1dc$ |
| 87 | $C_{4h}^5$ | $I4/m$ | $F4/m$ | 111 | $D_{2d}^1=V_d^1$ | $P\bar{4}2m$ | $C\bar{4}m2$ |
| 88 | $C_{4h}^6$ | $I4_1/a$ | $F4_1/a$ | 112 | $D_{2d}^2=V_d^2$ | $P\bar{4}2c$ | $C\bar{4}c2$ |
| 89 | $D_4^1$ | $P422$ | $C422$ | 113 | $D_{2d}^3=V_d^3$ | $P\bar{4}2_1m$ | $C\bar{4}m2_1$ |
| 90 | $D_4^2$ | $P42_12$ | $C422_1$ | 114 | $D_{2d}^4=V_d^4$ | $P\bar{4}2_1c$ | $C\bar{4}c2_1$ |
| 91 | $D_4^3$ | $P4_122$ | $C4_122$ | 115 | $D_{2d}^5=V_d^5$ | $P\bar{4}m2$ | $C\bar{4}2m$ |
| 92 | $D_4^4$ | $P4_12_12$ | $C4_122_1$ | 116 | $D_{2d}^6=V_d^6$ | $P\bar{4}c2$ | $C\bar{4}2c$ |
| 93 | $D_4^5$ | $P4_222$ | $C4_222$ | 117 | $D_{2d}^7=V_d^7$ | $P\bar{4}b2$ | $C\bar{4}2b$ |
| 94 | $D_4^6$ | $P4_22_12$ | $C4_222_1$ | 118 | $D_{2d}^8=V_d^8$ | $P\bar{4}n2$ | $C\bar{4}2n$ |
| 95 | $D_4^7$ | $P4_322$ | $C4_322$ | 119 | $D_{2d}^9=V_d^9$ | $I\bar{4}m2$ | $F\bar{4}2m$ |
| 96 | $D_4^8$ | $P4_32_12$ | $C4_322_1$ | 120 | $D_{2d}^{10}=V_d^{10}$ | $I\bar{4}c2$ | $F\bar{4}2c$ |
| 97 | $D_4^9$ | $I422$ | $F422$ | 121 | $D_{2d}^{11}=V_d^{11}$ | $I\bar{4}2m$ | $F\bar{4}m2$ |
| 98 | $D_4^{10}$ | $I4_122$ | $F4_122$ | 122 | $D_{2d}^{12}=V_d^{12}$ | $I\bar{4}2d$ | $F\bar{4}d2$ |

## TETRAGONAL SYSTEM

| No. of space group | Schoenflies symbol | Short symbols | | Full symbols | |
|---|---|---|---|---|---|
| | | a b c (standard) | (a±b) (b∓a) c | a b c | (a±b) (b∓a) c |
| 123 | $D_{4h}^{1}$ | $P4/mmm$ | $C4/mmm$ | $P\frac{4}{m}\frac{2}{m}\frac{2}{m}$ | $C\frac{4}{m}\frac{2}{m}\frac{2}{m}$ |
| 124 | $D_{4h}^{2}$ | $P4/mcc$ | $C4/mcc$ | $P\frac{4}{m}\frac{2}{c}\frac{2}{c}$ | $C\frac{4}{m}\frac{2}{c}\frac{2}{c}$ |
| 125 | $D_{4h}^{3}$ | $P4/nbm$ | $C4/nmb$ | $P\frac{4}{n}\frac{2}{b}\frac{2}{m}$ | $C\frac{4}{n}\frac{2}{m}\frac{2}{b}$ |
| 126 | $D_{4h}^{4}$ | $P4/nnc$ | $C4/ncn$ | $P\frac{4}{n}\frac{2}{n}\frac{2}{c}$ | $C\frac{4}{n}\frac{2}{c}\frac{2}{n}$ |
| 127 | $D_{4h}^{5}$ | $P4/mbm$ | $C4/mmb$ | $P\frac{4}{m}\frac{2_1}{b}\frac{2}{m}$ | $C\frac{4}{m}\frac{2}{m}\frac{2_1}{b}$ |
| 128 | $D_{4h}^{6}$ | $P4/mnc$ | $C4/mcn$ | $P\frac{4}{m}\frac{2_1}{n}\frac{2}{c}$ | $C\frac{4}{m}\frac{2}{c}\frac{2_1}{n}$ |
| 129 | $D_{4h}^{7}$ | $P4/nmm$ | $C4/nmm$ | $P\frac{4}{n}\frac{2_1}{m}\frac{2}{m}$ | $C\frac{4}{n}\frac{2}{m}\frac{2_1}{m}$ |
| 130 | $D_{4h}^{8}$ | $P4/ncc$ | $C4/ncc$ | $P\frac{4}{n}\frac{2_1}{c}\frac{2}{c}$ | $C\frac{4}{n}\frac{2}{c}\frac{2_1}{c}$ |
| 131 | $D_{4h}^{9}$ | $P4_2/mmc$ | $C4_2/mcm$ | $P\frac{4_2}{m}\frac{2}{m}\frac{2}{c}$ | $C\frac{4_2}{m}\frac{2}{c}\frac{2}{m}$ |
| 132 | $D_{4h}^{10}$ | $P4_2/mcm$ | $C4_2/mmc$ | $P\frac{4_2}{m}\frac{2}{c}\frac{2}{m}$ | $C\frac{4_2}{m}\frac{2}{m}\frac{2}{c}$ |
| 133 | $D_{4h}^{11}$ | $P4_2/nbc$ | $C4_2/ncb$ | $P\frac{4_2}{n}\frac{2}{b}\frac{2}{c}$ | $C\frac{4_2}{n}\frac{2}{c}\frac{2}{b}$ |
| 134 | $D_{4h}^{12}$ | $P4_2/nnm$ | $C4_2/nmn$ | $P\frac{4_2}{n}\frac{2}{n}\frac{2}{m}$ | $C\frac{4_2}{n}\frac{2}{m}\frac{2}{n}$ |
| 135 | $D_{4h}^{13}$ | $P4_2/mbc$ | $C4_2/mcb$ | $P\frac{4_2}{m}\frac{2_1}{b}\frac{2}{c}$ | $C\frac{4_2}{m}\frac{2}{c}\frac{2_1}{b}$ |
| 136 | $D_{4h}^{14}$ | $P4_2/mnm$ | $C4_2/mmn$ | $P\frac{4_2}{m}\frac{2_1}{n}\frac{2}{m}$ | $C\frac{4_2}{m}\frac{2}{m}\frac{2_1}{n}$ |
| 137 | $D_{4h}^{15}$ | $P4_2/nmc$ | $C4_2/ncm$ | $P\frac{4_2}{n}\frac{2_1}{m}\frac{2}{c}$ | $C\frac{4_2}{n}\frac{2}{c}\frac{2_1}{m}$ |
| 138 | $D_{4h}^{16}$ | $P4_2/ncm$ | $C4_2/nmc$ | $P\frac{4_2}{n}\frac{2_1}{c}\frac{2}{m}$ | $C\frac{4_2}{n}\frac{2}{m}\frac{2_1}{c}$ |
| 139 | $D_{4h}^{17}$ | $I4/mmm$ | $F4/mmm$ | $I\frac{4}{m}\frac{2}{m}\frac{2}{m}$ | $F\frac{4}{m}\frac{2}{m}\frac{2}{m}$ |
| 140 | $D_{4h}^{18}$ | $I4/mcm$ | $F4/mmc$ | $I\frac{4}{m}\frac{2}{c}\frac{2}{m}$ | $F\frac{4}{m}\frac{2}{m}\frac{2}{c}$ |
| 141 | $D_{4h}^{19}$ | $I4_1/amd$ | $F4_1/adm$ | $I\frac{4_1}{a}\frac{2}{m}\frac{2}{d}$ | $F\frac{4_1}{a}\frac{2}{d}\frac{2}{m}$ |
| 142 | $D_{4h}^{20}$ | $I4_1/acd$ | $F4_1/adc$ | $I\frac{4_1}{a}\frac{2}{c}\frac{2}{d}$ | $F\frac{4_1}{a}\frac{2}{d}\frac{2}{c}$ |

## TRIGONAL SYSTEM

| No. of space group | Schoenflies symbol | Short symbol | Full symbol |
|---|---|---|---|
| 143 | $C_3^1$ | $P3$ | |
| 144 | $C_3^2$ | $P3_1$ | |
| 145 | $C_3^3$ | $P3_2$ | |
| 146 | $C_3^4$ | $R3$ | |
| 147 | $C_{3i}^1$ | $P\bar{3}$ | |
| 148 | $C_{3i}^2$ | $R\bar{3}$ | |
| 149 | $D_3^1$ | $P312$ | |
| 150 | $D_3^2$ | $P321$ | |
| 151 | $D_3^3$ | $P3_112$ | |
| 152 | $D_3^4$ | $P3_121$ | |
| 153 | $D_3^5$ | $P3_212$ | |
| 154 | $D_3^6$ | $P3_221$ | |
| 155 | $D_3^7$ | $R32$ | |
| 156 | $C_{3v}^1$ | $P3m1$ | |
| 157 | $C_{3v}^2$ | $P31m$ | |
| 158 | $C_{3v}^3$ | $P3c1$ | |
| 159 | $C_{3v}^4$ | $P31c$ | |
| 160 | $C_{3v}^5$ | $R3m$ | |
| 161 | $C_{3v}^6$ | $R3c$ | |
| 162 | $D_{3d}^1$ | $P\bar{3}1m$ | $P\bar{3}1\frac{2}{m}$ |
| 163 | $D_{3d}^2$ | $P\bar{3}1c$ | $P\bar{3}1\frac{2}{c}$ |
| 164 | $D_{3d}^3$ | $P\bar{3}m1$ | $P\bar{3}\frac{2}{m}1$ |
| 165 | $D_{3d}^4$ | $P\bar{3}c1$ | $P\bar{3}\frac{2}{c}1$ |
| 166 | $D_{3d}^5$ | $R\bar{3}m$ | $R\bar{3}\frac{2}{m}$ |
| 167 | $D_{3d}^6$ | $R\bar{3}c$ | $R\bar{3}\frac{2}{c}$ |

## HEXAGONAL SYSTEM

| No. of space group | Schoenflies symbol | Short symbol | Full symbol |
|---|---|---|---|
| 168 | $C_6^1$ | $P6$ | |
| 169 | $C_6^2$ | $P6_1$ | |
| 170 | $C_6^3$ | $P6_5$ | |
| 171 | $C_6^4$ | $P6_2$ | |
| 172 | $C_6^5$ | $P6_4$ | |
| 173 | $C_6^6$ | $P6_3$ | |
| 174 | $C_{3h}^1$ | $P\bar{6}$ | |
| 175 | $C_{6h}^1$ | $P6/m$ | |
| 176 | $C_{6h}^2$ | $P6_3/m$ | |
| 177 | $D_6^1$ | $P622$ | |
| 178 | $D_6^2$ | $P6_122$ | |
| 179 | $D_6^3$ | $P6_522$ | |
| 180 | $D_6^4$ | $P6_222$ | |
| 181 | $D_6^5$ | $P6_422$ | |
| 182 | $D_6^6$ | $P6_322$ | |
| 183 | $C_{6v}^1$ | $P6mm$ | |
| 184 | $C_{6v}^2$ | $P6cc$ | |
| 185 | $C_{6v}^3$ | $P6_3cm$ | |
| 186 | $C_{6v}^4$ | $P6_3mc$ | |
| 187 | $D_{3h}^1$ | $P\bar{6}m2$ | |
| 188 | $D_{3h}^2$ | $P\bar{6}c2$ | |
| 189 | $D_{3h}^3$ | $P\bar{6}2m$ | |
| 190 | $D_{3h}^4$ | $P\bar{6}2c$ | |
| 191 | $D_{6h}^1$ | $P6/mmm$ | $P\frac{6}{m}\frac{2}{m}\frac{2}{m}$ |
| 192 | $D_{6h}^2$ | $P6/mcc$ | $P\frac{6}{m}\frac{2}{c}\frac{2}{c}$ |
| 193 | $D_{6h}^3$ | $P6_3/mcm$ | $P\frac{6_3}{m}\frac{2}{c}\frac{2}{m}$ |
| 194 | $D_{6h}^4$ | $P6_3/mmc$ | $P\frac{6_3}{m}\frac{2}{m}\frac{2}{c}$ |

## CUBIC SYSTEM

| No. of space group | Schoenflies symbol | Short symbol | Full symbol | No. of space group | Schoenflies symbol | Short symbol | Full symbol |
|---|---|---|---|---|---|---|---|
| 195 | $T^1$ | $P23$ | | 213 | $O^7$ | $P4_132$ | |
| 196 | $T^2$ | $F23$ | | 214 | $O^8$ | $I4_132$ | |
| 197 | $T^3$ | $I23$ | | 215 | $T_d^1$ | $P\bar{4}3m$ | |
| 198 | $T^4$ | $P2_13$ | | 216 | $T_d^2$ | $F\bar{4}3m$ | |
| 199 | $T^5$ | $I2_13$ | | 217 | $T_d^3$ | $I\bar{4}3m$ | |
| 200 | $T_h^1$ | $Pm3$ | $P\frac{2}{m}\bar{3}$ | 218 | $T_d^4$ | $P\bar{4}3n$ | |
| 201 | $T_h^2$ | $Pn3$ | $P\frac{2}{n}\bar{3}$ | 219 | $T_d^5$ | $F\bar{4}3c$ | |
| 202 | $T_h^3$ | $Fm3$ | $F\frac{2}{m}\bar{3}$ | 220 | $T_d^6$ | $I\bar{4}3d$ | |
| 203 | $T_h^4$ | $Fd3$ | $F\frac{2}{d}\bar{3}$ | 221 | $O_h^1$ | $Pm3m$ | $P\frac{4}{m}\bar{3}\frac{2}{m}$ |
| 204 | $T_h^5$ | $Im3$ | $I\frac{2}{m}\bar{3}$ | 222 | $O_h^2$ | $Pn3n$ | $P\frac{4}{n}\bar{3}\frac{2}{n}$ |
| 205 | $T_h^6$ | $Pa3$ | $P\frac{2_1}{a}\bar{3}$ | 223 | $O_h^3$ | $Pm3n$ | $P\frac{4_2}{m}\bar{3}\frac{2}{n}$ |
| 206 | $T_h^7$ | $Ia3$ | $I\frac{2_1}{a}\bar{3}$ | 224 | $O_h^4$ | $Pn3m$ | $P\frac{4_2}{n}\bar{3}\frac{2}{m}$ |
| 207 | $O^1$ | $P432$ | | 225 | $O_h^5$ | $Fm3m$ | $F\frac{4}{m}\bar{3}\frac{2}{m}$ |
| 208 | $O^2$ | $P4_232$ | | 226 | $O_h^6$ | $Fm3c$ | $F\frac{4}{m}\bar{3}\frac{2}{c}$ |
| 209 | $O^3$ | $F432$ | | 227 | $O_h^7$ | $Fd3m$ | $F\frac{4_1}{d}\bar{3}\frac{2}{m}$ |
| 210 | $O^4$ | $F4_132$ | | 228 | $O_h^8$ | $Fd3c$ | $F\frac{4_1}{d}\bar{3}\frac{2}{c}$ |
| 211 | $O^5$ | $I432$ | | 229 | $O_h^9$ | $Im3m$ | $I\frac{4}{m}\bar{3}\frac{2}{m}$ |
| 212 | $O^6$ | $P4_332$ | | 230 | $O_h^{10}$ | $Ia3d$ | $I\frac{4_1}{a}\bar{3}\frac{2}{d}$ |

Appendix 8

# CHARACTER TABLES FOR THE 32 POINT GROUPS

Our usual notation for each point group is given on the top left of each table. For the symmetry operations, which are grouped into classes as always in character tables, we have used the Schoenflies notation. This notation lends itself to this kind of grouping. The Mulliken or chemical notation is used for the irreducible representations. The 1-dimensional irreducible representations are labelled with the letters A or B, the 2-dimensional ones with E, the 3-dimensional ones with T (F is used by some authors). The subscripts g and u occur for point groups with a center of inversion as a symmetry operation. If the irreducible representation is symmetric (transforms into +1 times itself) under the inversion operations, then it is g (gerade); if it is antisymmetric, then it is u (ungerade). See Wilson, Decius and Cross, Appendix 10, for an explanation of the number subscripts. Most group theory books have a full explanation of character tables, see Burns, for example, Section 4-2.

## Non–Axial Groups

| $1(C_1)$ | E |
|---|---|
| A | 1 |

| $\bar{1}(S_2)$ | E | i | | |
|---|---|---|---|---|
| $A_g$ | 1 | 1 | $R_x, R_y, R_z$ | $x^2, y^2, z^2$, xy, xz, yz |
| $A_u$ | 1 | -1 | x, y, z | |

| $m(C_{1h})$ | E | $\sigma_h$ | | |
|---|---|---|---|---|
| A' | 1 | 1 | x, y, $R_z$ | $x^2, y^2$, $z^2$, xy |
| A" | 1 | -1 | z, $R_x, R_y$ | yz, xz |

## $C_n$ Groups

| 2($C_2$) | E | $C_2$(z) | | |
|---|---|---|---|---|
| A | 1 | 1 | z, $R_z$ | $x^2$, $y^2$, $z^2$, xy |
| B | 1 | -1 | x, y, $R_x$, $R_y$ | yz, xz |

| 3($C_3$) | | E | $C_3$(z) | $C_3^2$ | $\varepsilon=\exp(2\pi i/3)$ | |
|---|---|---|---|---|---|---|
| A | | 1 | 1 | 1 | z, $R_z$ | $x^2+y^2$, $z^2$ |
| E | { | 1 | $\varepsilon$ | $\varepsilon^*$ | x+iy; $R_x+iR_y$ } | ($x^2-y^2$, xy) |
| | { | 1 | $\varepsilon^*$ | $\varepsilon$ | x-iy; $R_x-iR_y$ } | (yz, xz) |

| 4($C_4$) | | E | $C_4$(z) | $C_2$ | $C_4^3$ | | |
|---|---|---|---|---|---|---|---|
| A | | 1 | 1 | 1 | 1 | z, $R_z$ | $x^2+y^2$, $z^2$ |
| B | | 1 | -1 | 1 | -1 | | $x^2-y^2$, xy |
| E | { | 1 | i | -1 | -i | x+iy; $R_x+iR_y$ } | (yz, xz) |
| | { | 1 | -i | -1 | i | x-iy; $R_x-iR_y$ } | |

| 6($C_6$) | | E | $C_6$ | $C_3$ | $C_2$ | $C_3^2$ | $C_6^5$ | $\varepsilon=\exp(2\pi i/6)$ | |
|---|---|---|---|---|---|---|---|---|---|
| A | | 1 | 1 | 1 | 1 | 1 | 1 | z, $R_z$ | $x^2+y^2$, $z^2$ |
| B | | 1 | -1 | 1 | -1 | 1 | -1 | | |
| $E_1$ | { | 1 | $\varepsilon$ | $-\varepsilon^*$ | -1 | $-\varepsilon$ | $\varepsilon^*$ | x+iy; $R_z+iR_y$ } | (xz, yz) |
| | { | 1 | $\varepsilon^*$ | $-\varepsilon$ | -1 | $-\varepsilon^*$ | $\varepsilon$ | x-iy; $R_x-iR_y$ } | |
| $E_2$ | { | 1 | $-\varepsilon^*$ | $-\varepsilon$ | 1 | $-\varepsilon^*$ | $-\varepsilon$ } | | ($x^2-y^2$, xy) |
| | { | 1 | $-\varepsilon$ | $-\varepsilon^*$ | 1 | $-\varepsilon$ | $-\varepsilon^*$ } | | |

## $C_{nv}$ Groups

| mm2($C_{2v}$) | E | $C_2(z)$ | $\sigma_v(xz)$ | $\sigma'_v(yz)$ | | |
|---|---|---|---|---|---|---|
| $A_1$ | 1 | 1 | 1 | 1 | z | $x^2$, $y^2$, $z^2$ |
| $A_2$ | 1 | 1 | -1 | -1 | $R_z$ | xy |
| $B_1$ | 1 | -1 | 1 | -1 | x, $R_y$ | xz |
| $B_2$ | 1 | -1 | -1 | 1 | y, $R_x$ | yz |

| 3m($C_{3v}$) | E | $2C_3(z)$ | $3\sigma_v$ | | |
|---|---|---|---|---|---|
| $A_1$ | 1 | 1 | 1 | z | $x^2+y^2$, $z^2$ |
| $A_2$ | 1 | 1 | -1 | $R_z$ | |
| E | 2 | -1 | 0 | (x, y) ($R_x$, $R_y$) | ($x^2-y^2$, xy) (xz, yz) |

| 4mm($C_{4v}$) | E | $2C_4(z)$ | $C_2$ | $2\sigma_v$ | $2\sigma_d$ | | |
|---|---|---|---|---|---|---|---|
| $A_1$ | 1 | 1 | 1 | 1 | 1 | z | $x^2+y^2$, $z^2$ |
| $A_2$ | 1 | 1 | 1 | -1 | -1 | $R_z$ | |
| $B_1$ | 1 | -1 | 1 | 1 | -1 | | $x^2-y^2$ |
| $B_2$ | 1 | -1 | 1 | -1 | 1 | | xy |
| E | 2 | 0 | -2 | 0 | 0 | (x, y) ($R_x$, $R_y$) | (xz, yz) |

| 6mm($C_{6v}$) | E | $2C_6(z)$ | $2C_3(z)$ | $C_2(z)$ | $3\sigma_v$ | $3\sigma_d$ | | |
|---|---|---|---|---|---|---|---|---|
| $A_1$ | 1 | 1 | 1 | 1 | 1 | 1 | z | $x^2+y^2$, $z^2$ |
| $A_2$ | 1 | 1 | 1 | 1 | -1 | -1 | $R_z$ | |
| $B_1$ | 1 | -1 | 1 | -1 | 1 | -1 | | |
| $B_2$ | 1 | -1 | 1 | -1 | -1 | 1 | | |
| $E_1$ | 2 | 1 | -1 | -2 | 0 | 0 | (x, y) ($R_x$, $R_y$) | (xz, yz) |
| $E_2$ | 2 | -1 | -1 | 2 | 0 | 0 | | ($x^2-y^2$, xy) |

# $C_{nh}$ Groups

| $2/m(C_{2h})$ | E | $C_2(z)$ | i | $\sigma_h$ | | |
|---|---|---|---|---|---|---|
| $A_g$ | 1 | 1 | 1 | 1 | $R_z$ | $x^2, y^2, z^2, xy$ |
| $B_g$ | 1 | -1 | 1 | -1 | $R_x, R_y$ | xz, yz |
| $A_u$ | 1 | 1 | -1 | -1 | z | |
| $B_u$ | 1 | -1 | -1 | 1 | x, y | |

| $\bar{6}(C_{3h})$ | E | $C_3(z)$ | $C_3^2$ | $\sigma_h$ | $S_3$ | $S_3^5$ | | $\varepsilon = \exp(2\pi i/3)$ |
|---|---|---|---|---|---|---|---|---|
| A' | 1 | 1 | 1 | 1 | 1 | 1 | $R_z$ | $x^2+y^2, z^2$ |
| E' | 1 | $\varepsilon$ | $\varepsilon^*$ | 1 | $\varepsilon$ | $\varepsilon^*$ | x+iy | $(x^2-y^2, xy)$ |
| | 1 | $\varepsilon^*$ | $\varepsilon$ | 1 | $\varepsilon^*$ | $\varepsilon$ | x-iy | |
| A" | 1 | 1 | 1 | -1 | -1 | -1 | z | |
| E" | 1 | $\varepsilon$ | $\varepsilon^*$ | -1 | $-\varepsilon$ | $-\varepsilon^*$ | $R_x+iR_y$ | (xz, yz) |
| | 1 | $\varepsilon^*$ | $\varepsilon$ | -1 | $-\varepsilon^*$ | $-\varepsilon$ | $R_x-iR_y$ | |

| $4/m(C_{4h})$ | E | $C_4(z)$ | $C_2$ | $C_4^3$ | i | $S_4^3$ | $\sigma_h$ | $S_4$ | | |
|---|---|---|---|---|---|---|---|---|---|---|
| $A_g$ | 1 | 1 | 1 | 1 | 1 | 1 | 1 | 1 | $R_z$ | $x^2+y^2, z^2$ |
| $B_g$ | 1 | -1 | 1 | -1 | 1 | -1 | 1 | -1 | | $x^2-y^2, xy$ |
| $E_g$ | 1 | i | -1 | -i | 1 | i | -1 | -i | $R_x+iR_y$ | (xz, yz) |
| | 1 | -i | -1 | i | 1 | -i | -1 | i | $R_x-iR_y$ | |
| $A_u$ | 1 | 1 | 1 | 1 | -1 | -1 | -1 | -1 | z | |
| $B_u$ | 1 | -1 | 1 | -1 | -1 | 1 | -1 | 1 | | |
| $E_u$ | 1 | i | -1 | -i | -1 | -i | 1 | i | x+iy | |
| | 1 | -i | -1 | i | -1 | i | 1 | -i | x-iy | |

## $D_n$ Groups

| $222(D_2)$ | E | $C_2(z)$ | $C_2(y)$ | $C_2(x)$ | | |
|---|---|---|---|---|---|---|
| A | 1 | 1 | 1 | 1 | | $x^2, y^2, z^2$ |
| $B_1$ | 1 | 1 | -1 | -1 | $z, R_z$ | $xy$ |
| $B_2$ | 1 | -1 | 1 | -1 | $y, R_y$ | $xz$ |
| $B_3$ | 1 | -1 | -1 | 1 | $x, R_x$ | $yz$ |

| $422(D_4)$ | E | $2C_4(z)$ | $C_2(\equiv C_4^2)$ | $2C'_2$ | $2C''_2$ | | |
|---|---|---|---|---|---|---|---|
| $A_1$ | 1 | 1 | 1 | 1 | 1 | | $x^2+y^2, z^2$ |
| $A_2$ | 1 | 1 | 1 | -1 | -1 | $z, R_z$ | |
| $B_1$ | 1 | -1 | 1 | 1 | -1 | | $x^2-y^2$ |
| $B_2$ | 1 | -1 | 1 | -1 | 1 | | $xy$ |
| E | 2 | 0 | -2 | 0 | 0 | $(x, y)$ $(R_x, R_y)$ | $(xz, yz)$ |

## $D_{nd}$ Groups

| $\bar{4}2m(D_{2d})$ | E | $2S_4$ | $C_2(z)$ | $2C'_2$ | $2\sigma_d$ | | |
|---|---|---|---|---|---|---|---|
| $A_1$ | 1 | 1 | 1 | 1 | 1 | | $x^2+y^2, z^2$ |
| $A_2$ | 1 | 1 | 1 | -1 | -1 | $R_z$ | |
| $B_1$ | 1 | -1 | 1 | 1 | -1 | | $x^2-y^2$ |
| $B_2$ | 1 | -1 | 1 | -1 | 1 | $z$ | $xy$ |
| E | 2 | 0 | -2 | 0 | 0 | $(x, y)$ $(R_x, R_y)$ | $(xz, yz)$ |

| $\bar{3}m(D_{3d})$ | E | $2C_3$ | $3C'_2$ | i | $2S_6$ | $3\sigma_d$ | | |
|---|---|---|---|---|---|---|---|---|
| $A_{1g}$ | 1 | 1 | 1 | 1 | 1 | 1 | | $x^2+y^2, z^2$ |
| $A_{2g}$ | 1 | 1 | -1 | 1 | 1 | -1 | $R_z$ | |
| $E_g$ | 2 | -1 | 0 | 2 | -1 | 0 | $(R_x, R_y)$ | $(x^2-y^2, xy)$ $(xz, yz)$ |
| $A_{1u}$ | 1 | 1 | 1 | -1 | -1 | -1 | | |
| $A_{2u}$ | 1 | 1 | -1 | -1 | -1 | 1 | $z$ | |
| $E_u$ | 2 | -1 | 0 | -2 | 1 | 0 | $(x, y)$ | |

# $D_{nh}$ Groups

| mmm($D_{2h}$) | E | $C_2(z)$ | $C_2(y)$ | $C_2(x)$ | i | $\sigma(xy)$ | $\sigma(xz)$ | $\sigma(yz)$ | |
|---|---|---|---|---|---|---|---|---|---|
| $A_g$ | 1 | 1 | 1 | 1 | 1 | 1 | 1 | 1 | |
| $B_{1g}$ | 1 | 1 | -1 | -1 | 1 | 1 | -1 | -1 | $R_z$ |
| $B_{2g}$ | 1 | -1 | 1 | -1 | 1 | -1 | 1 | -1 | $R_y$ |
| $B_{3g}$ | 1 | -1 | -1 | 1 | 1 | -1 | -1 | 1 | $R_x$ |
| $A_u$ | 1 | 1 | 1 | 1 | -1 | -1 | -1 | -1 | |
| $B_{1u}$ | 1 | 1 | -1 | -1 | -1 | -1 | 1 | 1 | z |
| $B_{2u}$ | 1 | -1 | 1 | -1 | -1 | 1 | -1 | 1 | y |
| $B_{3u}$ | 1 | -1 | -1 | 1 | -1 | 1 | 1 | -1 | x |

| $\bar{6}m2(D_{3h})$ | E | $2C_3(z)$ | $3C_2'$ | $\sigma_h(xy)$ | $2S_3$ | $3\sigma_v$ | | |
|---|---|---|---|---|---|---|---|---|
| $A_1'$ | 1 | 1 | 1 | 1 | 1 | 1 | | $x^2+y^2$, $z^2$ |
| $A_2'$ | 1 | 1 | -1 | 1 | 1 | -1 | $R_z$ | |
| E' | 2 | -1 | 0 | 2 | -1 | 0 | (x, y) | $(x^2-y^2, xy)$ |
| $A_1''$ | 1 | 1 | 1 | -1 | -1 | -1 | | |
| $A_2''$ | 1 | 1 | -1 | -1 | -1 | 1 | z | |
| E" | 2 | -1 | 0 | -2 | 1 | 0 | $(R_x, R_y)$ | (xz, yz) |

| 4/mmm($D_{4h}$) | E | $2C_4(z)$ | $C_2$ | $2C_2'$ | $2C_2''$ | i | $2S_4$ | $\sigma_h$ | $2\sigma_v$ | $2\sigma_d$ | | |
|---|---|---|---|---|---|---|---|---|---|---|---|---|
| $A_{1g}$ | 1 | 1 | 1 | 1 | 1 | 1 | 1 | 1 | 1 | 1 | | $x^2+y^2$, $z^2$ |
| $A_{2g}$ | 1 | 1 | 1 | -1 | -1 | 1 | 1 | 1 | -1 | -1 | $R_z$ | |
| $B_{1g}$ | 1 | -1 | 1 | 1 | -1 | 1 | -1 | 1 | 1 | -1 | | $x^2-y^2$ |
| $B_{2g}$ | 1 | -1 | 1 | -1 | 1 | 1 | -1 | 1 | -1 | 1 | | xy |
| $E_g$ | 2 | 0 | -2 | 0 | 0 | 2 | 0 | -2 | 0 | 0 | $(R_x, R_y)$ | (xz, yz) |
| $A_{1u}$ | 1 | 1 | 1 | 1 | 1 | -1 | -1 | -1 | -1 | -1 | | |
| $A_{2u}$ | 1 | 1 | 1 | -1 | -1 | -1 | -1 | -1 | 1 | 1 | z | |
| $B_{1u}$ | 1 | -1 | 1 | 1 | -1 | -1 | 1 | -1 | -1 | 1 | | |
| $B_{2u}$ | 1 | -1 | 1 | -1 | 1 | -1 | 1 | -1 | 1 | -1 | | |
| $E_u$ | 2 | 0 | -2 | 0 | 0 | -2 | 0 | 2 | 0 | 0 | (x, y) | |

| $6/mmm(D_{6h})$ | $E$ | $2C_6(z)$ | $2C_3$ | $C_2$ | $3C_2'$ | $3C_2''$ | $i$ | $2S_3$ | $2S_6$ | $\sigma_h(xy)$ | $3\sigma_d$ | $3\sigma_v$ | | |
|---|---|---|---|---|---|---|---|---|---|---|---|---|---|---|
| $A_{1g}$ | 1 | 1 | 1 | 1 | 1 | 1 | 1 | 1 | 1 | 1 | 1 | 1 | | $x^2+y^2, z^2$ |
| $A_{2g}$ | 1 | 1 | 1 | 1 | -1 | -1 | 1 | 1 | 1 | 1 | -1 | -1 | $R_z$ | |
| $B_{1g}$ | 1 | -1 | 1 | -1 | 1 | -1 | 1 | -1 | 1 | -1 | 1 | -1 | | |
| $B_{2g}$ | 1 | -1 | 1 | -1 | -1 | 1 | 1 | -1 | 1 | -1 | -1 | 1 | | |
| $E_{1g}$ | 2 | 1 | -1 | -2 | 0 | 0 | 2 | 1 | -1 | -2 | 0 | 0 | $(R_x, R_y)$ | $(xz, yz)$ |
| $E_{2g}$ | 2 | -1 | -1 | 2 | 0 | 0 | 2 | -1 | -1 | 2 | 0 | 0 | | $(x^2-y^2, xy)$ |
| $A_{1u}$ | 1 | 1 | 1 | 1 | 1 | 1 | -1 | -1 | -1 | -1 | -1 | -1 | | |
| $A_{2u}$ | 1 | 1 | 1 | 1 | -1 | -1 | -1 | -1 | -1 | -1 | 1 | 1 | $z$ | |
| $B_{1u}$ | 1 | -1 | 1 | -1 | 1 | -1 | -1 | 1 | -1 | 1 | -1 | 1 | | |
| $B_{2u}$ | 1 | -1 | 1 | -1 | -1 | 1 | -1 | 1 | -1 | 1 | 1 | -1 | | |
| $E_{1u}$ | 2 | 1 | -1 | -2 | 0 | 0 | -2 | -1 | 1 | 2 | 0 | 0 | $(x, y)$ | |
| $E_{2u}$ | 2 | -1 | -1 | 2 | 0 | 0 | -2 | 1 | 1 | -2 | 0 | 0 | | |

## $S_n$ Groups

| $\bar{4}(S_4)$ | $E$ | $S_4$ | $C_2(z)$ | $S_4^3$ | | |
|---|---|---|---|---|---|---|
| $A$ | 1 | 1 | 1 | 1 | $R_z$ | $x^2+y^2, z^2$ |
| $B$ | 1 | -1 | 1 | -1 | $z$ | $x^2-y^2, xy$ |
| $E$ | 1 | $i$ | -1 | $-i$ | $x+iy; R_x+iR_y$ | $(xz, yz)$ |
| | 1 | $-i$ | -1 | $i$ | $x-iy; R_x-iR_y$ | |

| $\bar{3}(S_6)$ | $E$ | $C_3(z)$ | $C_3^2$ | $i$ | $S_6^5$ | $S_6$ | $\varepsilon=\exp(2\pi i/3)$ | |
|---|---|---|---|---|---|---|---|---|
| $A_g$ | 1 | 1 | 1 | 1 | 1 | 1 | $R_z$ | $x^2+y^2, z^2$ |
| $E_g$ | 1 | $\varepsilon$ | $\varepsilon^*$ | 1 | $\varepsilon$ | $\varepsilon^*$ | $R_x+iR_y$ | $(x^2-y^2, xy)$ $(xz, yz)$ |
| | 1 | $\varepsilon^*$ | $\varepsilon$ | 1 | $\varepsilon^*$ | $\varepsilon$ | $R_x-iR_y$ | |
| $A_u$ | 1 | 1 | 1 | -1 | -1 | -1 | $z$ | |
| $E_u$ | 1 | $\varepsilon$ | $\varepsilon^*$ | -1 | $-\varepsilon$ | $-\varepsilon^*$ | $x+iy$ | |
| | 1 | $\varepsilon^*$ | $\varepsilon$ | -1 | $-\varepsilon^*$ | $-\varepsilon$ | $x-iy$ | |

## Cubic Groups

| $23(T)$ | $E$ | $4C_3$ | $4C_3^2$ | $3C_2$ | $\varepsilon = \exp(2\pi i/3)$ | |
|---|---|---|---|---|---|---|
| $A$ | 1 | 1 | 1 | 1 | | $x^2+y^2+z^2$ |
| $E$ | 1 | $\varepsilon$ | $\varepsilon^*$ | 1 | | $(x^2-y^2,\ 2z^2-x^2-y^2)$ |
| | 1 | $\varepsilon^*$ | $\varepsilon$ | 1 | | |
| $T$ | 3 | 0 | 0 | -1 | $(x, y, z), (R_x, R_y, R_z)$ | $(xy, xz, yz)$ |

| $m3(T_h)$ | $E$ | $4C_3$ | $4C_3^2$ | $3C_2$ | $i$ | $4S_6^5$ | $4S_6$ | $3\sigma_h$ | $\varepsilon = \exp(2\pi i/3)$ | |
|---|---|---|---|---|---|---|---|---|---|---|
| $A_g$ | 1 | 1 | 1 | 1 | 1 | 1 | 1 | 1 | | $x^2+y^2+z^2$ |
| $E_g$ | 1 | $\varepsilon$ | $\varepsilon^*$ | 1 | 1 | $\varepsilon$ | $\varepsilon^*$ | 1 | | $(x^2-y^2,\ 2z^2-x^2-y^2)$ |
| | 1 | $\varepsilon^*$ | $\varepsilon$ | 1 | 1 | $\varepsilon^*$ | $\varepsilon$ | 1 | | |
| $T_g$ | 3 | 0 | 0 | -1 | 3 | 0 | 0 | -1 | $(R_x, R_y, R_z)$ | $(xy, xz, yz)$ |
| $A_u$ | 1 | 1 | 1 | 1 | -1 | -1 | -1 | -1 | | |
| $E_u$ | 1 | $\varepsilon$ | $\varepsilon^*$ | 1 | -1 | $-\varepsilon$ | $-\varepsilon^*$ | -1 | | |
| | 1 | $\varepsilon^*$ | $\varepsilon$ | 1 | -1 | $-\varepsilon^*$ | $-\varepsilon$ | -1 | | |
| $T_u$ | 3 | 0 | 0 | -1 | -3 | 0 | 0 | 1 | $(x, y, z)$ | |

| $\bar{4}3m(T_d)$ | $E$ | $8C_3$ | $3C_2$ | $6S_4$ | $6\sigma_d$ | | |
|---|---|---|---|---|---|---|---|
| $A_1$ | 1 | 1 | 1 | 1 | 1 | | $x^2+y^2+z^2$ |
| $A_2$ | 1 | 1 | 1 | -1 | -1 | | |
| $E$ | 2 | -1 | 2 | 0 | 0 | | $(2z^2-x^2-y^2,\ x^2-y^2)$ |
| $T_1$ | 3 | 0 | -1 | 1 | -1 | $(R_x, R_y, R_z)$ | |
| $T_2$ | 3 | 0 | -1 | -1 | 1 | $(x, y, z)$ | $(xy, xz, yz)$ |

| $432(O)$ | $E$ | $8C_3$ | $6C_2'$ | $6C_4$ | $3C_2(\equiv C_4^2)$ | | |
|---|---|---|---|---|---|---|---|
| $A_1$ | 1 | 1 | 1 | 1 | 1 | | $x^2+y^2+z^2$ |
| $A_2$ | 1 | 1 | -1 | -1 | 1 | | |
| $E$ | 2 | -1 | 0 | 0 | 2 | | $(x^2-y^2,\ 2z^2-x^2-y^2)$ |
| $T_1$ | 3 | 0 | -1 | 1 | -1 | $(x, y, z)\ (R_x, R_y, R_z)$ | |
| $T_2$ | 3 | 0 | 1 | -1 | -1 | | $(xy, xz, yz)$ |

| $m3m(O_h)$ | E | $8C_3$ | $6C_2$ | $6C_4$ | $3C_2(=C_4^2)$ | i | $6S_4$ | $8S_6$ | $3\sigma_h$ | $6\sigma_d$ | | |
|---|---|---|---|---|---|---|---|---|---|---|---|---|
| $A_{1g}$ | 1 | 1 | 1 | 1 | 1 | 1 | 1 | 1 | 1 | 1 | | $x^2+y^2+z^2$ |
| $A_{2g}$ | 1 | 1 | -1 | -1 | 1 | 1 | -1 | 1 | 1 | -1 | | |
| $E_g$ | 2 | -1 | 0 | 0 | 2 | 2 | 0 | -1 | 2 | 0 | | $(2z^2-x^2-y^2, x^2-y^2)$ |
| $T_{1g}$ | 3 | 0 | -1 | 1 | -1 | 3 | 1 | 0 | -1 | -1 | $(R_x, R_y, R_z)$ | |
| $T_{2g}$ | 3 | 0 | 1 | -1 | -1 | 3 | -1 | 0 | -1 | 1 | | $(xz, yz, xy)$ |
| $A_{1u}$ | 1 | 1 | 1 | 1 | 1 | -1 | -1 | -1 | -1 | -1 | | |
| $A_{2u}$ | 1 | 1 | -1 | -1 | 1 | -1 | 1 | -1 | -1 | 1 | | |
| $E_u$ | 2 | -1 | 0 | 0 | 2 | -2 | 0 | 1 | -2 | 0 | | |
| $T_{1u}$ | 3 | 0 | -1 | 1 | -1 | -3 | -1 | 0 | 1 | 1 | $(x, y, z)$ | |
| $T_{2u}$ | 3 | 0 | 1 | -1 | -1 | -3 | 1 | 0 | 1 | -1 | | |

For the irreducible representations we have been using the Mulliken notation. Here we list a few examples of these representations in the Bethe and in the Bouckaert-Smoluchowski-Wigner notation.

| $O_h$ Mulliken (Chemical) | $O_h$ Bethe | $O_h$ BSW | $D_{4h}$ Mulliken (Chemical) | $D_{4h}$ Bethe | $D_{4h}$ BSW |
|---|---|---|---|---|---|
| $A_{1g}$ | $\Gamma_1^+$ | $\Gamma_1$ | $A_{1g}$ | $\Gamma_1^+$ | $M_1$ |
| $A_{2g}$ | $\Gamma_2^+$ | $\Gamma_2$ | $A_{2g}$ | $\Gamma_2^+$ | $M_2$ |
| $E_g$ | $\Gamma_3^+$ | $\Gamma_{12}$ | $B_{1g}$ | $\Gamma_3^+$ | $M_3$ |
| $T_{1g}$ | $\Gamma_4^+$ | $\Gamma_{15}'$ | $B_{2g}$ | $\Gamma_4^+$ | $M_4$ |
| $T_{2g}$ | $\Gamma_5^+$ | $\Gamma_{25}'$ | $E_g$ | $\Gamma_5^+$ | $M_5$ |
| $A_{1u}$ | $\Gamma_1^-$ | $\Gamma_1'$ | $A_{1u}$ | $\Gamma_1^-$ | $M_1'$ |
| $A_{2u}$ | $\Gamma_2^-$ | $\Gamma_2'$ | $A_{2u}$ | $\Gamma_2^-$ | $M_2'$ |
| $E_u$ | $\Gamma_3^-$ | $\Gamma_{12}'$ | $B_{1u}$ | $\Gamma_3^-$ | $M_3'$ |
| $T_{1u}$ | $\Gamma_4^-$ | $\Gamma_{15}$ | $B_{2u}$ | $\Gamma_4^-$ | $M_4'$ |
| $T_{2u}$ | $\Gamma_5^-$ | $\Gamma_{25}$ | $E_u$ | $\Gamma_5^-$ | $M_5'$ |

Appendix 9

# SYMMETRY OPERATIONS FOR THE 230 SPACE GROUPS

These tables, taken from Kovalev's book, show how to write the symmetry operations for all of the space groups. These operations are all taken with respect to a fixed origin in the unit cell as discussed in Section 6-5d, where other aspects of these tables are also discussed. Kovalev's book also contains a great deal of other information, including single group and double group representation tables for all the special points and lines in the Brillouin Zone. Note that in Kovalev's tables both planes and directions are denoted in parentheses. (Printed with permission of the publisher, Gordon and Breach.) (The corrections noted by J. L. Warren, Rev. Mod. Phys. 40, 38 (1968) have already been inserted in the tables that appear below.)

A. The class $O_h$. The first system of rectangular coordinates. Elements of symmetry:

| | | | |
|---|---|---|---|
| $h_1 = (x, y, z)$ | | —identity transformation | |
| $h_2 = (x, \bar{y}, \bar{z})$ | 180° | —rotation about | $(1, 0, 0)$ |
| $h_3 = (\bar{x}, y, \bar{z})$ | 180° | —rotation about | $(0, 1, 0)$ |
| $h_4 = (\bar{x}, \bar{y}, z)$ | 180° | —rotation about | $(0, 0, 1)$ |
| $h_5 = (y, z, x)$ | 240° | —rotation about | $(1, 1, 1)$ |
| $h_6 = (y, \bar{z}, \bar{x})$ | 120° | —rotation about | $(1, 1, \bar{1})$ |
| $h_7 = (\bar{y}, z, \bar{x})$ | 120° | —rotation about | $(\bar{1}, 1, 1)$ |
| $h_8 = (\bar{y}, \bar{z}, x)$ | 120° | —rotation about | $(1, \bar{1}, 1)$ |
| $h_9 = (z, x, y)$ | 120° | —rotation about | $(1, 1, 1)$ |
| $h_{10} = (z, \bar{x}, \bar{y})$ | 240° | —rotation about | $(1, \bar{1}, 1)$ |
| $h_{11} = (\bar{z}, x, \bar{y})$ | 240° | —rotation about | $(1, 1, \bar{1})$ |
| $h_{12} = (\bar{z}, \bar{x}, y)$ | 240° | —rotation about | $(\bar{1}, 1, 1)$ |
| $h_{13} = (\bar{y}, \bar{x}, \bar{z})$ | 180° | —rotation about | $(\bar{1}, 1, 0)$ |

The elements of symmetry $h_{14}, h_{15}, \ldots, h_{24}$ are successively obtained by right multiplication of the above listed elements by $h_{13}$, i.e $h_{j+12} = h_j \cdot h_{13}$ These elements are:

| | | | |
|---|---|---|---|
| $h_{14} = (\bar{y}, x, z)$ | 90° | —rotation about | $(0, 0, 1)$ |
| $h_{15} = (y, \bar{x}, z)$ | 270° | —rotation about | $(0, 0, 1)$ |
| $h_{16} = (y, x, \bar{z})$ | 180° | —rotation about | $(1, 1, 0)$ |
| $h_{17} = (\bar{x}, \bar{z}, \bar{y})$ | 180° | —rotation about | $(0, \bar{1}, 1)$ |
| $h_{18} = (\bar{x}, z, y)$ | 180° | —rotation about | $(0, 1, 1)$ |
| $h_{19} = (x, \bar{z}, y)$ | 90° | —rotation about | $(1, 0, 0)$ |
| $h_{20} = (x, z, \bar{y})$ | 270° | —rotation about | $(1, 0, 0)$ |
| $h_{21} = (\bar{z}, \bar{y}, \bar{x})$ | 180° | —rotation about | $(\bar{1}, 0, 1)$ |
| $h_{22} = (\bar{z}, y, x)$ | 270° | —rotation about | $(0, 1, 0)$ |
| $h_{23} = (z, \bar{y}, x)$ | 180° | —rotation about | $(1, 0, 1)$ |
| $h_{24} = (z, y, \bar{x})$ | 90° | —rotation about | $(0, 1, 0)$ |
| $h_{25} = (\bar{x}, \bar{y}, \bar{z})$ | | —inversion. | |

If we multiply all of the above-listed elements by an inversion, we obtain all of the remaining elements of symmetry in the class $O_h$, i. $h_{24+k} = h_k \cdot h_{25} = h_{25} \cdot h_k \; (k = 1, 2, \ldots, 24)$,

$h_{26} = (\bar{x}, y, z)$ —reflection in the plane (1, 0, 0),
$h_{27} = (x, \bar{y}, z)$ —reflection in the plane (0, 1, 0),
$h_{28} = (x, y, \bar{z})$ —reflection in the plane (0, 0, 1),
$h_{29} = h_5 \cdot h_{25} = (\bar{y}, \bar{z}, \bar{x})$,
$h_{30} = h_6\ h_{25} = (\bar{y}, z, x)$,
$h_{31} = h_7 \cdot h_{25} = (y, \bar{z}, x)$,
$h_{32} = h_8 \cdot h_{25} = (y, z, \bar{x})$,
$h_{33} = h_9 \cdot h_{25} = (\bar{z}, \bar{x}, \bar{y})$,
$h_{34} = h_{10} \cdot h_{25} = (\bar{z}, x, y)$,
$h_{35} = h_{11} \cdot h_{25} = (z, \bar{x}, y)$,
$h_{36} = h_{12} \cdot h_{25} = (z, x, \bar{y})$,
$h_{37} = (y, x, z)$ —reflection in the plane ($\bar{1}$, 1, 0),
$h_{38} = (y, \bar{x}, \bar{z})$ —270° mirror rotation about (0, 0, 1)
$h_{39} = (\bar{y}, x, \bar{z})$ —90° mirror rotation about (0, 0, 1)
$h_{40} = (\bar{y}, \bar{x}, z)$ —reflection in the plane (1, 1, 0),
$h_{41} = (x, z, y)$ —reflection in the plane (0, $\bar{1}$, 1),
$h_{42} = (x, \bar{z}, \bar{y})$ —reflection in the plane (0, 1, 1),
$h_{43} = (\bar{x}, z, \bar{y})$ —270° mirror rotation about (1, 0, 0)
$h_{44} = (\bar{x}, \bar{z}, y)$ —90° mirror rotation about (1, 0, 0)
$h_{45} = (z, y, x)$ —reflection in the plane ($\bar{1}$, 0, 1),
$h_{46} = (z, \bar{y}, \bar{x})$ —90° mirror rotation about (0, 1, 0)
$h_{47} = (\bar{z}, \bar{y}, \bar{x})$ —reflection in the plane (1, 0, 1),
$h_{48} = (\bar{z}, \bar{y}, x)$ —270° mirror rotation about (0, 1, 0)

For clarity, below there is a picture of a cube on whose surface we

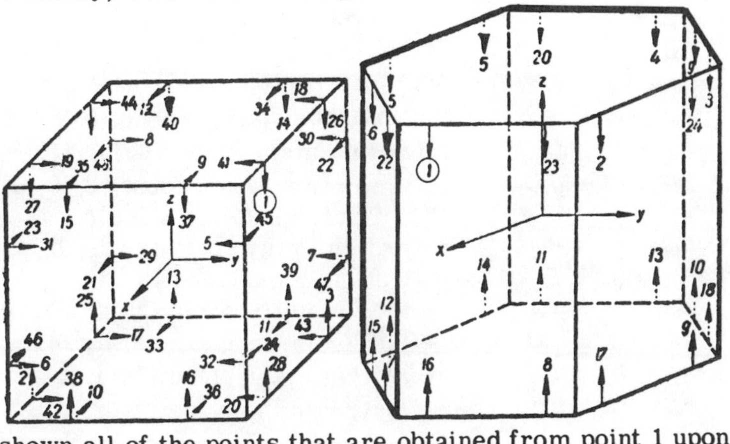

have shown all of the points that are obtained from point 1 upon application of the appropriate elements of symmetry $h_j$ in the point group $O_h$. Multiplication tables for the elements $h_1, h_2, \ldots, h_{24}$ in the class $O_h$ (they generate the point group $O$) are given in Appendix A. The multiplication rule for the remaining elements in the class $O_h$ is: if

$$h_j \cdot h_k = h_l \qquad (j,\ k,\ l = 1,\ 2, \ldots, 24),$$

then

$$h_{j+24} \cdot h_k = h_j \cdot h_{k+24} = h_{l+24} \text{ and } h_{j+24} \cdot h_{k+24} = h_l.$$

B. The class $D_{6h}$. Skew coordinate system. The $z$ axis is directed along a sixth-order axis and forms a right angle with the $x$ and $y$ axes. The angle between these last is 120 degrees. The unit vectors $\vec{e}_x$, $\vec{e}_y$, and $\vec{e}_z$ are directed along the corresponding coordinate axes. For each element of symmetry, a triple of numbers represents the contravariant coordinates of the vector into which the vector $\vec{x}e_x + \vec{y}e_y + \vec{z}e_z$. is transformed. Elements of symmetry:

$h_1 = (x, y, z)$ —identity transformation
$h_2 = (x - y, x, z)$ 60° —rotation about (0, 0, 1)
$h_3 = (\bar{y}, x - y, z)$ 120° —rotation about (0, 0, 1)
$h_4 = (\bar{x}, \bar{y}, z)$ 180° —rotation about (0, 0, 1)
$h_5 = (y - x, \bar{y}, z)$ 240° —rotation about (0, 0, 1)
$h_6 = (y, y - x, z)$ 300° —rotation about (0, 0, 1)
$h_7 = (\bar{x}, y - x, \bar{z})$ 180° —rotation about (0, 1, 0)
$h_8 = (\bar{y}, \bar{x}, \bar{z})$ 180° —rotation about ($\bar{1}$, 1, 0)
$h_9 = (x - y, \bar{y}, \bar{z})$ 180° —rotation about (1, 0, 0)
$h_{10} = (x, x - y, \bar{z})$ 180° —rotation about (2, 1, 0)
$h_{11} = (y, x, \bar{z})$ 180° —rotation about (1, 1, 0)
$h_{12} = (y - x, y, \bar{z})$ 180° —rotation about (1, 2, 0)
$h_{13} = (\bar{x}, \bar{y}, \bar{z})$ —inversion
$h_{14} = (y - x, \bar{x}, \bar{z})$ —240° mirror rotation about (0, 0, 1)
$h_{15} = (y, y - x, \bar{z})$ —300° mirror rotation about (0, 0, 1)
$h_{16} = (x, y, \bar{z})$ —reflection in the plane (0, 0, 1),
$h_{17} = (x - y, x, \bar{z})$ —60° mirror rotation about (0, 0, 1)
$h_{18} = (\bar{y}, x - y, z)$ —120° mirror rotation about (0, 0, 1)
$h_{19} = (x, x - y, z)$ —reflection in the plane-(0, 1, 0),
$h_{20} = (y, x, z)$ —reflection in the plane (1, 1, 0).
$h_{21} = (y - x, y, z)$ —reflection in the plane (1, 0, 0),
$h_{22} = (\bar{x}, y - x, z)$ —reflection in the plane (2, 1, 0),
$h_{23} = (\bar{y}, \bar{x}, z)$ —reflection in the plane (1, 1, 0),
$h_{24} = (x - y, \bar{y}, z)$ —reflection in the plane (1, 2, 0).

Figure 1 shows a six-sided prism with all points into which the point 1 is transformed by rotations or mirror rotations.

Appendix B contains a multiplication table for all elements in the class $D_{6h}$.

## 2. Bravais lattices

We will use the following notation for description of the Bravais lattices of crystals: $\vec{a}_1$, $\vec{a}_2$, $\vec{a}_3$ are the fundamental periods of the lattices; $2\tau_x$, $2\tau_y$, and $2\tau_2$ are the periods of a lattice along the corresponding axes of a rectangular coordinate system.

### Triclinic system

$\Gamma_{tr}$ — simple lattice: different angles between the vectors $\vec{a}_1, \vec{a}_2, \vec{a}_3$

### Monoclinic system

$\Gamma_m$ — simple lattice; $\vec{a}_1$ lies in the plane $z = 0$, $\vec{a}_2 = (0, 2\tau_y, 0)$, $\vec{a}_3 = (0, 0, 2\tau_z)$.

$\Gamma_m^b$ — side-centered; $\vec{a}_1$ lies in the plane $z = 0$, $\vec{a}_2 = (0, \tau_y, -\tau_z)$, $\vec{a}_3 = (0, \tau_y, \tau_z)$.

### Orthorhombic system

$\Gamma_0$ — simple lattice; $\vec{a}_1 = (2\tau_x, 0, 0)$, $\vec{a}_2 = (0, 2\tau_y, 0)$, $\vec{a}_3 = (0, 0, 2\tau_z)$.

$\Gamma_0^b$ — base-centered lattice; $\vec{a}_1 = (\tau_x, \tau_y, 0)$, $\vec{a}_2 = (-\tau_x, \tau_y, 0)$, $\vec{a}_3 = (0, 0, 2\tau_z)$.

$\Gamma_0^f$ — face-centered lattice; $\vec{a}_1 = (0, \tau_y, \tau_z)$, $\vec{a}_2 = (\tau_x, 0, \tau_z)$, $\vec{a}_3 = (\tau_x, \tau_y, 0)$.

$\Gamma_0^v$ — body-centered lattice; $\vec{a}_1 = (-\tau_x, \tau_y, \tau_z)$, $\vec{a}_2 = (\tau_x, -\tau_y, \tau_z)$, $\vec{a}_3 = (\tau_x, \tau_y, -\tau_z)$.

### Tetragonal system $(\tau_x = \tau_y = \tau)$

$\Gamma_q$ — simple lattice; $\vec{a}_1 = (2\tau, 0, 0)$, $\vec{a}_2 = (0, 2\tau, 0)$, $\vec{a}_3 = (0, 0, 2\tau_z)$.

$\Gamma_q^v(a)$ — body-centered lattice; $\vec{a}_1 = (-\tau, \tau, \tau_z)$, $\vec{a}_2 = (\tau, -\tau, \tau_z)$, $\vec{a}_3 = (\tau, \tau, -\tau_z)$.

$\Gamma_q^v(b)$ — also body-centered, but the fundamental periods are chosen differently: $\vec{a}_1 = (0, \tau, \tau_z)$, $\vec{a}_2 = (\tau, 0, \tau_z)$, $\vec{a}_3 = (\tau, \tau, 0)$.

### Cubic system $(\tau_x = \tau_y = \tau_z = \tau)$

$\Gamma_c$ — simple lattice; $\vec{a}_1 = (2\tau, 0, 0)$, $\vec{a}_2 = (0, 2\tau, 0)$, $\vec{a}_3 = (0, 0, 2\tau)$.

$\Gamma_c^v$ — body-centered lattice; $\vec{a}_1 = (-\tau, \tau, \tau)$, $\vec{a}_2 = (\tau, -\tau, \tau)$, $\vec{a}_3 = (\tau, \tau, -\tau)$.

$\Gamma_c^f$ — face-centered lattice; $\vec{a}_1 = (0, \tau, \tau)$, $\vec{a}_2 = (\tau, 0, \tau)$, $\vec{a}_3 = (\tau, \tau, 0)$.

### Rhombohedral system

$\Gamma_{rh}$—three vectors $\vec{a}_1$, $\vec{a}_2$ & $\vec{a}_3$ with equal length, do not lie in the same plane, and are located so that $\vec{a}_1 + \vec{a}_2 + \vec{a}_3 = (0, 0, 2\tau_z)$.

### Hexagonal system

$\Gamma_h$—the vector $\vec{a}_3$ is perpendicular to $\vec{a}_1$ and $\vec{a}_2$; the angle between $\vec{a}_1$ and $\vec{a}_2$ is 120 degrees; $a_1 = a_2 \neq a_3$; the vector $\vec{a}_1$ is directed alon $\vec{e}_x$, while the vector $\vec{a}_2$ is directed along $\vec{e}_y$.

### 3. Space Groups

Two space-group elements $g = t_{\vec{\alpha}} \cdot h_j$ and $g' = t_{\vec{\alpha}'} \cdot h_j$ with the same rotation $h_j$ differ only by translation through an integral number of lattice periods $\vec{\alpha}' - \vec{\alpha} = n_1\vec{a}_1 + n_2\vec{a}_2 + n_3\vec{a}_3$; in order to describe a spac group, therefore, it is sufficient for us to limit our list to only those elements $g$, that contain rotations or mirror rotations $h_j$. of different senses. The rotations or mirror rotations are given in the top line of the following table of all 230 space groups. In the line beginning with the notation for the space group, the characters for the given group of vectors $\vec{\alpha}$ along which translation occurs after the corresponding rotations or mirror rotations $h_j$. are given under the elements $h_i$. The vectors $\vec{\alpha}$, in the monoclinic system are written in the form of linear combinations of the vectors $\vec{a}_1$, $\vec{a}_2$, $\vec{a}_3$, which last are the fundamental periods of the lattice. In the remaining cases, the vectors $\vec{\alpha}$ are given by means of the components $\tau_x$, $\tau_y$, $\tau_z$ along the axes of a rectangular coordinate system. The second column shown the form of the Bravais lattice. The columns corresponding to the identity transformation $h_1$, are omitted.

The table of space groups was taken from [10] with small changes. These changes are associated with a different selection of the position of the origin inside the elementary crystal lattice and concern the groups in class $D_{4h}$ and the groups $D_3^4$, $D_3^6$, $D_{3d}^2$, $D_{3d}^6$, $D_{3h}^2$, $D_{3h}^4$, $D_{6h}^2$, $D_{6h}^3$*.

### Triclinic system. Lattice of type $\Gamma_{tr}$

Class $C_0$. The class contains one group $C_0^1$, consisting of only translations.

The Class $C_i = S_2$. The single group $C_i^1$ belonging to this class is the direct product of a subgroup of translations and an inversion.

[*In [10] there are errors in the descriptions of the groups $O^8$ and $O_h^{10}$

## Monclinic system

### Class $C_s$

| Group | Type | $h_{28}$ |
|---|---|---|
| $C_s^1$ | $\Gamma_m$ | |
| $C_s^2$ | $\Gamma_m$ | $\frac{\vec{a}_1}{2}$ |
| $C_s^3$ | $\Gamma_m^b$ | |
| $C_s^4$ | $\Gamma_m^b$ | $\frac{\vec{a}_1}{2}$ |

### Class $C_2$

| Group | Type | $h_4$ |
|---|---|---|
| $C_2^1$ | $\Gamma_m$ | |
| $C_2^2$ | $\Gamma_m$ | $\frac{\vec{a}_3}{2}$ |
| $C_2^3$ | $\Gamma_m^b$ | |

### Class $C_{2h}$

| Group | Type | $h_4$ | $h_{25}$ | $h_{28}$ |
|---|---|---|---|---|
| $C_{2h}^1$ | $\Gamma_m$ | | | |
| $C_{2h}^2$ | $\Gamma_m$ | $\frac{\vec{a}_3}{2}$ | $\frac{\vec{a}_3}{2}$ | |
| $C_{2h}^3$ | $\Gamma_m^b$ | | | |
| $C_{2h}^4$ | $\Gamma_m$ | | $\frac{\vec{a}_1}{2}$ | $\frac{\vec{a}_1}{2}$ |
| $C_{2h}^5$ | $\Gamma_m$ | $\frac{\vec{a}_3}{2}$ | $\frac{\vec{a}_1+\vec{a}_3}{2}$ | $\frac{\vec{a}_1}{2}$ |
| $C_{2h}^6$ | $\Gamma_m^b$ | | $\frac{\vec{a}_1}{2}$ | $\frac{\vec{a}_1}{2}$ |

## Orthorhombic system $D_{2h}$

### Class $C_{2v}$

| Group | Type | $h_4$ | $h_{26}$ | $h_{27}$ |
|---|---|---|---|---|
| $C_{2v}^1$ | $\Gamma_0$ | | | |
| $C_{2v}^2$ | $\Gamma_0$ | $0, 0, \tau_z$ | $0, 0, \tau_z$ | |
| $C_{2v}^3$ | $\Gamma_0$ | | $0, 0, \tau_z$ | $0, 0, \tau_z$ |
| $C_{2v}^4$ | $\Gamma_0$ | $\tau_x, 0, 0$ | | $\tau_x, 0, 0$ |
| $C_{2v}^5$ | $\Gamma_0$ | $\tau_x, 0, \tau_z$ | $0, 0, \tau_z$ | $\tau_x, 0, 0$ |

Continued

| Group | Type | $h_4$ | $h_{26}$ | $h_{27}$ |
|---|---|---|---|---|
| $C_{2v}^6$ | $\Gamma_0$ | $\tau_x, 0, 0$ | $0, 0, \tau_z$ | $\tau_x, 0, \tau_z$ |
| $C_{2v}^7$ | $\Gamma_0$ | $\tau_x, 0, \tau_z$ | | $\tau_x, 0, \tau_z$ |
| $C_{2v}^8$ | $\Gamma_0$ | $\tau_x, \tau_y, 0$ | $0, \tau_y, 0$ | $\tau_x, 0, 0$ |
| $C_{2v}^9$ | $\Gamma_0$ | $\tau_x, \tau_y, \tau_z$ | $0, \tau_y, \tau_z$ | $\tau_x, 0, 0$ |
| $C_{2v}^{10}$ | $\Gamma_0$ | $\tau_x, \tau_y, 0$ | $0, \tau_y, \tau_z$ | $\tau_x, 0, \tau_z$ |
| $C_{2v}^{11}$ | $\Gamma_0^b$ | | | |
| $C_{2v}^{12}$ | $\Gamma_0^b$ | $0, 0, \tau_z$ | | $0, 0, \tau_z$ |
| $C_{2v}^{13}$ | $\Gamma_0^b$ | | $0, 0, \tau_z$ | $0, 0, \tau_z$ |
| $C_{2v}^{18}$ | $\Gamma_0^f$ | | | |
| $C_{2v}^{19}$ | $\Gamma_0^f$ | $\frac{\tau_x}{2}, \frac{\tau_y}{2}, 0$ | $0, \frac{\tau_y}{2}, \frac{\tau_z}{2}$ | $\frac{\tau_x}{2}, 0, \frac{\tau_z}{2}$ |
| $C_{2v}^{20}$ | $\Gamma_0^v$ | | | |
| $C_{2v}^{21}$ | $\Gamma_0^v$ | $0, 0, \tau_z$ | $0, 0, \tau_z$ | |
| $C_{2v}^{22}$ | $\Gamma_0^v$ | | $\tau_x, 0, 0$ | $\tau_x, 0, 0$ |

Class $C_{2v}$

| Group | Type | $h_2$ | $h_{27}$ | $h_{28}$ |
|---|---|---|---|---|
| $C_{2v}^{14}$ | $\Gamma_0^b$ | | | |
| $C_{2v}^{15}$ | $\Gamma_0^b$ | | $0, \tau_y, 0$ | $0, \tau_y, 0$ |
| $C_{2v}^{16}$ | $\Gamma_0^b$ | | $0, 0, \tau_z$ | $0, 0, \tau_z$ |
| $C_{2v}^{17}$ | $\Gamma_0^b$ | | $0, \tau_y, \tau_z$ | $0, \tau_y, \tau_z$ |

Class $D_2 = V$

| Group | Type | $h_2$ | $h_3$ | $h_4$ |
|---|---|---|---|---|
| $D_2^1$ | $\Gamma_0$ | | | |
| $D_2^2$ | $\Gamma_0$ | | $0, 0, \tau_z$ | $0, 0, \tau_z$ |
| $D_2^3$ | $\Gamma_0$ | $\tau_x, \tau_y, 0$ | $\tau_x, \tau_y, 0$ | |
| $D_2^4$ | $\Gamma_0$ | $\tau_x, \tau_y, 0$ | $0, \tau_y, \tau_z$ | $\tau_x, 0, \tau_z$ |

Continued

| Group | Type | $h_2$ | $h_3$ | $h_4$ |
|---|---|---|---|---|
| $D_2^5$ | $\Gamma_0^b$ | $0, 0, \tau_z$ | | $0, 0, \tau_z$ |
| $D_2^6$ | $\Gamma_0^b$ | | | |
| $D_2^7$ | $\Gamma_0^f$ | | | |
| $D_2^8$ | $\Gamma_0^v$ | | | |
| $D_2^9$ | $\Gamma_0^v$ | $0, 0, \tau_z$ | $\tau_x, 0, 0$ | $0, \tau_y, 0$ |

Class $D_{2h}$

| Group | Type | $h_2$ | $h_3$ | $h_4$ | $h_{25}$ | $h_{26}$ | $h_{27}$ | $h_{28}$ |
|---|---|---|---|---|---|---|---|---|
| $D_{2h}^1$ | $\Gamma_0$ | | | | | | | |
| $D_{2h}^2$ | $\Gamma_0$ | | | | $\tau_x, \tau_y, t_z$ | $\tau_x, \tau_y, \tau_z$ | $\tau_x, \tau_y, \tau_z$ | $\tau_x, \tau_y, \tau_z$ |
| $D_{2h}^3$ | $\Gamma_0$ | | | | $0, 0, \tau_z$ | $0, 0, \tau_z$ | $0, 0, \tau_z$ | $0, 0, \tau_z$ |
| $D_{2h}^4$ | $\Gamma_0$ | | | | $\tau_x, \tau_y, 0$ | $\tau_x, \tau_y, 0$ | $\tau_x, \tau_y, 0$ | $\tau_x, \tau_y, 0$ |
| $D_{2h}^5$ | $\Gamma_0$ | | $0, 0, \tau_z$ | $0, 0, \tau_z$ | | | $0, 0, \tau_z$ | $0, 0, \tau_z$ |
| $D_{2h}^6$ | $\Gamma_0$ | | $0, 0, \tau_z$ | $0, 0, \tau_z$ | $\tau_x, \tau_y, 0$ | $\tau_x, \tau_y, 0$ | $\tau_x, \tau_y, \tau_z$ | $\tau_x, \tau_y, \tau_z$ |
| $D_{2h}^7$ | $\Gamma_0$ | | $0, 0, \tau_z$ | $0, 0, \tau_z$ | $\tau_x, 0, 0$ | $\tau_x, 0, 0$ | $\tau_x, 0, \tau_z$ | $\tau_x, 0, \tau_z$ |
| $D_{2h}^8$ | $\Gamma_0$ | | $0, 0, \tau_z$ | $0, 0, \tau_z$ | $0, \tau_y, 0$ | $0, \tau_y, 0$ | $0, \tau_y, \tau_z$ | $0, \tau_y, \tau_z$ |
| $D_{2h}^9$ | $\Gamma_0$ | $\tau_x, \tau_y, 0$ | $\tau_x, \tau_y, 0$ | | | $\tau_x, \tau_y, 0$ | $\tau_x, \tau_y, 0$ | |
| $D_{2h}^{10}$ | $\Gamma_0$ | $\tau_x, \tau_y, 0$ | $\tau_x, \tau_y, 0$ | | $\tau_x, \tau_y, \tau_z$ | $0, 0, \tau_z$ | $0, 0, \tau_z$ | $\tau_x, \tau_y, \tau_z$ |
| $D_{2h}^{11}$ | $\Gamma_0$ | $\tau_x, \tau_y, 0$ | $\tau_x, \tau_y, 0$ | | $0, \tau_y, 0$ | $\tau_x, 0, 0$ | $\tau_x, 0, 0$ | $0, \tau_y, 0$ |
| $D_{2h}^{12}$ | $\Gamma_0$ | $\tau_x, \tau_y, 0$ | $\tau_x, \tau_y, 0$ | | $0, 0, \tau_z$ | $\tau_x, \tau_y, \tau_z$ | $\tau_x, \tau_y, \tau_z$ | $0, 0, \tau_z$ |
| $D_{2h}^{13}$ | $\Gamma_0$ | $\tau_x, \tau_y, 0$ | $\tau_x, \tau_y, 0$ | | $\tau_x, \tau_y, 0$ | | | $\tau_x, \tau_y, 0$ |
| $D_{2h}^{14}$ | $\Gamma_0$ | $\tau_x, \tau_y, 0$ | $\tau_x, \tau_y, 0$ | | $\tau_x, 0, \tau_z$ | $0, \tau_y, \tau_z$ | $0, \tau_y, \tau_z$ | $\tau_x, 0, \tau_z$ |
| $D_{2h}^{15}$ | $\Gamma_0$ | $\tau_x, \tau_y, 0$ | $0, \tau_y, \tau_z$ | $\tau_x, 0, \tau_z$ | | $\tau_x, \tau_y, 0$ | $0, \tau_y, \tau_z$ | $\tau_x, 0, \tau_z$ |
| $D_{2h}^{16}$ | $\Gamma_0$ | $\tau_x, \tau_y, 0$ | $0, \tau_y, \tau_z$ | $\tau_x, 0, \tau_z$ | $\tau_x, \tau_y, 0$ | | $\tau_x, 0, \tau_z$ | $0, \tau_y, \tau_z$ |
| $D_{2h}^{17}$ | $\Gamma_0^b$ | $0, 0, \tau_z$ | | $0, 0, \tau_z$ | | $0, 0, \tau_z$ | | $0, 0, \tau_z$ |
| $D_{2h}^{18}$ | $\Gamma_0^b$ | $0, 0, \tau_z$ | | $0, 0, \tau_z$ | $0, \tau_y, 0$ | $0, \tau_y, \tau_z$ | $0, \tau_y, 0$ | $0, \tau_y, \tau_z$ |
| $D_{2h}^{19}$ | $\Gamma_0^b$ | | | | | | | |

Continued

| Group | Type | $h_2$ | $h_3$ | $h_4$ | $h_{25}$ | $h_{26}$ | $h_{27}$ | $h_{28}$ |
|---|---|---|---|---|---|---|---|---|
| $D_{2h}^{20}$ | $\Gamma_0^b$ | | | | $0, 0, \tau_z$ | $0, 0, \tau_z$ | $0, 0, \tau_z$ | $0, 0, \tau_z$ |
| $D_{2h}^{21}$ | $\Gamma_0^b$ | | | | $0, \tau_y, 0$ | $0, \tau_y, 0$ | $0, \tau_y, 0$ | $0, \tau_y, 0$ |
| $D_{2h}^{22}$ | $\Gamma_0^b$ | | | | $0, \tau_y, \tau_z$ | $0, \tau_y, \tau_z$ | $0, \tau_y, \tau_z$ | $0, \tau_y, \tau_z$ |
| $D_{2h}^{23}$ | $\Gamma_0^f$ | | | | | | | |
| $D_{2h}^{24}$ | $\Gamma_0^f$ | | | | $\frac{\tau_x}{2}, \frac{\tau_y}{2}, \frac{\tau_z}{2}$ | $\frac{\tau_x}{2}, \frac{\tau_y}{2}, \frac{\tau_z}{2}$ | $\frac{\tau_x}{2}, \frac{\tau_y}{2}, \frac{\tau_z}{2}$ | $\frac{\tau_x}{2}, \frac{\tau_y}{2}, \frac{\tau_z}{2}$ |
| $D_{2h}^{25}$ | $\Gamma_0^v$ | | | | | | | |
| $D_{2h}^{26}$ | $\Gamma_0^v$ | | | | $0, 0, \tau_z$ | $0, 0, \tau_z$ | $0, 0, \tau_z$ | $0, 0, \tau_z$ |
| $D_{2h}^{27}$ | $\Gamma_0^v$ | $0, 0, \tau_z$ | $\tau_x, 0, 0$ | $0, \tau_y, 0$ | | $0, 0, \tau_z$ | $\tau_x, 0, 0$ | $0, \tau_y, 0$ |
| $D_{2h}^{28}$ | $\Gamma_0^v$ | $0, 0, \tau_z$ | $\tau_x, 0, 0$ | $0, \tau_y, 0$ | $0, 0, \tau_z$ | | $\tau_x, 0, \tau_z$ | $0, \tau_y, \tau_z$ |

## Tetragonal system $D_{4h}$

### Class $C_4$

| Group | Type | $h_{14}$ | $h_4$ | $h_{15}$ |
|---|---|---|---|---|
| $C_4^1$ | $\Gamma_q$ | | | |
| $C_4^2$ | $\Gamma_q$ | $0, 0, \frac{\tau_z}{2}$ | $0, 0, \tau_z$ | $0, 0, \frac{3\tau_z}{2}$ |
| $C_4^3$ | $\Gamma_q$ | $0, 0, \tau_z$ | | $0, 0, \tau_z$ |
| $C_4^4$ | $\Gamma_q$ | $0, 0, \frac{3\tau_z}{2}$ | $0, 0 \tau_z$ | $0, 0, \frac{\tau_z}{2}$ |
| $C_4^5$ | $\Gamma_q^v (a)$ | | | |
| $C_4^6$ | $\Gamma_q^v (a)$ | $0, \tau, \frac{\tau_z}{2}$ | | $0, \tau, \frac{\tau_z}{2}$ |

### Class $S_4$

| Group | Type | $h_{39}$ | $h_4$ | $h_{38}$ |
|---|---|---|---|---|
| $S_4$ | $\Gamma_q$ | | | |
| $S_4^2$ | $\Gamma_q^v (a)$ | | | |

Class $C_{4v}$

| Group | Type | $h_{14}$ | $h_4$ | $h_{15}$ | $h_{37}$ | $h_{27}$ | $h_{40}$ | $h_{26}$ |
|---|---|---|---|---|---|---|---|---|
| $C_{4v}^1$ | $\Gamma_q$ | | | | | | | |
| $C_{4v}^3$ | $\Gamma_q$ | $0, 0, \tau_z$ | | $0, 0, \tau_z$ | | $0, 0, \tau_z$ | | $0, 0, \tau_z$ |
| $C_{4v}^5$ | $\Gamma_q$ | | | | $0, 0, \tau_z$ | $0, 0, \tau_z$ | $0, 0, \tau_z$ | $0, 0, \tau_z$ |
| $C_{4v}^7$ | $\Gamma_q$ | $0, 0, \tau_z$ | | $0, 0, \tau_z$ | $0, 0, \tau_z$ | | $0, 0, \tau_z$ | |
| $C_{4v}^2$ | $\Gamma_q$ | | | | $\tau, \tau, 0$ | $\tau, \tau, 0$ | $\tau, \ , 0$ | $\tau, \tau, 0$ |
| $C_{4v}^4$ | $\Gamma_q$ | $0, 0, \tau_z$ | | $0, 0, \ _z$ | $\tau, \tau, 0$ | $\tau, \tau, \tau_z$ | $\tau, \tau, 0$ | $\tau, \tau, \tau_z$ |
| $C_{4v}^6$ | $\Gamma_q$ | | | | $\tau, \tau, \tau_z$ | $\tau, \tau, \tau_z$ | $\tau, \tau, \tau_z$ | $\tau, \tau, \tau_z$ |
| $C_{4v}^8$ | $\Gamma_q$ | $0, 0, \tau_z$ | | $0, 0, \tau_z$ | $\tau, \tau, \tau_z$ | $\tau, \tau, 0$ | $\tau, \tau, \tau_z$ | $\tau, \tau, 0$ |
| $C_{4v}^9$ | $\Gamma_q^v(a)$ | | | | | | | |
| $C_{4v}^{10}$ | $\Gamma_q^v(a)$ | | | | $0, 0, \tau_z$ | $0, 0, \tau_z$ | $0, 0, \tau_z$ | $0, 0, \tau_z$ |
| $C_{4v}^{11}$ | $\Gamma_q^v(a)$ | $0, \tau, \frac{\tau_z}{2}$ | | $0, \tau, \frac{\tau_z}{2}$ | $0, \tau, \frac{\tau_z}{2}$ | | $0, \tau, \frac{\tau_z}{2}$ | |
| $C_{4v}^{12}$ | $\Gamma_q^v(a)$ | $0, \tau, \frac{\tau_z}{2}$ | | $0, \tau, \frac{\tau_z}{2}$ | $\tau, 0, \frac{\tau_z}{2}$ | $0, 0, \tau_z$ | $\tau, 0, \frac{\tau_z}{2}$ | $0, 0, \tau_z$ |

Class $C_{4h}$

| Group | Type | $h_{38}$ | $h_4$ | $h_{39}$ | $h_{28}$ | $h_{15}$ | $h_{25}$ | $h_{14}$ |
|---|---|---|---|---|---|---|---|---|
| $C_{4h}^1$ | $\Gamma_q$ | | | | | | | |
| $C_{4h}^2$ | $\Gamma_q$ | | | | $0, 0, \tau_z$ | $0, 0, \tau_z$ | $0, 0, \tau_z$ | $0, 0, \tau_z$ |
| $C_{4h}^3$ | $\Gamma_q$ | | | | $\tau, \tau, 0$ | $\tau, \tau, 0$ | $\tau, \tau, 0$ | $\tau, \tau, 0$ |
| $C_{4h}^4$ | $\Gamma_q$ | | | | $\tau, \tau, \tau_z$ | $\tau, \tau, \tau_z$ | $\tau, \tau, \tau_z$ | $\tau, \tau, \tau_z$ |
| $C_{4h}^5$ | $\Gamma_q^v(a)$ | | | | | | | |
| $C_{4h}^6$ | $\Gamma_q^v(a)$ | | | | $0, \tau, \frac{\tau_z}{2}$ | $0, \tau, \frac{\tau_z}{2}$ | $0, \tau, \frac{\tau_z}{2}$ | $0, \tau, \frac{\tau_z}{2}$ |

Class $D_{2d}$

| Group | Type | $h_{38}$ | $h_4$ | $h_{39}$ | $h_{37}$ | $h_3$ | $h_{40}$ | $h_2$ |
|---|---|---|---|---|---|---|---|---|
| $D_{2d}^1$ | $\Gamma_q$ | | | | | | | |
| $D_{2d}^2$ | $\Gamma_q$ | | | | $0, 0, \tau_z$ | $0, 0, \tau_z$ | $0, 0, \tau_z$ | $0, 0, \tau_z$ |

Continued

| Group | Type | $h_{38}$ | $h_4$ | $h_{39}$ | $h_{37}$ | $h_3$ | $h_{40}$ | $h_2$ |
|---|---|---|---|---|---|---|---|---|
| $D_{2d}^3$ | $\Gamma_q$ | | | | $\tau, \tau, 0$ | $\tau, \tau, 0$ | $\tau, \tau, 0$ | $\tau, \tau, 0$ |
| $D_{2d}^4$ | $\Gamma_q$ | | | | $\tau, \tau, \tau_z$ | $\tau, \tau, \tau_z$ | $\tau, \tau, \tau_z$ | $\tau, \tau, \tau_z$ |
| $D_{2d}^9$ | $\Gamma_q^v(b)$ | | | | | | | |
| $D_{2d}^{10}$ | $\Gamma_q^v(b)$ | | | | $\tau, \tau, \tau_z$ | $\tau, \tau, \tau_z$ | $\tau, \tau, \tau_z$ | $\tau, \tau, \tau_z$ |
| $D_{2d}^{11}$ | $\Gamma_q^v(a)$ | | | | | | | |
| $D_{2d}^{12}$ | $\Gamma_q^v(a)$ | | | | $\tau, 0, \frac{\tau_z}{2}$ | $\tau, 0, \frac{\tau_z}{2}$ | $\tau, 0, \frac{\tau_z}{2}$ | $\tau, 0, \frac{\tau_z}{2}$ |

Class $D_{2d}$

| Group | Type | $h_{38}$ | $h_4$ | $h_{39}$ | $h_{27}$ | $h_{16}$ | $h_{26}$ | $h_{13}$ |
|---|---|---|---|---|---|---|---|---|
| $D_{2d}^5$ | $\Gamma_q$ | | | | | | | |
| $D_{2d}^6$ | $\Gamma_q$ | | | | $0, 0, \tau_z$ | $0, 0, \tau_z$ | $0, 0, \tau_z$ | $0, 0, \tau_z$ |
| $D_{2d}^7$ | $\Gamma_q$ | | | | $\tau, \tau, 0$ | $\tau, \tau, 0$ | $\tau, \tau, 0$ | $\tau, \tau, 0$ |
| $D_{2d}^8$ | $\Gamma_q$ | | | | $\tau, \tau, \tau_z$ | $\tau, \tau, \tau_z$ | $\tau, \tau, \tau_z$ | $\tau, \tau, \tau_z$ |

Class $D_4$

| Group | Type | $h_{14}$ | $h_4$ | $h_{15}$ | $h_2$ | $h_{13}$ | $h_3$ | $h_{16}$ |
|---|---|---|---|---|---|---|---|---|
| $D_4^1$ | $\Gamma_q$ | | | | | | | |
| $D_4^2$ | $\Gamma_q$ | | | | $\tau, \tau, 0$ | $\tau, \tau, 0$ | $\tau, \tau, 0$ | $\tau, \tau, 0$ |
| $D_4^3$ | $\Gamma_q$ | $0, 0, \frac{\tau_z}{2}$ | $0, 0, \tau_z$ | $0, 0, \frac{3\tau_z}{2}$ | | $0, 0, \frac{3\tau_z}{2}$ | $0, 0, \tau_z$ | $0, 0, \frac{\tau_z}{2}$ |
| $D_4^4$ | $\Gamma_q$ | $0, 0, \frac{\tau_z}{2}$ | $0, 0, \tau_z$ | $0, 0, \frac{3\tau_z}{2}$ | $\tau, \tau, 0$ | $\tau, \tau, \frac{3\tau_z}{2}$ | $\tau, \tau, \tau_z$ | $\tau, \tau, \frac{\tau_z}{2}$ |
| $D_4^5$ | $\Gamma_q$ | $0, 0, \tau_z$ | | $0, 0, \tau_z$ | | $0, 0, \tau_z$ | | $0, 0, \tau_z$ |
| $D_4^6$ | $\Gamma_q$ | $0, 0, \tau_z$ | | $0, 0, \tau_z$ | $\tau, \tau, 0$ | $\tau, \tau, \tau_z$ | $\tau, \tau, \tau_z$ | $\tau, \tau, \tau_z$ |
| $D_4^7$ | $\Gamma_q$ | $0, 0, \frac{3\tau_z}{2}$ | $0, 0, \tau_z$ | $0, 0, \frac{\tau_z}{2}$ | | $0, 0, \frac{\tau_z}{2}$ | $0, 0, \tau_z$ | $0, 0, \frac{3\tau_z}{2}$ |

Continued

| Group | Type | $h_{14}$ | $h_4$ | $h_{15}$ | $h_2$ | $h_{13}$ | $h_3$ | $h_{16}$ |
|---|---|---|---|---|---|---|---|---|
| $D_4^8$ | $\Gamma_q$ | $0, 0, \frac{3z_z}{2}$ | $0, 0, \tau_z$ | $0, 0, \frac{\tau_z}{2}$ | $\tau, \tau, 0$ | $\tau, \tau, \frac{\tau_z}{2}$ | $\tau, \tau, \tau_z$ | $\tau, \tau, \frac{3\tau_z}{2}$ |
| $D_4^9$ | $\Gamma_q^v(a)$ | | | | | | | |
| $D_4^{10}$ | $\Gamma_q^v(a)$ | $0, \tau, \frac{\tau_z}{2}$ | | $0, \tau \frac{\tau_z}{2}$ | $0, \tau, \frac{\tau_z}{2}$ | | $0, \tau, \frac{\tau_z}{2}$ | |

Class $D_{4h}$. $h_{25}$ = inversion. Groups:

$D_{4h}^1 = D_4^1 + D_4^1 \times h_{25}$,

$D_{4h}^2 = D_4^1 + D_4^1 \times t_{(0, 0, \tau_z)} \cdot h_{25}$.

$D_{4h}^3 = D_4^1 + D_4^1 \times t_{(\tau, \tau, 0)} \cdot h_{25}$,

$D_{4h}^4 = D_4^1 + D_4^1 \times t_{(\tau, \tau, \tau_z)} \cdot h_{25}$,

$D_{4h}^5 = D_4^2 + D_4^2 \times h_{25}$.

$D_{4h}^6 = D_4^2 + D_4^2 \times t_{(0, 0, \tau_z)} \cdot h_{25}$

$D_{4h}^7 = D_4^2 + D_4^2 \times t_{(\tau, \tau, 0)} \cdot h_{25}$.

$D_{4h}^8 = D_4^2 + D_4^2 \times t_{(\tau, \tau, \tau_z)} \cdot h_{25}$.

$D_{4h}^9 = D_4^5 + D_4^5 \times h_{25}$

$D_{4h}^{10} = D_4^5 + D_4^5 \times t_{(0, 0, \tau_z)} \cdot h_{25}$,

$D_{4h}^{11} = D_4^5 + D_4^5 \times t_{(\tau, \tau, 0)} \cdot h_{25}$,

$D_{4h}^{12} = D_4^5 + D_4^5 \times t_{(\tau, \tau, \tau_z)} \cdot h_{25}$,

$D_{4h}^{13} = D_4^6 + D_4^6 \times h_{25}$,

$D_{4h}^{14} = D_4^6 + D_4^6 \times t_{(0, 0, \tau_z)} \cdot h_{25}$

$D_{4h}^{15} = D_4^6 + D_4^6 \times t_{(\tau, \tau, 0)} \cdot h_{25}$.

$D_{4h}^{16} = D_4^6 + D_4^6 \times t_{(\tau, \tau, \tau_z)} \cdot h_{25}$.

$D_{4h}^{17} = D_4^9 + D_4^9 \times h_{25}$.

$D_{4h}^{18} = D_4^9 + D_4^9 \times t_{(0, 0, \tau_z)} \cdot h_{25}$,

$D_{4h}^{19} = D_4^{10} + D_4^{10} \times t_{\left(0, \tau, \frac{\tau_z}{2}\right)} \cdot h_{25}$.

$D_{4h}^{20} = D_4^{10} + D_4^{10} \times t_{\left(0, \tau, \frac{3\tau_z}{2}\right)} \cdot h_{25}$.

Cubic system $O_h$

Class $T$

| Group | Type | $h_2$ | $h_3$ | $h_4$ | $h_5$ | $h_6$ | $h_7$ | $h_8$ | $h_9$ | $h_{10}$ | $h_{11}$ | $h_{12}$ |
|---|---|---|---|---|---|---|---|---|---|---|---|---|
| $T^1$ | $\Gamma_c$ | | | | | | | | | | | |
| $T^4$ | $\Gamma_c$ | $\tau, \tau, 0$ | $0, \tau, \tau$ | $\tau, 0, \tau$ | | $\tau, \tau, 0$ | $0, \tau, \tau$ | $\tau, 0, \tau$ | | $\tau, \tau, 0$ | $0, \tau, \tau$ | $\tau, 0, \tau$ |
| $T^2$ | $\Gamma_c^f$ | | | | | | | | | | | |
| $T^3$ | $\Gamma_c^v$ | | | | | | | | | | | |
| $T^5$ | $\Gamma_c^v$ | $0, 0, \tau$ | $\tau, 0, 0$ | $0, \tau, 0$ | | $0, 0, \tau$ | $\tau, 0, 0$ | $0, \tau, 0$ | | $0, 0, \tau$ | $\tau, 0, 0$ | $0, \tau, 0$ |

Class $O$. $h_{13}$ = 180° rotation about (1, $\bar{1}$, 0). Groups:

$O^1 = T^1 + T^1 \times h_{13}$,

$O^2 = T^1 + T^1 \times t_{(\tau,\tau,\tau)} \cdot h_{13}$,

$O^6 = T^4 + T^4 \times t_{\left(\frac{\tau}{2},\frac{\tau}{2},\frac{\tau}{2}\right)} \cdot h_{13}$,

$O^7 = T^4 + T^4 \times t_{\left(\frac{3\tau}{2},\frac{3\tau}{2},\frac{3\tau}{2}\right)} \cdot h_{13}$,

$O^3 = T^2 + T^2 \times h_{13}$,

$O^4 = T^2 + T^2 \times t_{\left(\frac{\tau}{2},\frac{\tau}{2},\frac{\tau}{2}\right)} \cdot h_{13}$,

$O^5 = T^3 + T^3 \times h_{13}$,

$O^8 = T^5 + T^5 \times t_{\left(\frac{\tau}{2},\frac{\tau}{2},\frac{\tau}{2}\right)} \cdot h_{13}$.

Class $T_h$. $h_{25}$ = inversion. Groups:

$T_h^1 = T^1 + T^1 \times h_{25}$,

$T_h^2 = T^1 + T^1 \times t_{(\tau,\tau,\tau)} \cdot h_{25}$,

$T_h^6 = T^4 + T^4 \times h_{25}$,

$T_h^3 = T^2 + T^2 \times h_{25}$,

$T_h^4 = T^2 + T^2 \times t_{\left(\frac{\tau}{2},\frac{\tau}{2},\frac{\tau}{2}\right)} \cdot h_{25}$,

$T_h^5 = T^3 + T^3 \times h_{25}$,

$T_h^7 = T^5 + T^5 \times h_{25}$.

Class $T_d$. $h_{37}$ = reflection in the plane ($\bar{1}$, 1, 0). Groups:

$T_d^1 = T^1 + T^1 \times h_{37}$,

$T_d^4 = T^1 + T^1 \times t_{(\tau,\tau,\tau)} \cdot h_{37}$,

$T_d^2 = T^2 + T^2 \times h_{37}$.

$T_d^5 = T^2 + T^2 \times t_{(\tau,\tau,\tau)} \cdot h_{37}$,

$T_d^3 = T^3 + T^3 \times h_{37}$,

$T_d^6 = T^5 + T^5 \times t_{\left(\frac{\tau}{2},\frac{\tau}{2},\frac{\tau}{2}\right)} \cdot h_{37}$

Class $O_h$. $h_{25}$ = inversion. Groups:

$O_h^1 = O^1 + O^1 \times h_{25}$

$O_h^2 = O^1 + O^1 \times t_{(\tau,\tau,\tau)} \cdot h_{25}$.

$O_h^3 = O^2 + O^2 \times h_{25}$,

$O_h^4 = O^2 + O^2 \times t_{(\tau,\tau,\tau)} \cdot h_{25}$,

$O_h^5 = O^3 + O^3 \times h_{25}$,

$O_h^6 = O^3 + O^3 \times t_{(\tau,\tau,\tau)} \cdot h_{25}$,

$O_h^7 = O^4 + O^4 \times t_{\left(\frac{\tau}{2},\frac{\tau}{2},\frac{\tau}{2}\right)} \cdot h_{25}$,

$O_h^8 = O^4 + O^4 \times t_{\left(\frac{3\tau}{2},\frac{3\tau}{2},\frac{3\tau}{2}\right)} \cdot h_{25}$,

$O_h^9 = O^5 + O^5 \times h_{25}$,

$O_h^{10} = O^8 + O^8 \times h_{25}$.

## Rhombohedral and Hexagonal systems

Class $C_3$

| Group | Type | $h_3$ | $h_5$ |
|---|---|---|---|
| $C_3^1$ | $\Gamma_h$ | | |
| $C_3^2$ | $\Gamma_h$ | $\frac{4\tau_z}{3}$ | $\frac{2\tau_z}{3}$ |
| $C_3^3$ | $\Gamma_h$ | $\frac{2\tau_z}{3}$ | $\frac{4\tau_z}{3}$ |
| $C_3^4$ | $\Gamma_{rh}$ | | |

Class $S_6$

| Group | Type | $h_3$ | $h_5$ | $h_{13}$ | $h_{15}$ | $h_{17}$ |
|---|---|---|---|---|---|---|
| $S_6^1$ | $\Gamma_h$ | | | | | |
| $S_6^2$ | $\Gamma_{rh}$ | | | | | |

Class $C_{3h}$

| Group | Type | $h_3$ | $h_5$ | $h_{14}$ | $h_{16}$ | $h_{18}$ |
|---|---|---|---|---|---|---|
| $C_{3h}^1$ | $\Gamma_h$ | | | | | |

Class $D_3$

| Group | Type | $h_3$ | $h_5$ | $h_7$ | $h_9$ | $h_{11}$ |
|---|---|---|---|---|---|---|
| $D_3^2$ | $\Gamma_h$ | | | | | |
| $D_3^4$ | $\Gamma_h$ | $0, 0, \frac{4\tau_z}{3}$ | $0, 0, \frac{2\tau_z}{3}$ | | $0, 0, \frac{4\tau_z}{3}$ | $0, 0, \frac{2\tau_z}{3}$ |
| $D_3^6$ | $\Gamma_h$ | $0, 0, \frac{2\tau_z}{3}$ | $0, 0, \frac{4\tau_z}{3}$ | | $0, 0, \frac{2\tau_z}{3}$ | $0, 0, \frac{4\tau_z}{3}$ |

| Group | Type | $h_3$ | $h_5$ | $h_8$ | $h_{10}$ | $h_{12}$ |
|---|---|---|---|---|---|---|
| $D_3^1$ | $\Gamma_h$ | | | | | |
| $D_3^3$ | $\Gamma_h$ | $0, 0, \frac{4\tau_z}{3}$ | $0, 0, \frac{2\tau_z}{3}$ | | $0, 0. \frac{4\tau_z}{3}$ | $0, 0, \frac{2\tau_z}{3}$ |
| $D_3^5$ | $\Gamma_h$ | $0, 0, \frac{2\tau_z}{3}$ | $0, 0, \frac{4\tau_z}{3}$ | | $0, 0. \frac{2\tau_z}{3}$ | $0, 0, \frac{4\tau_z}{3}$ |
| $D_3^7$ | $\Gamma_{rh}$ | | | | | |

Class $C_{3v}$

| Group | Type | $h_3$ | $h_5$ | $h_{19}$ | $h_{21}$ | $h_{23}$ |
|---|---|---|---|---|---|---|
| $C_{3v}^1$ | $\Gamma_h$ | | | | | |
| $C_{3v}^3$ | $\Gamma_h$ | | | $0, 0, \tau_z$ | $0, 0, \tau_z$ | $0\ 0, \tau_z$ |

Class $C_{3v}$

| Group | Type | $h_3$ | $h_5$ | $h_{20}$ | $h_{22}$ | $h_{24}$ |
|---|---|---|---|---|---|---|
| $C_{3v}^2$ | $\Gamma_h$ | | | | | |
| $C_{3v}^4$ | $\Gamma_h$ | | | 0, 0 $\tau_z$ | 0, 0, $\tau_z$ | 0, 0, $\tau_z$ |
| $C_{3v}^5$ | $\Gamma_{rh}$ | | | | | |
| $C_{3v}^6$ | $\Gamma_{rh}$ | | | 0, 0, $\tau_z$ | 0, 0 $\tau_z$ | 0, 0, $\tau_z$ |

Class $D_{3d}$. $h_{13}$ = inversion. Groups:

$D_{3d}^1 = D_3^1 + D_3^1 \times h_{13}$, $D_{3d}^4 = D_3^2 + D_3^2 \times t_{(0,\,0,\,\tau_z)} \cdot h_{13}$,

$D_{3d}^2 = D_3^1 + D_3^1 \times t_{(0,\,0,\,\tau_z)} \cdot h_{13}$, $D_{3d}^5 = D_3^7 + D_3^7 \times h_{13}$,

$D_{3d}^3 = D_3^2 + D_3^2 \times h_{13}$, $D_{3d}^6 = D_3^7 + D_3^7 \times t_{(0,\,0,\,\tau_z)} \cdot h_{13}$.

Class $D_{3h}$. $h_{16}$ = reflection in the plane (0, 0, 1). Groups:

$D_{3h}^1 = D_3^1 + D_3^1 \times h_{16}$ $D_{3h}^3 = D_3^2 + D_3^2 \times h_{16}$,

$D_{3h}^2 = D_3^1 + D_3^1 \times t_{(0,\,0,\,\tau_z)} \cdot h_{16}$, $D_{3h}^4 = D_3^2 + D_3^2 \times t_{(0,\,0,\,\tau_z)} \cdot h_{16}$.

Class $C_6$. Lattice $\Gamma_h$

| Group | $h_2$ | $h_3$ | $h_4$ | $h_5$ | $h_6$ |
|---|---|---|---|---|---|
| $C_6^1$ | | | | | |
| $C_6^2$ | 0, 0, $\frac{5\tau_z}{3}$ | 0, 0, $\frac{4\tau_z}{3}$ | 0, 0, $\tau_z$ | 0, 0, $\frac{2\tau_z}{3}$ | 0, 0 $\frac{\tau_z}{3}$ |
| $C_6^3$ | 0, 0 $\frac{\tau_z}{3}$ | 0, 0. $\frac{2\tau_z}{3}$ | 0, 0, $\tau_z$ | 0, 0. $\frac{4\tau_z}{3}$ | 0, 0, $\frac{5\tau_z}{3}$ |
| $C_6^4$ | 0, 0, $\frac{4\tau_z}{3}$ | 0, 0, $\frac{2\tau_z}{3}$ | | 0, 0, $\frac{4\tau_z}{3}$ | 0, 0. $\frac{2\tau_z}{3}$ |
| $C_6^5$ | 0, 0, $\frac{2\tau_z}{3}$ | 0, 0, $\frac{4\tau_z}{3}$ | | 0, 0, $\frac{2\tau_z}{3}$ | 0, 0 $\frac{4\tau_z}{3}$ |
| $C_6^6$ | 0, 0, $\tau_z$ | | 0, 0, $\tau_z$ | | 0, 0, $\tau_z$ |

Class $C_{6h}$. $h_{13}$ = inversion. Groups:

$C_{6h}^1 = C_6^1 + C_6^1 \times h_{13}$, $C_{6h}^2 = C_6^6 + C_6^6 \times h_{13}$.

Class $C_{6v}$. $h_{19}$ = reflection in the plane (0, 1, 0). Groups:

$C_{6v}^1 = C_6^1 + C_6^1 \times h_{19}$, $\quad C_{6v}^4 = C_6^6 + C_6^6 \times h_{19}$.

$C_{6v}^2 = C_6^1 + C_6^1 \times t_{(0,\,0,\,\tau_z)} \cdot h_{19}$, $\quad C_{6v}^3 = C_6^6 + C_6^6 \times t_{(0,\,0,\,\tau_z)} \cdot h_{19}$

Class $D_6$. $h_7$ = 180° rotation about (0, 1, 0). Groups:

$D_6^1 = C_6^1 + C_6^1 \times h_7$, $\quad D_6^4 = C_6^4 + C_6^4 \times h_7$

$D_6^2 = C_6^2 + C_6^2 \times h_7$, $\quad D_6^5 = C_6^5 + C_6^5 \times h_7$

$D_6^3 = C_6^3 + C_6^3 \times h_7$, $\quad D_6^6 = C_6^6 + C_6^6 \times h_7$

Class $D_{6h}$. $h_{13}$ — inversion. Groups:

$D_{6h}^1 = D_6^1 + D_6^1 \times h_{13}$, $\quad D_{6h}^3 = D_6^6 + D_6^6 \times t_{(0,\,0,\,\tau_z)} \cdot h_{13}$,

$D_{6h}^2 = D_6^1 + D_6^1 \times t_{(0,\,0,\,\tau_z)} \cdot h_{13}$ $\quad D_{6h}^4 = D_6^6 + D_6^6 \times h_{13}$.

# BIBLIOGRAPHY

## Tables

N.F.M. Henry and K. Lonsdale (1952,1965,1969). "International Tables for X-Ray Crystallography", Vol. 1. Kynoch, Birmingham. This is the book on space groups, and for brevity we usually refer to it as the International tables.

S. L. Altmann (1977). "Induced Representations in Crystals and Molecules". Academic Press, New York.

C.J. Bradley and A.P. Cracknell (1972). "The Mathematical Theory of Symmetry in Solids". Clarendon, Oxford. Full group-theoretical treatment of space groups and a very extensive bibliography.

D.K. Faddeyev (1964). "Tables of the Principal Unitary Representations of Fedorov Groups". Pergamon, Oxford.

V.A. Koptsik (1966). "Shubnikov Groups. Handbook on the Symmetry and Physical Properties of Crystal Structures". University Press, Moscow (in Russian).

O.V. Kovalev (1965). "Irreducible Representations of the Space Groups". Gordon and Breach, New York.

S.C. Miller and W.F. Love (1967). "Tables of Irreducible Representations of Space Groups and Co-representations of Magnetic Space Groups". Pruett, Colorado.

J. Zak, A. Casher, M. Glück, and Y. Gur (1969). "The Irreducible Representations of Space Groups". Benjamin, New York.

**Description of Space Groups**

W. Barlow (1894). On the geometric properties of homogeneous rigid structures and their application to crystals. Z. Krist. 23, 1 (in German).

M.J. Buerger (1956,1963). "Elementary Crystallography, an Introduction to the Fundamental Geometrical Features of Crystals". Wiley, New York.

M.J. Buerger (1971). "Introduction to Crystal Geometry". McGraw-Hill, New York.

J.J. Burckhardt (1966). "The Motion Groups of Crystallography". Birkhauser, Basel (in German).

J.J. Burckhardt (1967). The history of the discovery of the 230 space groups. Archs. Hist. Exact Sci. 4, 235 (in German).

E. S. Fedorov (1891). Symmetry of regular systems of figures. Vseross. min Obshch., Zap. (II) 28, 1 (in Russian). A full translation, by D. and K. Harker, is given in the American Crystallographic Association Monograph No. 7.

H. Hilton (1903). "Mathematical Crystallography and the Theory of Groups of Movements. Clarendon, Oxford; reprinted by Dover, New York, 1963.

H.D. Megaw (1973). "Crystal Structures: A Working Approach". Saunders, Philadelphia.

A. Schoenflies (1891). "Theory of Crystal Structure". Teubner, Leipzig (in German).

L. Sohncke (1879). "Development of a Theory of Crystal Structure". Teubner, Leipzig (in German).

P. Terpstra (1955). "Introduction to the Space Groups". Walters, Groningen.

R.W.G. Wyckoff (1930). "The Analytical Expression of the Results of the Theory of Space Groups". Carnegie Inst., Washington.

**General Crystallography**

Acta Crystallographica (1948- ). Munksgaard, Copenhagen.

S. Bhagavantum (1966). "Crystal Symmetry and Physical Properties". Academic Press, New York.

A.I. Kitaigorodskii (1955). "Organic Chemical Crystallography". U.S.S.R. Acad. Sci., Moscow (in Russian); translated by Consultants Bureau, New York 1961.

H. Lipson and W. Cochran (1966). "The Determination of Crystal Structures". Bell, London.

D. McKie and C. McKie (1974). "Crystalline Solids". Nelson, London.

H.D. Megaw — see under **Description of Space Groups**.

J.F. Nye (1957). "Physical Properties of Crystals". Clarendon, Oxford.

F.C. Phillips (1963). "An Introduction to Crystallography". Longmans, London.

V.C. Sinclair, J.M. Robertson, and A. McL. Mathieson (1950). The crystal and molecular structure of anthracene. Acta Cryst. 3, 234.

Structure Reports (1940- ). Oosthoek, Utrecht.

W.A. Wooster (1938). "Crystal Physics". Cambridge University Press.

R.W.G. Wyckoff (1963–1966,1968). "Crystal Structures", Vols. 1–5. Interscience, New York.

Zeitschrift für Kristallographie. Akademische Verlagsgesellschaft, Frankfurt.

**Group Theory**

L.P. Bouckaert, R. Smoluchowski, and E. Wigner (1936). Theory of Brillouin zones and symmetry properties of wave functions in crystals. Phys. Rev. 50, 58.

C.J. Bradley and A.P. Cracknell (1972). See under **Tables**.

G. Burns (1977). "Introduction to Group Theory with Applications". Academic Press, New York.

D.K. Faddeyev (1964). See under **Tables**.

P.J. Grout, J.W. Leech, and P.S. English (1975). The symmetry properties of the normal modes of vibration of crystalline carbon disulphide and chlorine. J. Phys. C: Sol. Stat. Phys. 8, 1620.

M. Hamermesh (1962). "Group Theory and its Application to Physical Problems". Addison-Wesley, Reading, Massachusetts.

H. Jones (1960). "The Theory of Brillouin Zones and Electronic States in Crystals. North-Holland, Amsterdam.

R.S. Knox and A. Gold (1964). "Symmetry in the Solid State". Benjamin, New York.

G.F. Koster (1957). Space groups and their representations. Sol. Stat. Phys. 5, 173.

O.V. Kovalev (1965). See under **Tables**.

M. Lax (1974). "Symmetry Principles in Solid State and Molecular Physics. Wiley, New York.

G.Ya. Lyubarskii (1960). "The Application of Group Theory in Physics". Pergamon, Oxford.

A.A. Maradudin and S.H. Vosko (1968). Symmetry properties of the normal vibration of crystals. Rev. Mod. Phys. 40, 1.

S.C. Miller and W.F. Love (1967). See under **Tables**.

H.W. Streitwolf (1967). "Group Theory in Solid State Physics". MacDonald, London.

J.L. Warren (1968). Further consideration on the symmetry properties of the normal vibrations of a crystal. Rev. Mod. Phys. 40, 38.

G. Weinreich (1965). "Solids: Elementary Theory for Advanced Students". Wiley, New York.

E.B. Wilson, Jr., J.C. Decius, and P.C. Cross (1955). "Molecular Vibrations – The Theory of Infrared and Raman Spectra". McGraw-Hill, New York.

H. Wondratschek and J. Neubüser (1967). "Determination of the symmetry elements of a space group from the general positions listed in International Tables for X-Ray Crystallography, Vol. I." Acta Cryst. 23, 349.

J. Zak, A. Casher, M. Glück, and Y. Gur (1969). See under **Tables**.

# INDEX